Student Manual with Daily Tasks

PRACTICE KIT FOR

Medical Front Office Skills

evolve

∵ *To access your Instructor Resources, visit:*

http://evolve.elsevier.com/Buck/practicekit/

Evolve Student Learning Resources for *Practice Kit for Medical Front Office Skills* offers the following features:

Bullet Items:

- **Audio Files**
  These MP3 files contain medical dictation files for transcription and telephone messages.

- **Forms Library**
  For your convenience, the forms from Appendix 5 are also included electronically.

- **Medisoft Base Data**
  This data, combined with your Medisoft CD, will allow you to create your South Padre Medical Office.

- **Patient Directory**
  As a helpful resource, a comprehensive list of all patients included in this kit is provided.

- **Content Updates**
  Continually updated information to provide the latest updates on relevant issues for medical front office skills.

Student Manual with Daily Tasks

PRACTICE KIT FOR
Medical Front Office Skills

Second Edition

CAROL J. BUCK, MS, CPC-I, CPC, CPC-H, CCS-P

Program Director, Retired
Medical Secretary Programs
Northwest Technical College
East Grand Forks, Minnesota

Technical Collaborator

CYNTHIA STAHL, CPC, CCS-P, CPC-H

Medical Coding Specialist
Lebanon, Indiana

SAUNDERS

ELSEVIER

11830 Westline Industrial Drive
St. Louis, Missouri 63146

STUDENT MANUAL WITH DAILY TASKS FOR PRACTICE   Part No. 9996059863
KIT FOR MEDICAL FRONT OFFICE SKILLS
Copyright © 2009, 2007 by Saunders, an imprint of Elsevier Inc.

Although for mechanical reasons some pages of this publication are perforated, only those pages imprinted with an Elsevier Inc. copyright notice are intended for removal.

Publisher: Michael S. Ledbetter
Associate Developmental Editor: Jennifer Bertucci
Associate Developmental Editor: Jenna Johnson
Publishing Services Manager: Catherine Jackson
Senior Project Manager: Karen M. Rehwinkel
Designer: Kimberly Denando

Printed in the United States of America

Last digit is the print number: 9 8 7 6 5 4 3 2 1

Working together to grow
libraries in developing countries

www.elsevier.com | www.bookaid.org | www.sabre.org

ELSEVIER   BOOK AID International   Sabre Foundation

This work is dedicated to students who approach every new project
with enthusiasm and determination to do their best.

Carol J. Buck

REVIEWERS

Ursula Cole, MEd, CMA (AAMA), CCS-P
Medical Program Coordinator/Medical Curriculum Chair
Indiana Business College
Terre Haute, Indiana

Teena Gregory-Gooding, MS, CPC
Medical Education Coordinator
Medical Reimbursement Programs
Medquest, Incorporated
Rapid City, South Dakota

PREFACE

The hub of the modern medical office is the computer. Practice management is accomplished by means of computer software designed to process and store medical records, appointments, billing, and numerous other medical office tasks. Many health care facilities are now paperless and others are in varying stages of transition to become paperless. There are, however, facilities that remain papered offices. The extent to which you will utilize a computer to accomplish your daily tasks will be determined by the facility in which you are employed, but regardless of the extent of the use of the computer, you will need to be familiar with a wide range of tasks that are standard in the medical office. For example, medical dictation may be transcribed and stored in electronic medium or printed on paper to be filed into the medical record. Either way, you need to be able to transcribe medical dictation, no matter what the terminal storage. The learning is what is important in the process, not whether the task is performed with or without a computer. To enhance your familiarity with all types of office settings and to give you the option of how to complete the tasks, many tasks may be accomplished using either a paper or computer approach, depending on your instructor's preference.

No matter which approach you use to complete the tasks in this packet, you will learn how to accomplish many of the basic medical office tasks and better prepare yourself to begin your new career in a medical setting.

Success is the sum of small efforts, repeated day in and day out.
Robert Collier

CONTENTS

 —recorded task   —electronic task   —hand-written task

Day Five

Day Six

Day Seven

Day Eight

Day Nine

Day Ten

Appendices

INTRODUCTION

Learning Objectives

Upon completion of this Practice Kit, you should be able to:

1. Demonstrate basic knowledge of confidentiality and HIPAA regulations.

2. Prepare the appointment schedule for appointment scheduling.

3. Schedule patient appointments according to office rules based on patient need, facility availability, and physician preference.

4. Schedule inpatient and outpatient admissions and procedures.

5. Prepare a daily Patient List.

6. File medical records.

7. Complete daily bank deposit ticket.

8. Reconcile a bank statement.

9. Post entries on a daysheet.

10. Perform accounts receivable procedures.

11. Perform accounts payable procedures.

12. Prepare monthly patient bills.

13. Perform collection procedures.

14. Establish a petty cash fund.

15. Post adjustments.

16. Process a credit balance.

17. Process refunds.

18. Post nonsufficient fund checks.

19. Post collection agency payments.

20. Obtain preauthorization for procedures.

21. Obtain managed care referrals and precertifications.

22. Apply the correct procedural and diagnosis codes for services provided.

23. Prepare an insurance claim form for Medicare, Medicaid, managed care carrier, and private health insurance carrier.

24. Use a fee schedule to correctly calculate payment for services.

25. Record a variety of telephone messages left on an answering machine.

26. Set up and maintain patient files.

27. Prepare draft documents for your supervisor's review.

28. Demonstrate understanding of risk management procedures.

29. Perform inventory of equipment.

30. Perform routine maintenance of administrative equipment.

31. Key documents from your supervisor's drafts.

32. Transcribe dictation from several people consisting of medical documents and general correspondence.

33. Use computer software to maintain systems.

Contents of the Practice Kit

The Practice Kit packet contains the following items:
- Student Manual with Daily Tasks (1)
- Patient Appointment Schedules (20)
- File Folders (36)
- File Labels (60: 30 preprinted; 30 plain)
- Check Register (1)
- Companion CD (1) with phone messages and dictation files, Forms Library, Medisoft base data, and Patient Directory
- Medisoft Advanced Version 14 Software CD (1)

STUDENT MANUAL WITH DAILY TASKS

This Student Manual with Daily Tasks provides you with directions for each of the tasks that you will be completing during your internship, along with reference materials and forms. The Supplies section of this manual contains many of the forms that you will be using while completing the various tasks. First, read through the information presented in "Your Internship Tasks" on p. xix.

PATIENT APPOINTMENT SCHEDULES

You will be scheduling the patient appointments on several days of your internship. Appendix 2 (p. 99) contains directions to guide you in the appointment-scheduling process.

FILE FOLDERS

This packet contains 36 file folders that you will use when establishing patient medical records and general supplies files.

FILE LABELS

Contained within this packet are two sheets of file labels (30 preprinted labels, 30 blank labels) that you will use to prepare patient medical records and general supplies files. On the job you would print labels using the computer; however, these labels have been prepared for you.

TASK TOOLS

The tasks in this practice kit contain instructions and supplies for both a paper-based office management system and software-based office management system. The kit can be completed using the paper-based system or in conjunction with the Medisoft Advanced Patient Accounting Software. **It is not recommended that you switch systems from one task to another because each task builds upon another.** For example, a task requires that you schedule Mr. Jones for a patient visit in the next available appointment period. You schedule this visit using the paper-based system. The next task may require that you schedule Mr. Smith for a patient visit. If for this task you choose to use the software to schedule the appointment, you may have scheduled both patients during the same time period because these systems cannot exchange this information.

Look for this symbol ✎ when you are to complete a task using paper supplies, and this symbol 💻 when you may complete a task using a computer.

COMPANION CD

The **companion** CD contains a patient directory, base data for Medisoft (to create the South Padre office), audio files, and the actual forms necessary to complete the tasks. This Forms Library (p. 169) is also provided in Appendix 5 at the back of this text. Please note that not all of these forms are intended to be completed electronically. They are simply provided on the CD and Evolve site for convenience.

The following forms are located in the Forms Library in Appendix 5, on the companion CD, and on the Evolve site:

- Check No. 999
- CMS-1500 Health Insurance Claim
- Continuation
- Deposit Ticket
- History and Physical Examination, South Padre Medical Center
- Interoffice Memo, South Padre Medical Center
- Journal of Daily Charges and Payments
- Letterhead, South Padre Medical Center
- Patient Information
- Petty Cash Journal
- Phone Record
- Referral
- Request for Inpatient Consultation
- Request for Preauthorization for Surgery
- Statement
- Subsequent Findings
- Superbill
- Surgical Request and Information
- Patient Health History
- Cardiology Report, South Padre Hospital
- Operative Report, South Padre Hospital
- Radiology Report, South Padre Hospital

For the software to work correctly, you must change the date on your computer to April 7, 2008. You do this by double clicking the time display on the bar at the lower right of the computer screen. When you double click the time display, a dialog box opens that allows you to reset the date. Reset the month to "April", the day to "7", the year to "2008", and you can leave the time as displayed. Now, your computer will keep time from the initial date of April 7, 2008.

On some of the forms that are completed electronically, a second page is sometimes necessary. In this instance, the second page will be automatically formatted, with the patient name (last name, first name, middle initial) in the upper left-hand corner.

To save a form that you have completed electronically, use the "Save As" feature on your computer and title the document with the task number and patient name, if applicable. Remember to save the document to a location on your computer that you can easily access in the future.

Audio Files on Companion CD

The **audio** portion of the CD and Evolve site contains medical dictation files for transcription and telephone messages. You will be transcribing the information on the CD as directed for specific tasks. These tasks will be identified by the icon 🎧 appearing next to the task. At the beginning of each item on the recording, the task number will be announced. For example, "This is Day Four, Task 4.1." The end of the transcribed item will also be announced. For example, "This is the end of Day Four, Task 4.1."

The tasks that use the audio will require various forms. These forms are located in the Supplies section (p. 195) of the Student Manual, in the Forms Library in Appendix 5 (p. 169), on the companion CD, or on the Evolve site at http://evolve.elsevier.com/Buck/practicekit/. You will be instructed as to which form(s) to use and the location of the form(s) within the directions for each task.

The following tasks have information dictated onto the companion CD (and included on the Evolve site):

TASK **1.3**	Scheduling Telephone Appointments and Inpatient Consultations
TASK **2.4**	Medical Transcription
TASK **3.2**	Medical Transcription
TASK **4.1**	Telephone Messages and Appointment Schedule
TASK **5.1**	Medical Transcription
TASK **6.3**	Telephone Messages
TASK **10.1**	Telephone Messages
TASK **10.3**	Medical Transcription

The following task uses the Internet for a research assignment.

TASK **6.1**	Internet Research

MEDISOFT CD

You may use the Medisoft software for scheduling appointments and completing insurance forms and various financial documentations. Appendix 4 of this text contains software operating instructions, including data backup and restoration, which must be done before and immediately after completion of daily assignments.

The following tasks may be completed using the Medisoft software.

TASK **1.2**	Preparing the Schedules
TASK **1.3**	Scheduling Telephone Appointments and Inpatient Consultations
TASK **1.5**	Records Management and Patient List
TASK **2.1**	Patient List
TASK **2.2**	Patient Reception
TASK **2.3**	Scheduling Appointments
TASK **2.5**	Scheduling Emergency or Urgent Appointments

Before You Begin

Read Appendix 1, Welcome (p. 97) now and then read Appendix 2, Policies and Procedures (p. 99), which explains the standard operating procedures of the Center. You will be following these Policies and Procedures during your internship. Be certain you complete all items requested in the directions in the Policies and Procedures information.

Pre-Task **1.1**

Routine Maintenance

SUPPLIES NEEDED:
- 1 file folder (blank)
- 1 file folder label (blank)

You are expected to perform routine maintenance on all administrative equipment that you use while an intern at the Center. At the end of each day, you are to wipe the computer screen with a dry, soft cloth. Never use any type of cleaner on the computer screen because it will damage the screen surface. Use a soft brush to sweep the keyboard at the end of each day. Organize your work and place all papers into the desk drawer at the end of the day and during your breaks. Gladys, Medical Office Assistant, will be your supervisor and will provide you with a key to your desk to be used to lock the desk at the end of the day and on your breaks. Always keep your area clear of patient information that could be seen by others. Clean the top of your desk at the end of each day using the spray cleaner located in the lower right-hand drawer of your desk.

We at the Center understand that each intern's training differs when it comes to use of the various office equipment. Gladys will provide a demonstration on the operation of all equipment you will be using during your internship. Should the equipment malfunction while you are using it, please contact Gladys for any help you require. You have begun your internship at a great time. The practice is just beginning to convert from a paper-based office management system to a computer-based office management system (Medisoft software). Although the paper-based system will be maintained during your internship, occasionally you will be asked to perform tasks that include use of the Medisoft software. You are to complete these tasks only when the Medisoft software is available for that specific task and if your instructor has directed you to use the software feature.

You will find a check-off form in the Supplies section (p. 196) of this Student Manual (labeled "Equipment Maintenance and Desk Security") that is dated for each day of your internship. Enter your name on the form. You are to use this form at the end of each day of your internship to check off that you have performed all necessary maintenance of your equipment and that you have secured your desk. At the end of your internship, you are to turn this form in to Gladys during your internship checkout meeting.

Locate a blank file folder and blank file folder label from your packet. Write "GENERAL" on the file folder label in capital letters and place the label on the file folder. Place the Equipment Maintenance and Desk Security form into the file folder.

Your Internship Tasks

You have completed your review of Appendices 1 (p. 97) and 2 (p. 99) that is required of all new interns and employees. You have completed your "Equipment Maintenance and Desk Security" form (p. 196) and are now ready to begin your work duties. All directions and materials necessary to complete the jobs are included either in the packet, this Student Manual, the companion CD, or the Medisoft CD. **It is important to complete all tasks in the order presented.**

Student Manual with Daily Tasks

PRACTICE KIT FOR
Medical Front Office Skills

STUDENT MANUAL

Make sure to check **evolve** for the latest content updates

Supplies from the supplies section (p. 195) are also located in the forms library on the companion CD and on the Evolve site at http://evolve.elsevier.com/Buck/practicekit/.

Monday, April 7, 2008

TASK **1.1**

Risk Management

Today, before you begin your internship, Gladys, Medical Office Assistant, tells you that she would like to share a very important part of her job with you—risk management. She explains that risk management procedures are used in the Center and are the responsibility of all staff members. Risk is defined as any occurrence that may result in a patient, staff member, or visitor being injured or any liability that could result in financial loss to the Center. A major risk factor to any health care facility is management of patient information and it is an important aspect of every health care facility member's job. Gladys has been designated the Privacy Officer for the Center and as such is responsible for ensuring that policies and procedures are in place and that all staff are trained in patient rights and the Health Insurance Portability and Accountability Act of 1996 (HIPAA). The primary function of HIPAA is to provide continuous insurance coverage for employees and their dependents when they change jobs or lose their jobs. Another function of HIPAA is to reduce the costs of managing the exchange of patient data. One part of the management of patient data is standardization of electronic transactions and another part is the implementation of security and privacy procedures that ensure confidentiality of patient information. Further, the Act ensures the patients have the legal right to restrict access to their health records and know who accesses their records. All staff members are responsible for complying with HIPAA and safeguarding all patient information.

Another important component of risk management reduction in the health care setting is for each employee to report any situation that may place patients, employees, or the facility at risk. For example, if you witness any behavior that would be considered risky, such as the odor of alcohol on a fellow employee, you should immediately report the behavior to your supervisor. Also, your attention to details that may present a risk in the

Center, such as a rug with a turned-up corner or a chair that is placed too far into a traffic path in the waiting room, is essential. You are to be alert to every possible detail in the office to ensure that the office space is as safe as we can make it. Each member of the health care team must assume the responsibility for safety in the Center.

You also will find a confidentiality statement in the Supplies section (p. 197). You are to now read the statement, sign it, and place it in the general file.

Preparing the Schedules

Gladys has asked you to prepare the schedule for November 10 to November 21 for appointments by blocking off the times when the physicians will not be available. Gladys previously prepared the schedules through November 9.

If you are completing the scheduling activities using the paper appointment sheets, please enter all information onto the schedule in pencil and print clearly. For all other handwritten documents you will use a pen.

SUPPLIES NEEDED:
- 10 appointment sheets dated Monday, November 10, to Friday, November 21
- 1 file folder and 1 file folder label

November 2008						
S	M	T	W	T	F	S
						1
2	3	4	5	6	7	8
9	10	11	12	13	14	15
16	17	18	19	20	21	22
23	24	25	26	27	28	29
30						

1. **Write the physicians' names on the appointment sheets.**
   - Note that on the Monday, November 10, appointment sheet, not only the date has been entered, but also the last name of each of the Center's four physicians. Using Monday's appointment sheet as a model, write the physicians' names at the top of each column on the schedule's remaining 9 days of the appointment sheets.

2. **Read about establishing an appointment sheet matrix.**
   - Matrixing means you mark off the times when a physician is not available for appointments. Referring to Appendix 2, Policies and Procedures (p. 99), in this text, locate Items I through M. These items contain the scheduling preferences of each physician.
   - *Caution:* Be sure to read all information regarding schedules contained in Items I through M **before** you begin to matrix the appointment schedules. Use a pencil for all entries on the schedule.
   - You will begin by marking off the times when Dr. Bond is unavailable for appointments for the weeks of November 10-21. According to Item I, Dr. Bond is unavailable before 10 AM on Mondays. You will note that on the Monday, November 10, appointment sheet, under Dr. Bond's

name, that the hours from 8 AM to 10 AM have been marked off by placing an X over the time period and writing "Unavailable" in the space. By marking off the times when the physician is unavailable for appointments, you can be certain that all office employees know not to schedule appointments for Dr. Bond before 10 AM on Monday.

3. **Read about and mark off lunch breaks on Dr. Bond's schedule.**
   - The directions in Item J, Physicians' Lunch Hours, indicate that when a physician begins his/her appointments at 10 AM, the lunch break is to be scheduled from 1 PM to 2 PM. Note Dr. Bond's lunch has been previously marked off on the Monday, November 10, appointment schedule from 1 PM to 2 PM in accordance with his stated preference. Referring to Dr. Bond's office hours in Item I and his lunch hour preferences in Item J, mark off Dr. Bond's lunch hours for the remainder of the week, Tuesday, November 11, through Friday, November 14.

4. **Mark off Dr. Bond's hospital rounds.**
   - According to Item M, Other Physician Scheduling Preferences, Dr. Bond has a board meeting scheduled from 7:30 AM to 8:45 AM on Thursday and he has requested you allow an additional 15 minutes after his meeting to allow him time to return to the Center. Mark off from 8 AM to 9 AM on Dr. Bond's Thursday appointment schedule and write "Board Meeting" on the schedule, as illustrated in **Figure 1-1.** This will ensure that all employees referencing Dr. Bond's schedule for that day will know that he is at a board meeting during that time period. The office staff does not schedule appointments in the times the physician has indicated he does not want to be scheduled. The office staff is not responsible for scheduling Dr. Bond's or any of the physicians' time before 8 AM or after 6 PM, unless specifically requested to do so.
   - On Tuesday and Wednesday, Dr. Bond has hospital rounds from 6 AM until 8:45 AM, plus the additional 15 minutes after his rounds to allow for time to return to the clinic. Mark off his schedule on Tuesday and Wednesday from 8 AM to 9 AM and write "Rounds" on the schedule.

Figure **1-1** **Board meeting marked off on appointment sheet.**

5. **Mark off Dr. Bond's surgery schedule.**
   - According to Item M, Other Physician Scheduling Preferences, Dr. Bond has requested his surgical procedures be scheduled beginning at 1 PM, with the last procedure scheduled with a starting time of no later than 4 PM on Wednesday and Thursday.
   - Mark off the 1 PM up to the 4:15 PM time period on Dr. Bond's schedule by placing a heavy line around the times reserved for scheduling surgeries.
   - **Figure 1-2** illustrates the placement of surgery hours on a physician's schedule. Note that in order to schedule a 4 PM surgery, you must leave the 4 PM to 4:15 PM line in the surgery block open to allow a patient's name to be placed on the 4 PM line.
   - Dr. Bond also has requested that the hour before his surgery schedule be marked off to allow him desk time and lunch and to ensure he will be on time for his first surgery. Mark off 12 to 1 PM on Wednesday and Thursday by placing an X though the time as illustrated in **Figure 1-2.**
   - The time from 4:15 PM to 6 PM on Dr. Bond's surgery days is to be marked off to allow for time to complete the surgical procedures begun between 1 PM and 4:00 PM. Mark off 4:15 PM to 6 PM on Dr. Bond's schedule on Wednesday and Thursday as "Unavailable," as illustrated in **Figure 1-3.**

6. **Mark off the end-of-day time blocks.**
   - On Tuesday and Friday Dr. Bond works until 5 PM. The time from 5 PM to 6 PM needs to be marked off so no one will inadvertently schedule an appointment that will begin at or continue past 5 PM. According to Item L, you are to do this by placing an X over the four time slots from 5 PM to 6 PM. Refer to **Figure 1-4** for an example of how this time is marked off. Mark off the time at the end of the day and label the time from 5 PM to 6 PM as "Unavailable."

Figure **1-2** Surgery hours marked off on appointment sheet.

1:00	
1:15	
1:30	
1:45	
2:00	
2:15	
2:30	
2:45	
3:00	
3:15	
3:30	
3:45	
4:00	
4:15	Unavailable
4:30	
4:45	
5:00	
5:15	
5:30	
5:45	

Figure **1-3** Unavailable time periods marked off on appointment sheet.

4:30	
4:45	
5:00	Unavailable
5:15	
5:30	
5:45	

Figure **1-4** End-of-day time marked off on appointment sheet.

7. **Review Dr. Bond's schedule.**
   - Dr. Bond's first weekly schedule is now completely matrixed and ready for scheduling appointments. Review Dr. Bond's Monday through Friday schedule again and ensure that you have written down the reason for each block of time marked off. All time marked off on the physician's schedule should be accounted for. If you do not know the reason, write "Unavailable" over the marked-off time. If you followed the preceding directions correctly, the five days of schedules for Dr. Bond should look similar to those illustrated in **Figure 1-5.**

8. **Matrix the remaining schedules for the week of Monday, November 10 to Friday, November 14.**
   - Mark off the remaining physicians' schedules using the information about their individual preferences provided to you in Items I through M.
   - Remember to mark off the entire day when Dr. Harkness and Dr. Clark are not in the office and indicate "Unavailable."

8

Figure 1-5 Dr. Bond's matrixed schedule for the week of November 10 to November 14.

DAY 1 TASK **1.2**

9. Matrix the four physicians' schedules for the week of November 17-21 using the same directions you used for the week of November 10-14.

10. Write "COMPLETED WORK" on the file folder label and place the label on the file folder. Place the completed matrixed schedules for November 10-21 in the Completed Work folder.

 If your instructor has directed the use of the medical practice software, follow these directions: Gladys has asked that you also prepare the schedule for each physician from November 10 to November 21 using the new software scheduling program. She has provided step-by-step instructions for blocking and labeling the time slots. These instructions are located in Appendix 4, Item A (p. 133). Following the physician scheduling preferences located in Appendix 2, Items I through M (p. 99), matrix the schedules for each physician.

Place the printed schedules in the following order:
- Dr. Bond
- Dr. Adams
- Dr. Harkness
- Dr. Clark

All of Dr. Bond's schedules will be in date order (lowest to highest) and placed first in the folder, followed by all Dr. Adams' schedules in date order, and so on.

Scheduling Telephone Appointments and Inpatient Consultations

SUPPLIES NEEDED (p. 199):

- Appointment sheets for Monday, April 7, to Friday, April 18
- Companion CD containing telephone messages from Saturday, April 5, and Sunday, April 6
- 8 blank Telephone Records (as illustrated in **Figure 1-6**) (located in the Supplies section)
- 3 blank Request for Inpatient Consultation forms (as illustrated in **Figure 1-7**) (located in the Supplies section)

1. Locate the "Telephone Messages" area on the companion CD (Task 1.3).
   - Requests for appointments came into the office over the weekend (April 5 and 6). Gladys has asked you to listen to the voice mail of the calls and complete a Telephone Record for each call.
   - Schedule the Appointments: If the patient requests a specific time for an appointment, and the time the patient requested is not available, schedule the patient as close as you can to the requested time. Refer to Appendix 2, Policies and Procedures, Item N, for directions on scheduling appointments.
   - Indicate on the Telephone Record the date and time of the tentative appointment in the "Response" block. Gladys will then review the appointments you made and call each of the patients to confirm the tentative appointment you made for them.
   - The voice mail messages may contain calls from other physicians who are requesting that a Center physician do a consultation for a hospital inpatient. For these calls, you are to complete a Request for Inpatient Consultation form. Gladys will review these requests for consultations and deliver them to the appropriate physician. You do not need to complete a Telephone Record for consultation requests for inpatients

PRIORITY ☐		Telephone Record
Patient _____ Age _____		Message _____
Caller _____		_____
Telephone _____		_____
Referred to _____		Temp _____ | Allergies _____
Chart # _____		Response _____
Chart Attached ☐ YES ☐ NO		_____
Date / / Time _____ Rec'd By _____		PHY/RN Initials | Date / / | Time | Handled By

Figure **1-6** **Telephone Record.**

REQUEST FOR INPATIENT CONSULTATION

To: ❑ Gerald Bond, MD   ATTENDING: _____
     ❑ Ray Adams, MD   TELEPHONE: _____
     ❑ Joyce Harkness, MD   Request Date and Time: _____
     ❑ Anthony Clark, MD

PATIENT: _____   ADMIT DATE: _____

FACILITY: _____   FLOOR: _____ ROOM: _____

REASON FOR CONSULTATION: _____

_____

_____

_____

PLEASE COMPLETE BY: _____ RECEIVED BY: _____
                         (DATE)

Figure **1-7** **Request for Inpatient Consultation form.**

because all of the necessary information is located on the Request for Inpatient Consultation form. When a physician requests that one of the Center physicians provide a consultation at the hospital, place the consultation on the appointment schedule. For example, Dr. Thompson requests an inpatient consultation Monday afternoon by Dr. Bond. You would identify adequate time on the schedule, at either the requested time or a convenient time for the Center physician, and enter the information about the patient (e.g., name, room number, reason for consultation, requesting physician, and if the patient was a new or established patient) onto the schedule. The necessary information will be provided. Remember to schedule 15 minutes of travel time before the consultation.

- Refer to Appendix 2, Policies and Procedures, Item F, for the step-by-step directions on how to complete the Telephone Record and the Request for Inpatient Consultation form.

2. Gladys has spoken with Dr. Bond about Dr. Thomas Thompson's request for a consultation on Charlie Burke at the SPH. Dr. Bond has indicated that he would like to go over to the hospital after lunch today and do the consultation. Gladys wants you to write the consultation information on Dr. Bond's schedule to ensure no one books an appointment for him from 2 PM to 3 PM today, April 7. In addition, she requests you mark off the remainder of the day because Dr. Bond has decided not to return to the office after the hospital consultation.

3. Gladys informs you that Dr. Harkness wants Marion Wilbert seen in consultation after Harriet Muir on Wednesday, April 9. Gladys directs you to schedule the travel from 5–5:15 PM, followed by the consultation, even

though there is only 30 minutes remaining on the schedule. Gladys indicates that Bridget Larson should be scheduled for a 30-minute preoperative visit as per direction Appendix 2, N (p. 110). Place the completed telephone messages, Request for Inpatient Consultation forms, and appointment sheets into the Completed Work folder behind the completed schedules from Task 1.2.

1. Using the completed Telephone Records, Request for Inpatient Consultation forms, and completed appointment sheets from Task 1.3, transfer the new appointments to the office software scheduling program. Gladys has provided step-by-step instructions for scheduling new, established, surgery, emergent, and nursing home appointments in Appendix 4, Item B.
   - Once you have completed scheduling the appointments, Gladys has asked that you print an Appointment List for Monday, April 7, and Wednesday, April 9 for physicians' schedules that changed. This report will allow her to compare the current paper schedule to the new software schedule. Instructions for printing this list are listed in Appendix 4, Item D.

2. Place the Appointment List in the Completed Work folder behind the completed schedules from Task 1.2.

DAY 1 TASK 1.3

Written Communications

SUPPLIES NEEDED (p. 209):
- Handwritten History and Physical Examination form by Dr. Adams for Gloria Hydorn (2 pages) (located in the Supplies section)
- Blank History and Physical Examination form (as illustrated in **Figure 1-8**) (located in the Supplies section)
- Handwritten Continuation note by Dr. Adams for Gloria Hydorn (located in the Supplies section)
- Blank Continuation form (as illustrated in **Figure 1-9**) (located in the Supplies section)

1. **History and physical examination.**
   - Last Thursday, April 3, 2008, Dr. Ray Adams saw a new patient, Gloria Hydorn, who recently moved to the area and wanted to establish a family practitioner. Dr. Adams performed a complete history and physical and completed handwritten notes that you will now key onto a History and Physical Examination (H&P) form.

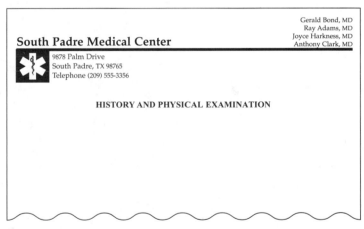

Figure **1-8**   **History and Physical Examination form.**

Figure **1-9**   **Continuation form.**

2. **Key Dr. Adams's handwritten notes onto the H&P form.**
   - After you have completed the H&P for Gloria Hydorn, set it aside until after the completion of all tasks on Day One because you will be creating a medical record for Gloria Hydorn in Task 1.5 and you will place both the H&P and Continuation form into the record.

3. **Key Dr. Adams's handwritten continuation notes (word for word) onto the Continuation form.**
   - Dr. Adams noted a left breast lump during Gloria's examination on Thursday and has requested that diagnostic mammography be performed on Friday, April 4. The radiologist performed the mammography and notified Dr. Adams of the findings. After completing the Continuation form, set it aside until after the completion of the medical record for this patient in Task 1.5.

Records Management and Patient List

SUPPLIES NEEDED (p. 219):

- 1 completed Patient Information form for Gloria Hydorn (as illustrated in **Figure 1-10**)
- 11 completed Patient Information sheets
- 11 completed Subsequent Findings sheets
- 12 file folder labels
- 12 file folders
- 2 blank pieces of paper for patient lists
- 1 Filing document

1. Using the completed work from Task 1.3, you will now establish a medical record for Gloria Hydorn.
   - Locate a file folder and a file label in the packet. The patient's name is in capital letters on a label with last name first, then the first name, and then middle initial (as illustrated in **Figure 1-11**). Secure the label to the file folder.

Figure **1-10** Patient Information sheet for Gloria Hydorn.

Figure **1-11**   Gloria Hydorn's patient medical record file folder.

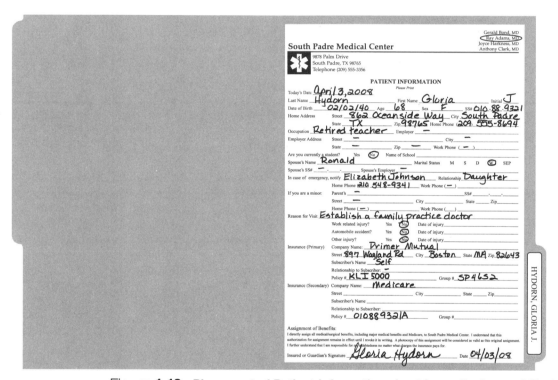

Figure **1-12**   Placement of Patient Information sheet in medical record file folder.

2. Assemble the patient's medical record.
    *   In the Supplies section you will find a completed Patient Information form for Gloria Hydorn. Place the information form first in the file with the top of the form to the left edge of the file, so when you place the file on the desk in front of you and open the file, the information sheet will be the first document and the heading will be at the top of the file (as shown in **Figure 1-12**).
    *   The second and third items in the file should be the History and Physical Examination form and the Continuation page you completed in Task 1.4. Place the papers in reverse chronological order. The order of the medical record for Gloria Hydorn from the first page to the last will be:

- Completed Patient Information sheet (first)
- Continuation page (second)
- History and Physical Examination form (pages 1 and 2) (last)

3. Assemble the established patient's medical records.
   - Using supplies located in this packet, you will now assemble the established patients' medical records for Monday, April 7, 2008.
     - Prepare a file folder for each of the established patients scheduled with Dr. Bond and Dr. Adams on Monday, April 7, 2008. Note that the patient's name is on the label in capital letters—last name, first name, middle initial.
     - Place the Patient Information form and Subsequent Findings form into the file folder with the Patient Information form first.
     - After completing the files, place all files in *alphabetic* order.

4. Using the information regarding a color-coded filing system in Appendix 2, Policies and Procedures, Item Q, of this Student Manual, indicate on the form in the Supplies section for this task the first two colors used on these patients' charts. For example, Carrie Anderson would be filed "Anderson, Carrie" and the color for the letter "A" is grey and the color for the letter "N" is green.

5. On the same form (from the Supplies section for this task), place in numeric order the 10 patient numbers previously taken from an accession ledger by Monday. Indicate the first two colors used in the color coding of these patient numbers. For example, 5678 (Kathy Sue Thompson) would be represented by 005678 and would be the first number in the list of 10. The color for the number "0" is grey and the first two colors for 005678 would be grey and grey.

6. Prepare a Patient List for Dr. Bond and Dr. Adams for Monday, April 7, 2008. An example of the format used for the Patient List is illustrated in **Figure 1-13**. Refer to Appendix 2, Item O for directions on Patient Lists.

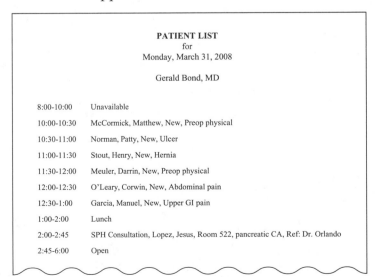

PATIENT LIST
for
Monday, March 31, 2008

Gerald Bond, MD

8:00-10:00	Unavailable
10:00-10:30	McCormick, Matthew, New, Preop physical
10:30-11:00	Norman, Patty, New, Ulcer
11:00-11:30	Stout, Henry, New, Hernia
11:30-12:00	Meuler, Darrin, New, Preop physical
12:00-12:30	O'Leary, Corwin, New, Abdominal pain
12:30-1:00	Garcia, Manuel, New, Upper GI pain
1:00-2:00	Lunch
2:00-2:45	SPH Consultation, Lopez, Jesus, Room 522, pancreatic CA, Ref: Dr. Orlando
2:45-6:00	Open

Figure **1-13** Sample Patient List. When preparing a Patient List using Medisoft, the patient's first name is listed first, followed by the last name.

7. Place the filing form, all file folders, and the Patient Lists into the Competed Work folder behind the work from Task 1.3.

Always place your completed work from one task behind the work from the previous task. So, the completed work from Task 1.2 is placed behind the work from Task 1.1. In this way, the completed work from Task 1.1 is always first in the Completed Work folder. If, as in this task, the completed work is folders, always place the work in alphabetic order. Anderson is in first position, Burthold in second, Carlisle in third, and so on. Once alphabetized, place the work in the completed work folder.

1. Enter Gloria Hydorn's patient information into the new software system using the completed Patient Information form. The step-by-step instructions for entering patient information are located in Appendix 4, Item E. Once all the demographic information has been entered, print a Patient Face Sheet to review the information for errors. The instructions for printing the Patient Face Sheet are located in Appendix 4, Item F.

2. Place the printed Patient Face Sheet in the Completed Work folder behind the work from Task 1.3.

DAY TWO

Make sure to check **evolve** for the latest content updates

Tuesday, April 8, 2008

TASK **2.1**   Patient List

TASK **2.2**   Patient Reception

TASK **2.3**   Scheduling Appointments

TASK **2.4**   Medical Transcription

TASK **2.5**   Scheduling Emergency or Urgent Appointments

TASK **2.1**

Patient List

SUPPLIES NEEDED:
- Appointment schedule for Tuesday, April 8, from Completed Work file
- 2 sheets of plain white paper

1. Prepare today's Patient Lists for Dr. Bond and Dr. Adams using the same format that you used in Task 1.5.

2. Place the completed Patient Lists in the Completed Work file.

1. Print today's Appointment List for Dr. Bond and Dr. Adams following the instructions listed in Appendix 4, Item D.

2. Place the Schedule Reports in the Completed Work file.

Patient Reception

SUPPLIES NEEDED (p. 269):

- Appointment schedule for Tuesday, April 8, 2008, from Completed Work file
- 6 file folders
- 6 completed file labels
- 6 completed Patient Information forms **(Figure 2-1)**
- 6 completed Patient Face Sheets from Medisoft **(Figure 2-2)**
- 6 blank Subsequent Findings forms **(Figure 2-3)**

1. This morning you will be working at the reception desk greeting the patients as they arrive. You will first need to read the Patient Reception directions in Appendix 2, Policies and Procedures, Item P.

Figure **2-1** **Patient Information form.**

South Padre Medical Center
Patient Face Sheet
4/8/2008

Patient Chart #:   D.O.B.:   Age:
Patient Name: Sex:
Street 1:   SSN:
Street 2:   Mar Status:
City: S.O.F:
Phone: Assigned Provider:

Employer Name:
Street 1:
City:
Phone:

Case Information

Case Desc: Diagnosis 1:
Last Visit: Diagnosis 2:
Referral: Diagnosis 3:
Guarantor Name: Diagnosis 4:
Street 1:
City:
Phone:
SSN:

Ins Co #:   Insured 1 Name:
Insurance 1:   Street 1:
Street 1:   Street 2:
Street 2:   Phone:
City: D.O.B.:   Sex:Male
Phone: Policy Number:
Ins-Start: Group Number:
End:

Ins Co #:   Insured 2 Name:
Insurance 2:   Street 1:
Street 1:   Street 2:
Street 2:   City:
City: Phone:
Phone: D.O.B.:
Ins-Start: Policy Number: Sex:
End: Group Number:

Ins Co #:   Insured 3 Name:
Insurance 3:   Street 1:
Street 1:   Street 2:
Street 2:   City:
City: Phone:
Phone: D.O.B.:   Sex:
Ins-Start: Policy Number:
End: Group Number:

Figure **2-2**   **Patient Face Sheet.**

South Padre Medical Center

Patient's Name _____ Age _____ Sex _____ Marital Status S M W D
Address _____ Insurance _____
Telephone _____ Referred _____

Date	Subsequent Findings

Figure **2-3**   **Subsequent Findings form.**

2. Assemble the patient's medical record.
   - Locate the 6 file folders and 6 completed labels.
   - Secure the completed label to each file folder.

3. In the Supplies section you will find 6 completed Patient Information forms **(Figure 2-1)** and 6 completed Patient Face Sheets from the new office management software **(Figure 2-2)** for Task 2.2. Using the Patient

Information forms, locate and circle any errors on the 6 Patient Face Sheets. Assume the patient is the stated age and that the policy number is correct. Place the Patient Information form in the file with the top of the form to the left edge of the file (see Figure 1-12).

4. The second item in the file should be the Subsequent Findings form, so the order of the medical record will be:
   1. Patient Information form
   2. Subsequent Findings form

   Once you have completed this task, place the completed files and Patient Face Sheets in your Completed Work folder directly behind Task 2.1.

1. Gladys has requested that you correct the demographic errors found on the Patient Face Sheets. Using the instructions from Appendix 4, Item E, correct the patient demographics within the software system.
2. Print a new Patient Face Sheet for each patient and place it in the Completed Work file behind the rest of the work for Task 2.2.

Scheduling Appointments

SUPPLIES NEEDED:
- Appointment schedules from your Completed Work file

1. Schedule patients for follow-up appointments
- Using the patient information from Task 2.2, this morning you will be scheduling three patients for follow-up visits with Dr. Bond for April 16 and 17:
  - Lewis Rock will need a recheck appointment on April 17 at 9 AM for 30 minutes.
  - Ed Goldman will need a recheck appointment on April 17 at 10 AM for 30 minutes. Note the patient's age and the mother's name on the appointment sheet.
  - Thomas Blair will need a recheck appointment on April 16 at 9 AM for 30 minutes for a varicocele recheck.

2. Once you have completed this task, place your work in your Completed Work folder directly behind Task 2.2.

1. Using the step-by-step instructions provided in Appendix 4, Items B and C, reschedule the appointments from Task 2.3 in the software scheduling program.

2. Once all appointments have been scheduled, print an Appointment List for Dr. Bond for April 16 and 17.

3. Place the Appointment List in your Completed Work folder behind Task 2.2.

Medical Transcription

SUPPLIES NEEDED (p. 305):
- Companion CD containing medical dictation for Monday, April 7 (Task 2.4)
- 6 Subsequent Findings forms (located in the Supplies section)

1. Locate the "Transcription" area on the companion CD (Task 2.4)
   - This afternoon Gladys is going to cover the receptionist desk and you are to key in the medical transcription that was dictated Monday, April 7.
   - You will key in dictation for six office visits.
   - Subsequent Findings forms are to be completed by hand and then attached to the transcription. To do this, write the patient's known demographic information at the top of the Subsequent Findings form on the lines provided. In the left-hand column of the form under the "Date" heading, write today's date (April 8) of the visit. In the right-hand column under the "Subsequent Finding" heading, write "See Dr. (physician's name here) dictation dated (April 8)." See **Figure 2-4, A** for an example of the format. Then, on a blank paper start your electronic transcription in the upper left-hand corner with the patient's name (last name, first name, middle initial) on the first line and the date on the second line. Leave two blank spaces and begin to key the physician's dictation. When you have finished keying in the dictation, create a signature line approximately $1\frac{1}{2}$ inches wide double spaced below the last line of the dictation. See **Figure 2-4, B** for an illustration of the placement of this line. After the line, key "MD". This is the line that the physician will use to sign the report after he/she has reviewed it. Next, place the physician's initials in capital letters a double space below the physician signature line, followed by a slash and your initials in lower case (refer to Figure 2-4, B). Enter another double space and key "DD" for date of dictation in capital letters followed by a colon and two blank spaces. On this line key the date the physician dictated the report. On the next line key "DT" for date of transcription in capital letters followed by a colon and two blank spaces. On this line key the date you are transcribing the report.

2. Once you have completed this task, place all forms in your Completed Work file.

South Padre Medical Center

A

Patient's Name ___Adam G. Hoverson___ Age __14__ Sex __M__ Marital Status (S) M W D

Address _____ Insurance _____

Telephone _____ Referred _____

Date	Subsequent Findings
04/08/08	See Dr. Adams' dictation dated 04/07/08.

B

Hoverson, Adam G.

04/07/08

PROBLEM: Clogged ears.

SUBJECTIVE: Adam returns to the clinic. He has had some clogged ears for the last couple of weeks. He denies any specific pain. He tried to clean his ears out and did not really get anything. He did have PE tubes about a year ago and he had apparently flat tympanograms at that time. He denies any runny nose, fever, or chills.

PAST MEDICAL HISTORY: He is on no meds and has no allergies.

PHYSICAL EXAMINATION reveals a well-developed, well-nourished young male in no obvious distress. Temperature is 96.6. Pulse is 72 and regular. Respirations 14 and unlabored. TMs are both slightly dull and red. They have tympanosclerosis. I cannot detect an obvious effusion but the TMs appear retracted.

ASSESSMENT:

1. Otitis media.
2. Tympanosclerosis.

PLAN: I have given him Bactrim DS b.i.d. for two weeks and Claritin-D one p.o. b.i.d., for two weeks. If he is not symptom free in two weeks he will let us know and we will have to do another tympanogram.

_____ , MD

RA/si

DD: 04/07/08
DT: 04/08/08

Figure **2-4**   **A, Subsequent Findings form and B, transcription format.**

Scheduling Emergency or Urgent Appointments

SUPPLIES NEEDED:
- Appointment schedule for Tuesday, April 8, 2008

1. Work the reception desk to schedule appointments.
   - The rest of the afternoon you will be working the reception desk. During the time you are at the reception desk, there will be three patients that present in need of emergency or urgent appointments.
   - Upon checking the appointment schedule, you will see that both Dr. Bond and Dr. Adams are available.

2. Schedule patients for emergency appointments.
   - Note that if there is not an exact time frame open when the patient arrives, you are to schedule with the physician that has the next available appointment time slot open. You would immediately notify the physician's nurse when an emergency patient arrives.
   - The patients will be arriving between 1 PM and 5 PM. All patients are established patients.
     - David Oakland (Est) arrives at 12:45 PM with a dog bite to the left hand. Schedule the patient with the physician who has an appointment time available. Block off 30 minutes for the appointment.
     - Larry Smith arrives at 3 PM with severe RLQ pain. Schedule this patient with the physician who has an appointment time open. Block off 45 minutes for the appointment.
     - Anne Meires (Est) arrives at 4:15 PM with a severe headache and some dizziness. Schedule this patient with the physician that has an appointment time open. Block off 30 minutes.

3. Once you have completed this task, place the appointment schedule into your Completed Work file. Make sure that your work is placed in order of day and task.

1. Using the step-by-step instructions provided in Appendix 4, Item B, schedule the appointments from Task 2.5 in the software scheduling program.

2. Once all appointments have been scheduled, print an Appointment List for Dr. Bond and Dr. Adams for today's schedule.

3. Place the Appointment List in your Completed Work folder behind Task 2.5.

DAY THREE

Wednesday, April 9, 2008

Make sure to check
evolve
for the latest
content updates

TASK **3.1**   Patient Reception and Referral

TASK **3.2**   Medical Transcription

TASK **3.3**   Insurance Claim Form

TASK **3.4**   Written Communications

TASK **3.5**   Preparing the Superbill

TASK **3.1**

Patient Reception and Referral

SUPPLIES NEEDED (p. 317):
- Appointment schedule for Wednesday, April 9, from Completed Work folder
- 2 completed Patient Face Sheets for Task 3.1 for Eskew and Kolper (located in the Supplies section)
- 2 blank Patient Information forms (located in the Supplies section)
- 2 blank Subsequent Finding forms (located in the Supplies section, Appendix 5 of the Student Manual, and in the Forms Library on the data CD)
- 1 blank referral form (located in the Supplies section)
- 2 file folders (located in the general *Practice Kit* envelope)
- 2 preprinted file labels (located in the general *Practice Kit* envelope)

1. This morning you will be working at the reception desk greeting patients as they arrive. There are two new patients scheduled with Dr. Harkness and Dr. Bond. Gladys has asked you to assemble a medical record for these two new patients scheduled today (Eskew and Kolper).

2. Assemble the patient's medical record.
   - Locate the file folders and preprinted file labels in the envelope. Secure the label to each file folder.
   - In the Supplies section you will find the Patient Face Sheets for Task 3.1 (see Figure 2-2 for the blank form). The information from the Patient Face Sheets and appointment schedule will be used to fill out Patient Information forms for each patient. Although the patients would complete the Patient Information forms themselves, today you will complete the forms to familiarize yourself with the data on the form.

DAY 3 TASK 3.1

Also, there are patients who, due to physical limitations, are unable to complete the forms themselves. Once you have completely filled out each Patient Information form, you will place the Patient Information form first in the file with the top of the form to the left edge of the file. Complete the top portion of the Subsequent Findings form and place it behind the Patient Information form.

3. Once you have completed all file folders for each new patient, place your completed work in your Completed Work folder directly behind Task 2.5.

4. Dr. Harkness has asked Gladys to handle arrangements for Henry Kolper to be referred to Dr. Morton Samson (1256 56th Avenue South, Houston, TX 99881) for his heart murmur. Dr. Morton Samson's office number is 956-934-6120. Gladys has asked you to complete a Referral form and request an appointment as soon as possible (ASAP). Place the form in the Completed Work folder.

Medical Transcription

SUPPLIES NEEDED (p. 331):
- Companion CD for Task 3.2—medical dictation from April 8
- 2 blank Subsequent Findings forms (located in the Supplies section)

Gladys will now take over the reception desk for the rest of the morning. Gladys has asked you to transcribe two of the emergency appointments that were dictated on Tuesday, April 8.

1. Key medical transcription. Locate the "Medical Transcription" area on the companion CD (Task 3.2).

2. Locate the Subsequent Findings forms. If necessary, see specific instructions regarding the format provided in Task 2.4. You are to write the patient's name, age, and sex on the form, but leave the other patient data areas blank (marital status, etc.). Another employee is responsible for obtaining and entering the data.

3. Once you have completed this task, place your completed work in the Completed Work folder directly behind Task 3.1.

Insurance Claim Form

SUPPLIES NEEDED (p. 335):

- 6 blank CMS-1500 health insurance forms (located in the Supplies section)
- 6 Patient Information and 6 Patient Face sheets from the Completed Work file from Task 2.2 for:
  - Lewis Rock
  - Edward Goldman
  - Thomas Blair
  - Jackie King
  - Joe Knight
  - Peter Silverman
- 6 superbills completed for the patients listed above from the Supplies section

1. Completion of CMS-1500 health insurance forms.
   - This afternoon you will be completing CMS-1500 health insurance forms on the six new patients that were seen yesterday, April 8 (Task 2.2). The CMS-1500 form is located in the Supplies section of the Student Manual and in the Forms Library on the companion CD. Appendix 3, Third-Party Payer List and Directions, contains a list of the information entered in each block of the form and the physicians' NPI numbers.
   - To complete each CMS-1500 health insurance form (as illustrated in **Figure 3-1**), you will need to use the Patient Information forms from Task 2.2. All patient information for Items 1 through 13 is included on the Patient Face Sheet or the Patient Information sheets completed in Task 2.2.
   - Complete Lewis Rock's form and then compare it to the information on the next page. Once you are certain of how to complete the form, complete the remaining 5 forms using the directions that begin on p. 119.
   - Using Lewis Rock's form as a guide, complete the CMS-1500 health insurance forms for the remaining five patients. The information can be taken from the Patient Information forms used in Task 2.2 and the superbills for April 8, 2008.
   - The Center's Federal ID number is 00789200 (p. 119) and is entered in Item 25 of the CMS-1500.

2. Once you have completed the CMS-1500 health insurance forms, place all forms in your Completed Work File directly behind Task 3.2. Return the Patient Information sheets to the correct location in the Completed Work folder directly behind Task 2.1.

Figure **3-1** CMS-1500 (08/05) health insurance form.

Item Number	How to Complete the Item
1	Place an X in the Medicare box
1a	201489201A
2	ROCK LEWIS L
3	03 06 1931
	Place an X in the "M" box
4	Blank
5	1000 BASS AVENUE
	SOUTH PADRE TX
	97865 (209) 555-2292
6	Place a check in the "Self" box
7	Blank
8	Place an X in the "Married" box
9	Blank
10	Place 3 Xs as follows:
	Employment, "NO"
	Auto Accident, "NO"
	Other Accident, "NO"
11	NONE

12	On "Signed" line place "SOF" (signature on file)
	Date: 04/09/08
13	On "Signed" line place "SOF"
14	Blank
15	Blank
16	Blank
17	THOMAS THOMPSON MD
17b	1100986210 (See p. 119)
18	Blank
19	Blank
20	Place an X in the "NO" box
21	On line 1, place 171.9
22	Blank
23	Blank
24a	04 08 08
24b	11
24c	Blank
24d	99204
24e	1
24f	105 00
24g	Blank
24h	Blank
24i	Blank
24j	4682943911 (See p. 119)
25	00789200, and an X in the "EIN" box (See p. 119)
26	Blank
27	Place an X in the "YES" box
28	105 00
29	Blank
30	105 00
31	Blank
32	SAME
33	(209)555-3356
	SOUTH PADRE MEDICAL CENTER
	9878 PALM DIRVE
	SOUTH PADRE TX 98765
33a	Blank
33b	8866905213 (See p. 119)

Written Communications

SUPPLIES NEEDED (p. 359):
- 1 blank Subsequent Findings form (located in the Supplies section)
- Handwritten progress note by Dr. Bond for Raymond Edwards

1. Progress note.
   - Earlier today Dr. Bond completed a handwritten note on Raymond Edwards, which you will now key onto a Subsequent Findings form (see instructions for completing the form provided in Task 2.4). Dr. Bond saw Mr. Edwards on Friday, April 4, 2008.

2. Once you have completed the progress note, place your completed work in the Completed Work folder directly behind Task 3.3.

Preparing the Superbill

SUPPLIES NEEDED (p. 363):
- 6 blank superbills (illustrated in **Figure 3-2**) (located in the Supplies section)
- April 10, 2008 Appointment Schedule
- 6 completed Patient Face Sheets for Task 3.5 (located in the Supplies section)

1. Preparing superbills for patient services.
   - Gladys has asked you to prepare the superbills for some of the patients scheduled for tomorrow. The shaded areas on the superbill in **Figure 3-2**

South Padre Medical Center

9878 Palm Drive
South Padre, TX 98765
Telephone (209) 555-3356

Gerald Bond, MD
Ray Adams, MD
Joyce Harkness, MD
Anthony Clark, MD

PATIENT'S LAST NAME	FIRST	ACCOUNT #	BIRTHDATE / /	SEX ☐ MALE ☐ FEMALE	TODAY'S DATE / /

INSURANCE COMPANY	SUBSCRIBER	GROUP/PLAN #	SUB. #	TIME

ASSIGNMENT: I hereby assign my insurance benefits to be paid directly to the undersigned physician. I am financially responsible for non-covered services.
SIGNED: (Patient, Or parent, if Minor)_____ DATE: / /

RELEASE: I hereby authorize the physician to release to my insurance carriers any information required to process this claim.
SIGNED: (Patient, Or Parent, if Minor) _____ DATE: / /

✓ DESCRIPTION	CPT	Diag.	FEE	✓ DESCRIPTION	CPT	Diag.	FEE	✓ DESCRIPTION	CPT	Diag.	FEE
OFFICE VISIT				IMMUNIZATIONS/INJECTIONS				PROCEDURES			
NEW PATIENT				Admin of Vaccine 1	90471			Inhalation treatment	94640		
Problem Focused				Admin of Vac 2+	90472			Demo/eval treatment	94664		
Exp Problem Focused	99202			TB Tine, skin	86486			Vital Capacity	94150		
Detailed	99203			Pneumococcal	90732			Spirometry	94010		
Comp/ Mod MDM	99204			Medicare code	G0009			EKG w/interpretation	93000		
Comp/ High MDM	99205			Influenza <3	90657	I&D abscess		10060			
ESTABLISHED PATEINT				Influenza 3 and >	90658			Remove skin tag <15	11200		
Minimal/Nurse Visit	99211			Medicare code	G0008			EXCISION BENIGN LESIONS (inc. margins)			
Problem Focused	99212			Varicella	90716			Trunk, arms, legs			
Exp Problem Forcused	99213			DPT	90701			0.5 cm or less	11400		
Detailed	99214			DT children	90702			0.6 to 1.0 cm	11401		
Comprehensive	99215			Td adult	90718			1.1 to 2.0 cm	11402		
CONSULTATION				DtaP	90700			2.1 to 3.0 cm	11403		
Problem Focused	99241			IPV	90713			Scalp, neck, hand, ft			
Exp Problem Focused	99242			Rubella	90706			0.5 cm or less	11420		
Detailed	99243			MMR	90707			0.6 to 1.0 cm	11421		
Comp/ Mod MDM	99244			Hep B Child	90744			1.1 to 2.0 cm	11422		
Comp/High MDM	99245			Hep B Adult	90746			2.1 to 3.0 cm	11423		
				IM Administration	96372			Face, ears, eyelids, lip			
Requesting Provider _____				Compazine	J0780			0.5 cm or less	11440		
Post-op Exam	99024	0.00		Demerol	J2175			0.6 to 1.0 cm	11441		
PREVENTIVE MEDICINE				Depo-Provera	J1055			1.1 to 2.0 cm	11442		
NEW PATIENT				Dexamethasone	J1100			2.1 to 3.0 cm	11443		
Infant – 1 yr	99381			Solumedrol	J1720			EXCISION MALIGNANT LESIONS (inc. margins)			
1 yr – 4 yr	99382			Antigen admin 1	95115			Trunk, arms, legs			
5 yr – 11 yr	99383			Antigen admin 2+	95117			0.5 cm or less	11600		
12 yr – 17 yr	99384			LABORATORY				0.6 to 1.0 cm	11601		
18 yr – 39 yr	99385			Blood collect Vein	36415			1.1 to 2.0 cm	11602		
40 yr – 64 yr	99386			Capillary	36416			2.1 to 3.0 cm	11603		
65 yr and over	99387			Hemoglobin	85018			Scalp, neck, hand, ft			
ESTABLISHED PATIENT				Glucose, reagent	82948			0.5 cm or less	11620		
Infant – 1 yr	99391			Pregnancy, Serum	84702			0.6 to 1.0 cm	11621		
1 yr – 4 yr	99392			Pregnancy, Urine	81025			1.1 to 2.0 cm	11622		
5 yr – 11 yr	99393			Health panel	80050			2.1 to 3.0 cm	11623		
12 yr – 17 yr	99394			B Met Pan Cal ion	80047			Face, ears, eyelids, lip			
18 yr – 39 yr	99395			B Met Pan Cal tot	80048			0.5 cm or less	11640		
40 yr – 64 yr	99396			C Metabolic panel	80053			0.6 to 1.0 cm	11641		
65 yr and over	99397			Ob panel	80055			1.1 to 2.0 cm	11642		
SUPPLIES				Lipid panel	80061			2.1 to 3.0 cm	11643		
Take home burn kit	99070			UA Auto w/o micro	81003			*Awaiting path report*	☐ *Yes*	☐ *No*	
Take home wound kit	99070			UA dip stck	81000			Wart destruction < 14	17110		
Miscellaneous				Strep test	87880			Cerumen removal	69210		
				Hemoccult	82270			Endometrial biopsy	58100		
MODIFIERS				Lab Handling	99000						
Significant/Sep EM provided with other service	-25			30 DAYS				60 DAYS		90 DAYS	
Unrelated EM in post op period	-24										
Repeat procedure, same physician, same day	-76										

DIAGNOSIS:	RETURN APPOINTMENT: (days) (wks) (mos) (PRN)	TODAY'S TOTAL	
1) _____	NEXT APPOINTMENT: M - T - W - TH - F - S	PREVIOUS BALANCE	
2) _____		AMOUNT REC'D TODAY REC'D BY _____	
3) _____	DATE / / TIME		
4) _____	Provider's Signature:	BALANCE DUE	

Figure **3-2** **Superbill with shading.**

illustrate those areas that you are to complete for this task using information from the appointment schedule and the Patient Face Sheets for Task 3.5.

- You will be completing the aging (length of time the amount has been owed) for each of the superbills you prepare. Complete a superbill for the following patients:

Patient	Previous Balance	30 Days	60 Days	90 Days
a. Mary Bogert	$206.73	$100.73	$106.00	0
b. Elizabeth Fenton	0	0	0	0
c. Amanda Foster	$934.58	0	$900.00	$34.58
d. Jack Masci	$509.00	0	0	$509.00
e. Jean Olson	0	0	0	0
f. Lori Whittaker	0	0	0	0

- In the "Today's Date" (upper right hand corner) space of the superbill, use the date 04/10/2008, as this is the date of service on which the patient will be seen.
- The "Account #" on the superbill is to be left blank.

2. Once you have completed all 6 superbills, place your completed work in alphabetic order in the Completed Work folder directly behind Task 3.4.

Good job! You have completed Day Three of your internship.

FOUR

Make sure to check
evolve
for the latest
content updates

Thursday, April 10, 2008

TASK **4.1**   Telephone Messages and Appointment Schedule

TASK **4.2**   Correspondence and Mail

TASK **4.3**   Scheduling Appointments

TASK **4.4**   Records Management

TASK **4.1**

Telephone Messages and Appointment Schedule

SUPPLIES NEEDED (p. 387):
- Appointment sheets for Thursday, April 10, to Friday, April 18, from your Completed Work folder
- Companion CD containing the telephone messages from April 9 (Task 4.1)
- 4 blank Telephone Records (located in the Supplies section)

1. Locate the "Telephone Messages" area on the companion CD (Task 4.1)
   - Telephone messages came into the office during the hours in which the clinic was closed. Gladys has asked you to listen to the voice mail of the calls and complete a Telephone Record for each call.
   - If a patient requests a specific time for an appointment, you are to schedule the appointment as close as possible to the time requested by the patient.
   - Indicate the date and time of the tentative appointment in the "Response" block on the Telephone Record.
   - If a message is left for an employee of the clinic staff, you are to record the message for the appropriate person on the Telephone Record.

2. Once you have completed all messages, place all Telephone Record forms into the Completed Work folder.

1. Using the step-by-step instructions provided in Appendix 2, Item N, schedule the appointments using the Telephone Records from Task 4.1 and the appointment sheets in the software scheduling program.

2. Once all appointments have been scheduled, print an Appointment List for Drs. Bond and Harkness for April 16.

3. Place the Appointment List in alphabetic order in your Completed Work folder behind Task 4.1.

Correspondence and Mail

SUPPLIES NEEDED (p. 389):
- Telephone records from this morning (Task 4.1)
- 2 letterhead forms (**Figure 4-1**) (located in the Supplies section)
- Incoming Mail form dated April 10 (located in the Supplies section)
- Mail Sorting form (**Figure 4-2**) (located in the Supplies section)

1. **Preparing correspondence and separating of mail.**
   - Per Gladys's instructions, you will be preparing letters for her signature. These letters will be in response to the patients that left telephone messages in Task 4.1, requesting appointments at a later date.
   - The address for Mr. Sven Johnson is 509 Mockingham Road, South Padre, TX, 98765, and the address for Mr. George Jones is 79892 Elf Street, South Padre, TX, 98765.
   - Prepare responses on letterhead to Sven Johnson and George Jones regarding their requested appointments. Give the date and time you have indicated on the Telephone Record in the "Response" block.
   - On completion of this first part of this task, file the two letters in the Completed Work folder.

   Once you have finished the correspondence, you will be sorting mail.

1. **Sorting of incoming mail.**
   - Gladys has given the instructions that you are to sort the mail by person and department. You will get all of the mail from the Incoming Mail form. You will sort the mail by doctor, insurance, accounts receivable, human resources, waiting room, and Gladys (Refer to Appendix 2, Policies and Procedures, Item G). You will indicate the mail received under the appropriate heading (see **Figure 4-2**).

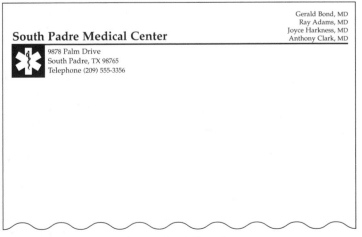

South Padre Medical Center

Gerald Bond, MD
Ray Adams, MD
Joyce Harkness, MD
Anthony Clark, MD

9878 Palm Drive
South Padre, TX 98765
Telephone (209) 555-3356

Figure **4-1** **South Padre Medical Center letterhead.**

```
┌─────────────────────────────────┐
│           MAIL SORTING          │
│                                 │
│  Dr. Bond                       │
│  1, 17                          │
│                                 │
│  Dr. Harkness                   │
│                                 │
│  Dr. Adams                      │
│                                 │
│  Dr. Clark                      │
│                                 │
│  Gladys                         │
│                                 │
│  Accounts receivable            │
│                                 │
│  Insurance                      │
│                                 │
│  Human Resources                │
│                                 │
│  Waiting Room                   │
│                                 │
└─────────────────────────────────┘
```

Figure **4-2**   Incoming Mail sorting form for Thursday, April 10.

2. Once you have completed this part of Task 4.2, place behind the first part of this task and place in Completed Work folder directly behind Task 4.1.

Scheduling Appointments

SUPPLIES NEEDED (p. 397):
* Appointment sheets dated Monday, April 7, to Friday, April 18 (located in the general *Practice Kit* envelope)
* Four previously completed Telephone Records, dated Thursday, April 10 (located in the Supplies section)

1. Work patient reception, answer the telephone, and schedule appointments.
   * The patient information to schedule each appointment is located on the Telephone Record (Task 4.3).
   * You will need to schedule each appointment as requested by the patient on the Telephone Record.
   * Indicate the date, time, and length of appointment on the Telephone Record.

   Lilly Rice is known to Dr. Clark, so Gladys directs you to schedule her for 60 minutes rather than the usual 30 minutes. Also, Gladys directs Kristie Olson be scheduled for 30 minutes.

2. Place completed appointment sheets in Completed Work folder. Place the Telephone Record in the Completed Work folder.

1. Using the step-by-step instructions provided in Appendix 2, Item N, schedule the appointments using the previously completed Telephone Records from Task 4.3 and the appointment sheets in the software scheduling program.

2. Once all appointments have been scheduled, print an Appointment List for Drs. Bond, Adams, and Clark for those days with new appointments.

3. Place the Appointment List in your Completed Work folder behind Task 4.2.

Records Management

SUPPLIES NEEDED (p. 399):
- 2 blank Patient Information forms (located in the Supplies section)
- 2 blank Subsequent Findings forms (located in the Supplies section)
- 2 file folder labels (located in the general *Practice Kit* envelope)
- 2 file folders (located in the general *Practice Kit* envelope)
- Telephone Records from Task 4.3

1. **You will now establish medical records for the two new patients from Task 4.3—Kristie Olson and Lilly Rice.**
   - Locate the file folders and the file labels in the packet.
   - Secure the labels for each patient to the file folders.

2. **Assemble the patient's medical record.**
   - Locate the Patient Information forms and complete the forms with only the information taken from the messages in Task 4.3 for Kristie Olson and Lilly Rice.
   - The order of the medical record for Kristie Olson and Lilly Rice should be:
     - Completed Patient Information form (first)
     - Subsequent Findings sheet (second)

3. **Once you have completed this task, place in alphabetic order in the Completed Work folder directly behind Task 4.3.**

   You have just finished Day Four; you're almost halfway through your internship. Good job! Let's go on to Day Five.

DAY FIVE

Make sure to check *evolve* for the latest content updates

Friday, April 11, 2008

TASK **5.1**   Medical Transcription

TASK **5.2**   Posting Charges to a Superbill

TASK **5.3**   Billing and Banking Procedures

TASK **5.4**   Petty Cash and Checking

TASK **5.1**

Medical Transcription

SUPPLIES NEEDED (p. 407):
- 2 Operative Report forms (**Figure 5-1**) (located in the Supplies section)
- Companion CD containing medical transcription from April 9 and 10, Task 5.1.

1. Locate the "Medical Transcription" area on the companion CD (Task 5.1).
   - Today you will start your morning by completing the transcription. Gladys is going to cover the reception desk and you are to key in operative reports dictated by Dr. Bond and Dr. Clark.

2. On completion of the medical transcription, place in the Completed Work folder directly behind Task 4.4.
   - From this point on, no directions will be provided for the location of forms. It will be assumed that you will get the forms from the Supplies section of this text, Appendix 5, the Forms Library on the companion CD, or the Evolve site.

DAY 5 TASK 5.1

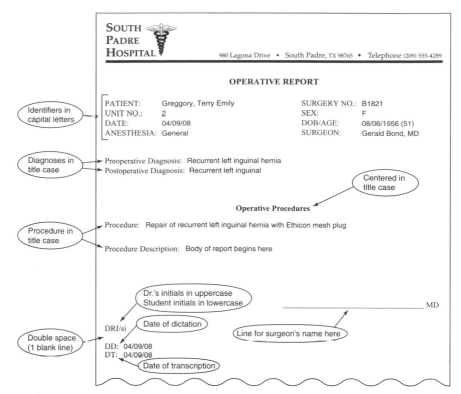

Figure **5-1** Operative Report form with explanations.

Posting Charges to a Superbill

SUPPLIES NEEDED:

- 6 superbills from Completed Task folder from Task 3.5
- Fee Schedule (displayed below in **Figure 5-2**)

1. Gladys has asked you to post charges for the patients seen yesterday. Normally the diagnosis codes and services provided during the patients' visits would already be entered either by provider or clinical staff; however, in order to assist you in becoming more familiar with the superbill you will be entering the service(s) provided for these patients, and completing the requested future appointments area if indicated. You are **not** to schedule the appointments indicated, just enter any future appointment onto the superbill in the "Return Appointment" area. Using the superbills completed in Task 3.5, indicate the following services and diagnosis codes for these patients:

√	DESCRIPTION	CPT	Diag.	FEE
	OFFICE VISIT			
	NEW PATIENT			
	Problem Focused			
	Exp Problem Focused	99202		75.00
	Detailed	99203		95.00
	Comp/ Mod MDM	99204		105.00
	Comp/ High MDM	99205		120.00
	ESTABLISHED PATEINT			
	Minimal/Nurse Visit	99211		45.00
	Problem Focused	99212		55.00
	Exp Problem Forcused	99213		65.00
	Detailed	99214		85.00
	Comprehensive	99215		105.00
	CONSULTATION			
	Problem Focused	99241		120.00
	Exp Problem Focused	99242		140.00
	Detailed	99243		160.00
	Comp/ Mod MDM	99244		200.00
	Comp/High MDM	99245		250.00
	Requesting Provider _____			
	Post-op Exam	99024		0.00
	PREVENTIVE MEDICINE			
	NEW PATIENT			
	Infant – 1 yr	99381		95.00
	1 yr – 4 yr	99382		110.00
	5 yr – 11 yr	99383		110.00
	12 yr – 17 yr	99384		135.00
	18 yr – 39 yr	99385		150.00
	40 yr – 64 yr	99386		170.00
	65 yr and over	99387		200.00
	ESTABLISHED PATIENT			
	Infant – 1 yr	99391		80.00
	1 yr – 4 yr	99392		80.00
	5 yr – 11 yr	99393		80.00
	12 yr – 17 yr	99394		100.00
	18 yr – 39 yr	99395		120.00
	40 yr – 64 yr	99396		140.00
	65 yr and over	99397		160.00

Figure **5-2** Fee schedule.

Patient	Service	Diagnosis Code
a. Mary Bogert	99213	599.0
Dr. Adams has requested a return visit in 10 days		
b. Elizabeth Fenton	99387	V70.0
c. Amanda Foster	99213	V22.2
Dr. Adams has requested a return visit in 1 month		
d. Jack Masci	99214	531.0
Dr. Clark has requested a return visit in 10 days		
e. Jean Olson	99205	278.00
Dr. Clark has requested a return visit in 15 days		
f. Lori Whittaker	99244	455.9
Physician requesting consultation was Dr. Blackburn		

2. **Figure 5-2** illustrates the office visit area of the superbill. For your use, Gladys has written the fee schedule on a superbill. You will be using these amounts to post the charges for the patient services to each of the superbills you have just completed. You are not to total the balance due yet. You will be instructed to do that in Task 5.3. However, be certain to enter "Today's Total" in the appropriate box on the form.

3. Once you have completed all six superbills, place in alphabetic order and go on to Task 5.3, where you will enter further information onto these superbills.

56

Billing and Banking Procedures

SUPPLIES NEEDED (p. 411):
- 6 superbills completed in Task 5.2
- 1 Journal of Daily Charges and Payments (located in the Supplies section)
- 6 blank patient statements (located in the Supplies section)
- 7 partially completed patient statements (located in the Supplies section)
- 1 deposit ticket (located in the Supplies section)

1. Gladys asks you to post payments to the superbills for some of the patients seen yesterday. Usually, Kerri Marshall, the insurance specialist, would post payments the day the payments were received, but Gladys wanted you to have an opportunity to process the payments as a part of your internship experience. **Figure 5-3** illustrates the blocks where payment information is to be entered on the superbill. The following are checks received from the patients represented on the superbills. Be certain to calculate the Balance Due and place your initials on the line next to the "Rec'd by". If the patient pays nothing, initial and enter zero in the amount paid.

Patient	Payment
a. Mary Bogert, 2502 32nd Avenue South, South Padre, Texas 98765	$25.00
b. Elizabeth Fenton, 201 2nd Avenue North, South Padre, Texas 98765	$125.00
c. Amanda Foster, 1603 Todd Avenue, South Padre, Texas 98765	$0
d. Jack Masci, 809 Heights Drive, South Padre, Texas 98765	$75.00
e. Jean Olson, 2405 Elm Way Drive, South Padre, Texas 98765	$50.00
f. Lori Whittaker, 3204 34th Avenue South, South Padre, Texas 98765	$100.00

2. Next, you are to enter the above payments two more times: once onto a statement for the patient and once onto the Journal of Daily Charges and Payments. **Figure 5-4** illustrates the placement of the payment data on Mary Bogert's patient statement. Note that the "DATE" is the date the service was provided to the patient, not the date the charges and payments were posted. **Figure 5-5** illustrates the Journal of Daily Charges and Payments areas that you will be completing for the patient Mary Bogert. You will enter the payments on the patient statement and the Journal of Daily Charges and Payments.

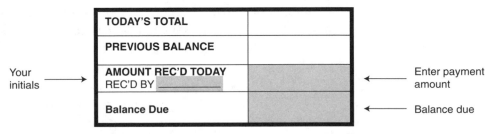

Figure **5-3** **Superbill payment placement area to be completed.**

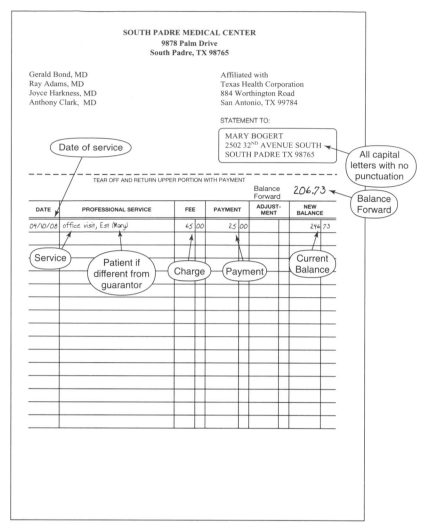

Figure **5-4** **Patient statement for Mary Bogert.**

JOURNAL OF DAILY CHARGES & PAYMENTS

	DATE	PROFESSIONAL SERVICE	FEE		PAYMENT		ADJUST-MENT	NEW BALANCE		OLD BALANCE		PATIENT'S NAME	
1	04/10/08	office visit, Est (Mary)	65	00	25	00		246	73	206	73	Bogert, Mary	1
2													2

Figure **5-5** **Journal of Daily Charges and Payments.**

Complete the patient statements as follows:

Statement to:	Patient's name and address in capital letters with no punctuation
Balance Forward:	The previous amount from the last statement
Date:	Date the service was provided
Professional Service:	The type of service, such as "office visit", and if the patient is an established patient "(Est)" or new patient "(New)". Also include the name of the patient if different from the guarantor (the person responsible for paying the bill).
Fee:	The charge for the service

Payment: The payment made to the account
New Balance: The amount due after adding charges and subtracting payments

3. Now record the following payments made today onto the Journal of Daily Charges and Payments and also onto the patient statements. The partially completed statements for these patients are located in the Supplies section. Use today's date in the DATE column of the Journal of Daily Charges and Payments.

a. Thomas Blair $26.00   Check number 890
b. Maynard Hovlett $150.00   Cash
c. Larry Smith $35.00   Check number 15346
d. Anne Meires $55.00   Cash
e. Edward Goldman $50.00   Check number 90001
f. Jasper Hunt $100.00   Check number 236
g. Lewis Rock $200.00   Check number 101011

4. Now that you have entered all payment information onto the Journal of Daily Charges and Payments, you are ready to proof the posting. You do this by adding up columns A through E (illustrated in **Figure 5-6**) and placing the totals on line 31 of the journal sheet under the bold line (see Figure 5-6).

Complete the Journal of Daily Charges and Payments as follows:
Date: The date of the service was provided
Professional Service: The type of service, such as "office visit", and if the patient is an established patient (Est) or a new patient (New). Also include the name of the patient if different from the guarantor (the person responsible for paying the bill)
Fee: The charge for the service
Payment: The payment made to the account
New Balance: The amount due after adding charges and subtracting payments
Old Balance: The amount brought forward from last month
Patient's Name: Last name, comma, first name

These totals are then transferred to the "Arithmetic Posting Proof" area of the form (see Figure 5-6). Your entries are correct when the resulting number from the proofing equals the number in column D ("New Balance") on the journal form.

5. Gladys has asked that you prepare a deposit ticket (**Figure 5-7**) for all the cash and checks you have posted to the journal sheet. Complete the deposit ticket now. The total of the bank deposit should be the same as the total in column B ("Payments") of the journal.

6. When you have finished entering all the information for this task, place all the documentation in the Completed Work folder after Task 5.1.

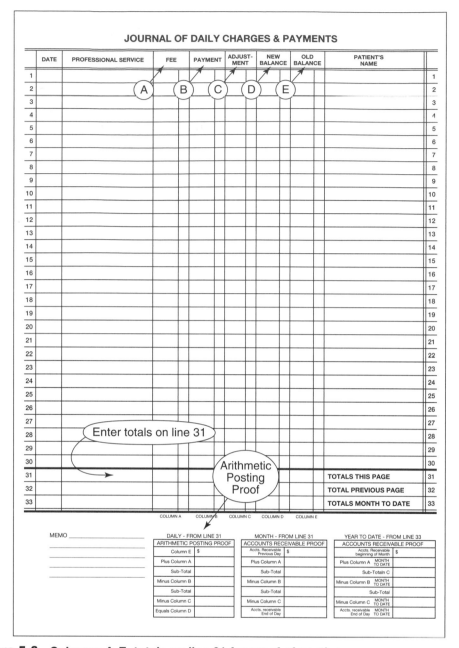

Figure **5-6** Columns A-E, totals on line 31 for proof of posting.

1. Using the completed superbills from Task 5.3, Gladys wants you to enter the charges and payments for each patient into the new software system. She has given you step-by-step instructions for entry of both charges and payments in Appendix 4, Items G through H.

2. Once you have entered the charges and payments for all the superbills, print a Patient Ledger for each of these patient accounts. Directions on how to print these are located in Appendix 4, Item I.

DEPOSIT TICKET

SOUTH PADRE MEDICAL CENTER
9878 PALM DRIVE
SOUTH PADRE, TX 98765

FIRST NATIONAL BANK
100 FIRST STREET
SOUTH PADRE, TX 98765

DATE _____
DEPOSITS MAY NOT BE AVAILABLE FOR IMMEDIATE WITHDRAWAL

		DOLLARS	CENTS
CURRENCY			
COIN			
CHECKS	LIST EACH SEPARATELY		
1			
2			
3			
4			
5			
6			
7			
8			
9			
10			
11			
12			
13			
14			
15			
16			
17			
18			
19			
20			
21			
22			
23			
24			
25			
26			
27			
28			
TOTAL FROM OTHER SIDE OR ATTACHED LIST			
PLEASE RE-ENTER TOTAL HERE	TOTAL		

00001001002005

$

Total

Checks and other items are received for deposit subject to the provisions of the Uniform Commercial Code or any applicable colllection agreement.

Figure **5-7** **Deposil ticket entry of total.**

3. Next, print a Patient Day Sheet User Match Report for April 11. Directions on how to print the report are in Appendix 4, Item J.

4. Place the Patient Ledgers and Patient Day Sheet User Match Report in your Completed Work folder behind Task 5.2.

DAY 5 TASK **5.3**

Petty Cash and Checking

SUPPLIES NEEDED (p. 441):

- 1 letterhead form
- 2 checks (located in the Supplies section)
- 1 petty cash journal form (located in the Supplies section)
- 1 check register (located in the general *Practice Kit* envelope)
- 2 completed statements (Field and Zacharizison) (located in the Supplies section)
- Patient statement for Jack Masci from Task 5.3.

1. Today Gladys has requested that you write a letter (use letterhead) to Jack Masci regarding his account, on which $509 is in the 90 days aged category. Prepare the letter for Gladys to sign. Although Mr. Masci has made a payment, he has not sufficiently paid down the balance. Messages requesting payment on the account have been sent to Mr. Masci on three previous occasions. Inform Mr. Masci that he should contact Kerri Marshall to make arrangements for payment of the account or the account will be turned over to the collection agency. A $75 payment was posted to Mr. Masci's account in Task 5.3.

2. Gladys has asked you to write a check for $100 to be used to set up a petty cash fund for the office. The check is to be written paid to the order of the "First National Bank—Cash" and recorded on the Check Register. The address of the bank is to be listed on lines 2 and 3 of the "To The Order Of" area on the sample check as illustrated in **Figure 5-8.** When you have the check prepared, you are to begin the journal that Gladys drafted that will be used to keep track of how the petty cash funds are spent by

South Padre Medical Center	**FIRST NATIONAL BANK**	98-95
9878 Palm Drive	100 FIRST STREET	1251
SOUTH PADRE, TX 98765	SOUTH PADRE, TX 98765	

NO   872

PAY *Fifty Dollars and no/100* _____ DOLLARS

DATE	CHECK NO.	AMOUNT
10/30/07	872	50 00

TO THE ORDER OF *First National Bank*
100 First Street
South Padre, TX 98765

⑈0⑈0123⑈ ⑆4567⑈8901⑇ ⑈1234567890⑈

Figure **5-8** **Sample check.**

entering the beginning balance at the top right-hand corner of the petty cash journal.

3. You are now to write a check to reimburse a patient for a credit balance, post a nonsufficient fund check, and post a collection agency payment. You will record each transaction on the Check Register. The following is the information to perform these tasks:
   - Write a check to Gloria Hydorn for $26.89 to reimburse her for a credit balance on her account. Her address is 862 Oceanside Way, South Padre, TX 98765. Kerri has already recorded the refund on Gloria's account. Enter this check information on the Check Register.
   - A check deposited last week has been returned for nonsufficient funds (NSF). The check is from David Oakland for $56.00. Kerri has made the notation of NSF check on the patient statement. You are to record the NSF check on the Check Register by writing "David Oakland" in the "Paid To" column, using today's date in the "Date" column, NSF in the "Check Number" and "Description" columns, and deducting the $56.00 from the balance in the Check Register.
   - Record a check on the Check Register that was received from the Island Collection Agency today in the amount of $309.32. Kerri has already credited the various patients' accounts represented by this check. In the "Description" column indicate "Collections" and record the $309.32 in the deposit column.

4. Kerri has asked you to post a credit to Norma Field's patient statement in the amount of $100 and to make an adjustment to the account for $80 because today Kerri received an explanation of benefits (EOB, an explanation of the payments and adjustments), number 2001134. Kerri explained to you that the $80 was the amount that Medicare would not pay and that we cannot charge the patient this amount because our physicians participate in the Medicare program. The $80 becomes a write-off to the clinic, which means that the amount is deducted from the patient's account as if it were never charged.

5. Kerri has asked that you reconcile the clinic's bank statement for her. Reconciliation of a bank statement is a procedure in which the balance from a bank statement, as illustrated in **Figure 5-9**, is compared with the customer's checkbook balance with the addition of any deposits and/or deductions since the bank statement was issued. Kerri provides a bank statement that indicates the balance was $21,028.02 as of April 9. Since then, Kerri deposited checks in the amount of $5,020.69 on April 10. Using the check register you used earlier today, determine if the clinic's check register balance is the same as the bank's balance using the following formula:

   A. Bank statement balance $21,028.02_____
      a. Less outstanding checks (there are 3, from Check Register)   _____
      b. Plus deposits not shown (there are 2)   _____
   B. Corrected bank balance   _____
      a. Less any NSF or bank charges (there is 1)   _____
   C. Corrected checkbook balance   _____

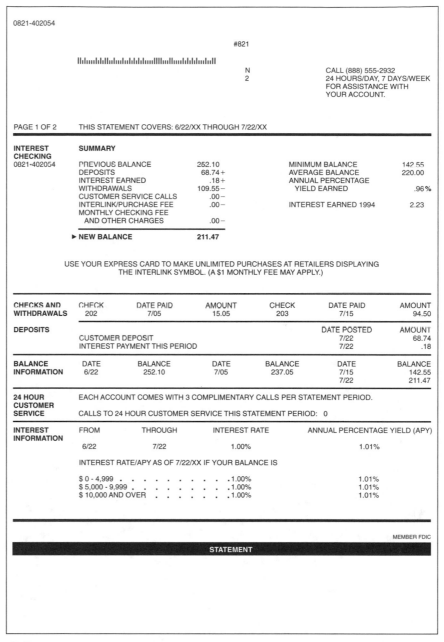

0821-402054

#821

|ldunldllludadldluuIIIlludlundddualdl

N
2

CALL (888) 555-2932
24 HOURS/DAY, 7 DAYS/WEEK
FOR ASSISTANCE WITH
YOUR ACCOUNT.

PAGE 1 OF 2   THIS STATEMENT COVERS: 6/22/XX THROUGH 7/22/XX

INTEREST CHECKING
0821-402054

SUMMARY

PREVIOUS BALANCE	252.10		MINIMUM BALANCE	142.55
DEPOSITS	68.74+		AVERAGE BALANCE	220.00
INTEREST EARNED	.18+		ANNUAL PERCENTAGE	
WITHDRAWALS	109.55−		YIELD EARNED	.96%
CUSTOMER SERVICE CALLS	.00−			
INTERLINK/PURCHASE FEE	.00−		INTEREST EARNED 1994	2.23
MONTHLY CHECKING FEE AND OTHER CHARGES	.00−			
▶ **NEW BALANCE**	**211.47**			

USE YOUR EXPRESS CARD TO MAKE UNLIMITED PURCHASES AT RETAILERS DISPLAYING
THE INTERLINK SYMBOL. (A $1 MONTHLY FEE MAY APPLY.)

CHECKS AND WITHDRAWALS

CHECK	DATE PAID	AMOUNT	CHECK	DATE PAID	AMOUNT
202	7/05	15.05	203	7/15	94.50

DEPOSITS

	DATE POSTED	AMOUNT
CUSTOMER DEPOSIT	7/22	68.74
INTEREST PAYMENT THIS PERIOD	7/22	.18

BALANCE INFORMATION

DATE	BALANCE	DATE	BALANCE	DATE	BALANCE
6/22	252.10	7/05	237.05	7/15	142.55
				7/22	211.47

24 HOUR CUSTOMER SERVICE

EACH ACCOUNT COMES WITH 3 COMPLIMENTARY CALLS PER STATEMENT PERIOD.

CALLS TO 24 HOUR CUSTOMER SERVICE THIS STATEMENT PERIOD: 0

INTEREST INFORMATION

FROM	THROUGH	INTEREST RATE	ANNUAL PERCENTAGE YIELD (APY)
6/22	7/22	1.00%	1.01%

INTEREST RATE/APY AS OF 7/22/XX IF YOUR BALANCE IS

$ 0 - 4,999 . . . . .1.00%		1.01%
$ 5,000 - 9,999 . . . . .1.00%		1.01%
$ 10,000 AND OVER 1.00%		1.01%

MEMBER FDIC

STATEMENT

Figure **5-9** **Example of bank statement.** *(From Young AP and Kennedy DB: Kinn's the medical assistant: an applied learning approach, ed 9, St. Louis, 2003, Saunders.)*

The checkbook balances when the amount on line C of the formula is the same as the last balance in the check register.

6. Kerri asked that you post a $37.50 credit to Maynard Zacharizison's account based on a check received from the Island Collection Agency. Mr. Zacharizison's account balance was $200 and the collection agency made an agreement with him that if he would pay $75 total on the account, the remainder of the bill would be removed, which he has now done. You are to credit the account with the second payment of $37.50 and adjust the account (enter $125.00 in the "Adjustment" column). Mr. Zacharizison's balance will now be zero.

7. You will place all work in the Completed Work folder directly behind Task 5.3.

Well, you're over halfway there. Great job so far! Now let's move on to Day Six.

DAY SIX

Make sure to check **evolve** for the latest content updates

Monday, April 14, 2008

TASK **6.1**

Internet Research

SUPPLIES NEEDED:
- Computer with access to the Internet
- 1 file folder
- 1 file folder label

1. Research "Incident To"
   - This morning Gladys has a special project for you to do. You will be going onto the Internet and researching "Incident To" for the physicians. "Incident to" services are those that are furnished at the same time as the physician's professional service.

2. Work from a computer with Internet access
   - Do a search typing in the words "incident to" using a search engine such as www.google.com or www.yahoo.com. Place quotation marks at the beginning and end of the entry to ensure that you locate the entire statement, not just one of the two words of the search. You are looking for information on "Incident To" as it relates to billing requirements for Medicare patients. Locate what you think is the best information on the subject and print five copies.

3. Prepare a file folder with file folder label
   - Locate the file folder and file label. Type or write "INCIDENT TO" in capital letters on the label. Secure the label to the file folder.
   - Place the research papers in the folder and file in the Completed Work folder.

DAY 6 TASK 6.1

Establishing a Meeting

SUPPLIES NEEDED (p. 453):
* Patient appointment sheet for Wednesday, April 16, from your Completed Work folder
* 5 memo forms (located in the Supplies section)

1. Assist Gladys with establishing a meeting.
   * You will be assisting Gladys with establishing a meeting with the information you researched on "Incident To" in Task 6.1. The physicians requested the information on "Incident To" and would like Gladys to present the information researched at a meeting of all clinic physicians. The meeting is to be scheduled for Wednesday, April 16, from 12 PM to 1 PM.
   * First, you will need to review the appointment schedule for Wednesday, April 16, to determine if each physician is available at the time indicated. Once you have established that all physicians are available, mark the schedule for the meeting by placing an X though the time block of 12 PM though 1 PM and noting "Office Meeting" on each physician's schedule.
   * You will need 5 memo forms. Gladys has asked you to prepare a memo to each of the physicians (Drs. Bond, Adams, Harkness, and Clark) and one for Gladys as a reminder.

2. What to include in the memo.
   * The memo will include today's date and all physicians' complete names followed by "MD". Be sure to **bold** each name that pertains to the physician it is sent to (as illustrated in **Figure 6-1**). The memo will also

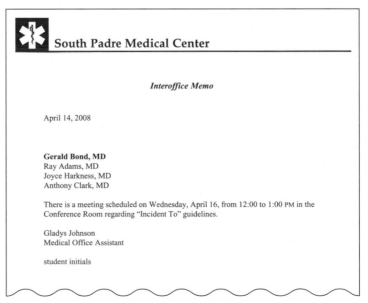

Figure **6-1** Interoffice memo.

state the date and time of the meeting, the place where the meeting will be held (Conference Room), and the topic to be discussed.

3. Once you have completed all memos, place in the folder you prepared and then in the Completed Work folder directly behind Task 6.1.

1. Enter the "Incident To" meeting into the software for all Center physicians.

Telephone Messages

SUPPLIES NEEDED (p. 463):
- Companion CD containing the telephone messages for Task 6.3
- 5 blank Telephone Records (located in the Supplies section)

1. Locate the "Telephone Messages" area on the companion CD (Task 6.3).
   - Telephone messages came into the office during the lunch hour. Gladys has asked you to listen to the voice mail of the calls and complete a Telephone Record for each call.
   - If a patient requests an appointment, you will be completing the request in Task 6.4.

TASK **6.4** ▐█████████████████████████████████████

Scheduling Appointments

SUPPLIES NEEDED (p. 467):
- 10 previously dated appointment sheets for Monday, April 7, to Friday, April 18, from your Completed Work file
- 2 file folders
- 2 preprinted file labels
- 2 blank Patient Information forms (located in the Supplies section)
- Telephone Records from Task 6.3

1. Assemble the patient's medical record.
   - Locate the file folders and the file labels in the packet. Using the Telephone Records from Task 6.3, locate the labels for the two new patients that are requesting appointments. Secure the label to each file folder.
   - For each new patient, fill out the Patient Information form that is supplied for you with data from the Telephone Record. Place the form for each patient into the correct patient file folder.

2. Schedule appointments.
   - Finish this task by scheduling the two new and one established patient appointments as requested from the Telephone Records.
   - Once you have scheduled the appointment that is indicated on the Telephone Record, indicate the appointment date and time on the Telephone Record in the "Reponse" block.

3. Once you have finished this task, place the Telephone Records (Task 6.3) directly behind Task 6.2. and place the file folders with the Patient Information forms inside each folder into the Completed Work folder directly behind Task 6.3.

1. Schedule appointments using the Telephone Records from Task 6.3 and the appointment sheets in the software scheduling program.

2. Once all appointments have been scheduled, print an Appointment List for all providers for each day an appointment was scheduled during this task.

3. Place the Appointment Lists in your Completed Work folder behind Task 6.3.

DAY 6 TASK 6.4

DAY SEVEN

Make sure to check **evolve** for the latest content updates

Tuesday, April 15, 2008

TASK **7.1**   Insurance Claim Forms

TASK **7.2**   Patient Reception

TASK **7.3**   Scheduling Nursing Home Services

TASK **7.1**

Insurance Claim Forms

SUPPLIES NEEDED (p. 471):

- 6 blank CMS-1500 health insurance forms (located in the Supplies section)
- 6 Patient Face Sheets from Completed Work folder from Task 3.5
- 6 completed superbills from Completed Work folder from Task 5.2 (used again in Task 5.3)

1. Prepare CMS-1500 health insurance forms.
   - This morning Gladys has asked you to complete CMS-1500 health insurance forms using the information from the Patient Face Sheet and the completed superbills from Task 5.2 and used in Task 5.3.
   - Included on the CMS-1500 health insurance forms will be the patient information, date of service, and type of insurance.
   - See Appendix 3 for detailed directions on completing the CMS-1500

2. The employment and marital status of each patient is:
   Many Bogert is married.
   Elizabeth Fenton is married.
   Amanda Foster is married and employed.
   Jack Masci is married and employed.
   Jean Olson is single and employed.
   Lori Whittaker is single and was referred by Theodore Blackburn, MD. Gladys has also requested that no "Amount Paid" be recorded on the CMS-1500.

3. Once you have completed all the information for each patient on the CMS-1500 health insurance forms, place them in alphabetic order in the Completed Work folder directly behind Task 6.4. Return to their correct locations in the Completed Work folder the Patient List (behind Task 3.4) and superbills (behind Task 5.2).

DAY 7 TASK 7.1

Patient Reception

SUPPLIES NEEDED (p. 483):
- Appointment schedule for April 15 and 16 from your Completed Work file
- 3 file folders
- 3 preprinted file labels
- 3 blank Patient Information forms (located in the Supplies section)
- 3 blank Subsequent Findings forms (located in the Supplies section)

The remainder of the morning will be spent working at the reception desk. Gladys has asked you to prepare a new patient file folder for three of the new patients that are scheduled on Tuesday, April 15, and Wednesday, April 16.

1. **Assemble the patient's medical record.**
   - Locate the file folders and the file labels in the packet. On the appointment schedule for April 15 you will see that Li Wong and Lillian Schultz are new patients scheduled with Dr. Adams, and on April 16 George Jones has been scheduled with Dr. Harkness. Prepare a medical record for each of these three new patients. Gladys has already prepared the record for Fred Peterson.

2. **Patient Information forms.**
   - Prepare a Patient Information form for each patient. Once you have completed the Patient Information form with as much information as possible, place each form into the patient's folder.
   - Next, prepare a Subsequent Findings form to be placed into the patient's folder as the second sheet in the folder.
   - Once you have completed this task, place all your work in the Completed Work folder directly behind Task 7.1.

Scheduling Nursing Home Services

SUPPLIES NEEDED:
- Appointment schedules for April 16 and April 17, from the Completed Work folder

Once a month Gladys schedules appointments for the physicians to see their patients at the South Padre Nursing Home. Today Gladys will have you perform this duty. Dr. Adams, Dr. Harkness, and Dr. Clark have stated that they would like to have a full morning or afternoon to go to the nursing home. If a full morning or afternoon is not available, schedule as much time as possible for the nursing home visit. They all also have requested that they see patients at the nursing home on either Wednesday, April 16, or Thursday, April 17.

The travel time will not be scheduled separately. For example, Dr. Harkness has lunch from 1–2 PM and 2–6 PM is marked off for the nursing home visit.

1. You will check the appointment schedule for each of these two days indicated and block off either a morning or afternoon for each of the three physicians. You will do this by placing an X through the time period that is open for each physician. Indicate "Nursing Home" on the blocked-off time.

2. Once you have completed this task, place the appointment schedule back in your Completed Work folder.

1. Using the step-by-step instructions for matrixing the schedule located in Appendix 4, Item A, block off time for nursing home visits for Dr. Adams, Dr. Harkness, and Dr. Clark. Follow the guidelines for time requested as in Task 7.3.

2. Print an Appointment List for each provider for April 17.

3. Place the Appointment List in your Completed Work folder behind Task 7.2.

This completes your tasks for Day Seven. On to Day Eight. You're doing a great job!

EIGHT

Wednesday, April 16, 2008

TASK **8.1**   Arrange for Physician Travel

TASK **8.2**   Scheduling Surgeries

TASK **8.3**   Inventory Management

TASK **8.1**

Arranging for Physician Travel

SUPPLIES NEEDED (p. 495):
- Travel schedule for Dr. Harkness (located in the Supplies section)
- Blank piece of paper

1. Gladys has supplied you with a handwritten itinerary from which you will prepare an itinerary (as illustrated in **Figure 8-1**) for Dr. Harkness's overnight trip. Once you have completed Dr. Harkness's itinerary, place it in your Completed Work folder behind Task 7.3.

> *Itinerary for Dr. Joyce Harkness*
> *New York City Cardiac Conference*
>
> 4:45 am   Friday, April 18, arrive at South Padre Airport
>
> 5:30 am   Flight 19 leaves South Padre, destination New York City

Figure **8-1** **Travel schedule for Dr. Harkness.**

DAY **8** TASK **8.1**

Scheduling Surgeries

SUPPLIES NEEDED (p. 497):
- Appointment schedule for April 17 from your Completed Work file
- 6 Preauthorization forms (as illustrated in **Figure 8-2**) (located in the Supplies section)
- 6 physician-completed Surgical Request and Information forms (a blank form is illustrated in **Figure 8-3**)
- 6 completed Patient Information forms

This afternoon you will be working with Joan Bothum, a medical assistant who schedules surgeries for the surgeons and obtains preauthorizations for those surgeries scheduled. All surgeries are performed at the South Padre Hospital.

1. **Complete the Request for Preauthorization for Surgery forms.**
   - Using the Surgical Request and Information forms and the Patient Information forms, complete a Request for Preauthorization for Surgery form for each patient. Be sure to fill out the Preauthorization form as completely as possible as illustrated in **Figure 8-4**. Use 04/17/08 as the "Admit Date."

2. **Schedule surgery times for each physician.**
   - Using the appointment schedule for Thursday, April 17, and the Surgical Request and Information forms that were previously completed, schedule each patient with the appropriate physician on the Center's appointment schedule. On the first line of the schedule, write the patient's last name, followed by the first name and any initials. The next line will be the type of surgery to be performed (such as "Kidney Biopsy"). The last line will be the diagnosis for which the surgery is being performed (such as "Dx: Renal Failure). The length of time for each surgery is located in Appendix 2, Item N. If the patient information does not fill in the lines for the allotted time, block the remaining time frame with Xs (as illustrated in **Figure 8-5**).

REQUEST FOR PREAUTHORIZATION FOR SURGERY

Surgeon: (circle one) Gerald Bond, MD
Ray Adams, MD
Joyce Harkness, MD
Anthony Clark, MD

PATIENT NAME: _____   FACILITY: _____

DATE OF BIRTH: _____   ADMIT DATE: _____

ACCOUNT #: _____   SURGERY DATE: _____

INSURANCE: _____   POLICY#: _____

PROCEDURE: _____

DIAGNOSIS: _____

AUTHORIZATION: _____

COMPLETED BY: _____

DATE COMPLETED: _____

Figure **8-2**   **Request for Preauthorization for Surgery form.**

South Padre Medical Center

SURGICAL REQUEST AND INFORMATION

This portion is to be completed by requesting surgeon.

Surgeon:
❑ Gerald Bond, MD
❑ Ray Adams, MD
❑ Joyce Harkness, MD
❑ Anthony Clark, MD

Schedule: ❑ URGENT ❑ IMMEDIATE ❑ PATIENT CONVENIENCE

Date Requested: _____ Time Requested: _____

Patient Name: _____

Procedure: _____

Procedure Code(s): _____

Diagnosis(es): _____

Diagnosis(es) Code(s): _____

Estimated Surgery Time: _____

Surgical Assistant Requested: _____

Additional Information: _____

This portion is to be completed by scheduling personnel.

Surgery Date: _____ Time: _____
                    Day   Date

Authorization Obtained: ❑ YES ❑ NO ❑ REQUESTED

If authorization has been requested and response is pending, list date and contact information from the initial request.

Requested From: _____ Date: _____
                        (Carrier and person)

Telephone: _____ Ext: _____

Completed By: _____

Date Completed: _____

Figure 8-3 Blank Surgical Request and Information form.

REQUEST FOR PREAUTHORIZATION FOR SURGERY

Surgeon:
(circle one)
(Gerald Bond, MD)
Ray Adams, MD
Joyce Harkness, MD
Anthony Clark, MD

Date of surgery unless otherwise specified

PATIENT NAME: Sam Klint
DATE OF BIRTH: 02/11/46 (62)
ACCOUNT #: 00000-0012
INSURANCE: BC/BS of Texas

FACILITY: S. Padre Hospital
ADMIT DATE: 04/17/08
SURGERY DATE: 04/17/08
POLICY#: MKL2211

PROCEDURE: Kidney BX   50200
DIAGNOSIS: Renal Failure   586
AUTHORIZATION: BC/BS of Texas
COMPLETED BY: Student's name
DATE COMPLETED: 04/16/08

Figure 8-4 Completed Request for Preauthorization for Surgery form.

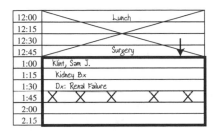

Figure **8-5** **Example of matrixing appointment time for surgery.**

Schedule the surgeries in the following order:

Klint, Sam J.
Harkland, Emmy L.
Bates, Michelle L.
Adams, Tony W.
Anderson, Charlie M.
Wood, Tina J.

Once you have entered the surgeries onto the schedule, complete the bottom portion of the Surgical Request and Information form by entering the date and time the surgery has been scheduled as illustrated in **Figure 8-6.**

South Padre Medical Center

SURGICAL REQUEST AND INFORMATION

This portion is to be completed by requesting surgeon.

Surgeon: ☒ Gerald Bond, MD
☐ Ray Adams, MD
☐ Joyce Harkness, MD
☐ Anthony Clark, MD

Schedule: ☐ URGENT ☒ IMMEDIATE ☐ PATIENT CONVENIENCE

Date Requested: ___04-16-08___ Time Requested: ___8:10 AM___

Patient Name: ___KLINT, SAM J.___ ACCOUNT #: 00000-0012

Procedure: ___BIOPSY OF KIDNEY___

Procedure Code(s): ___50200___

Diagnosis(es): ___RENAL FAILURE___

Diagnosis(es) Code(s): ___586___

Estimated Surgery Time: ___1 HOUR___ OUTPATIENT

Surgical Assistant Requested: ___—___

Additional Information: ___—___

This portion is to be completed by scheduling personnel.

Surgery Date: ___Thursday___ ___04/17/08___ Time: ___1:00 pm___
　　　　　　　　Day　　　　　　　　Date

Authorization Obtained: ☒ YES ☐ NO ☐ REQUESTED

If authorization has been requested and response is pending, list date and contact information from the initial request.

Requested From: _____ Date: _____
　　　　　　　　(Carrier and person)

Telephone: _____ Ext: _____

Completed By: ___Student's Name___

Date Completed: ___04/16/08___

Figure **8-6** **Surgical Request and Information form.**

DAY 8 TASK 8.2

Also indicate that insurance authorization has been received for all six patients by placing an X in the box next to "YES" on the Authorization Obtained line. Sign your name and date the form.

- Using the Surgical Request and Information forms you just completed, you would schedule the inpatient and outpatient surgeries with the hospital. You are to assume that the staff member whom you called at the hospital approved all of the procedure times as requested and scheduled.

3. **Once you have completed this task, place all of your completed work and the appointment schedule in the Completed Work folder after Task 8.1.**

1. Using the completed Surgical Request and Information forms from Task 8.2, schedule the inpatient and outpatient surgeries in the software scheduling program.

2. Print an Appointment List for each provider for April 17 and place it in your Completed Work folder behind Task 8.2.

Inventory Management

SUPPLIES NEEDED (p. 533):
- Reception inventory sheet (located in the Supplies section)

1. Complete an inventory sheet.
   - Gladys has asked you to inventory the furniture in the patient waiting room after office hours today. She refers you to Appendix 2, Policies and Procedures, Item R, for details on how to complete the inventory sheet. Inventory the items in the office reception photo **(Figure 8-7)** with the inventory sheet in the Supplies Section for this task.
   - Place the work in the Completed Work folder.

   That's it for Day Eight. Great work! You have learned so much so far, so let's learn a little more. On to Day Nine.

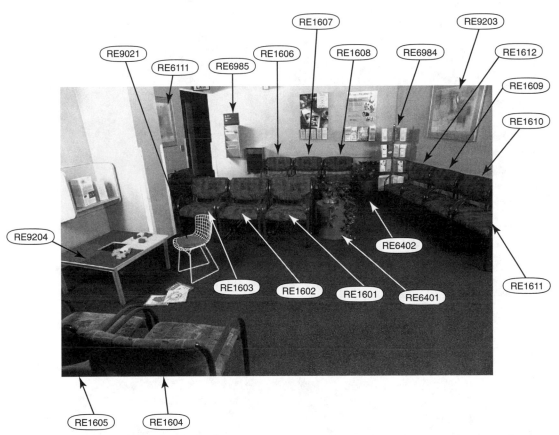

Figure **8-7** **Office inventory.** *(From Potter BP: Medical office administration: a worktext, Philadelphia, 2003, Saunders.)*

Make sure to check **evolve** for the latest content updates

Thursday, April 17, 2008

TASK **9.1**   Medical Records

TASK **9.1**

Medical Records

SUPPLIES NEEDED (p. 535):

- 6 file folders
- 6 preprinted file labels
- 6 completed Patient Information sheets from Task 8.2 supplies
- 6 blank Subsequent Findings forms (located in the Supplies section)

This afternoon you will be responsible for assembling patient files for each patient that is scheduled for surgery today. All of these patients will be coming in for postoperative visits, and will need a patient file.

1. Assemble the patient medical record.
   - Locate the file folders and file labels in the packet. The patient's name is in capital letters on each label, with last name first followed by the patient's first name and middle initial. The patients are from are Task 8.2. Secure the labels to each file folder.

2. Place each Patient Information sheet in the patient's file folder, making sure the Patient Information sheet is placed first in the correct file folder.

3. Subsequent Findings form.
   - You will also need to place a Subsequent Findings form in each of the file folders. Using the information from the Patient Information forms from Task 8.2, complete the information on the top of each Subsequent Findings form. This will be the second page to be placed in the patient's file folder.

4. Once you have completed this task, place the file folders with both of the completed forms in the proper file folders in your Completed Work folder.

1. Enter into the new software program the demographic information from the completed Patient Information forms for each patient from Task 8.2. The step-by-step instruction for entering patient information is located in Appendix 4, Item E. Once all the demographic information has been entered, print a Patient Face Sheet for each patient and review the information for errors. The instructions for printing the Patient Face Sheet are located in Appendix 4, Item F.

2. Place the printed Patient Face Sheets in the Completed Work folder.

   This completes Day Nine; one more day to go.

TEN

Make sure to check
evolve
for the latest
content updates

Friday, April 18, 2008

TASK **10.1**   Telephone Messages

TASK **10.2**   Scheduling Appointments

TASK **10.3**   Medical Transcription

TASK **10.1**

Telephone Messages

SUPPLIES NEEDED (p. 547):
- Companion CD containing the telephone messages for April 18 (Task 10.1)
- 5 blank Telephone Records (located in the Supplies section)

Today is your final day of your internship with South Padre Medical Center.

1. Locate the "Telephone Messages" area on the companion CD (Task 10.1)
   - Telephone messages came into the office during the time the clinic was closed. Gladys has asked you to listen to the voice mail and complete a Telephone Record for each call.
   - If a message is left for a member of the clinic staff, you are to write the message for the appropriate person indicated in the telephone message.
   - For patients who requested appointments for today, set those messages aside because you will be scheduling these appointments in Task 10.2.
   - Refer patients who are calling regarding laboratory results to Gladys.

DAY 10 TASK 10.1

Scheduling Appointments

SUPPLIES NEEDED:
- Appointment schedule for Friday, April 18, 2008
- Completed Telephone Records from Task 10.1

1. Scheduling appointments from the telephone records.
   - Now that you have received the messages from the voice mail, you need to schedule any requests for appointments with Dr. Adams; all other physicians are unavailable today. All of the information needed to schedule the appointments is taken from the Telephone Record from Task 10.1. Once you have scheduled the appointments, indicate the appointment date and time on the Telephone Record in the "Response" section.

2. Gladys informs you that Dr. Bond was called out of town on a family emergency and will not be in the office today and asks you to mark this on his schedule.

3. Once you have scheduled the appointments requested from the messages, place the appointment schedule back in your Completed Work folder and return the Telephone Record (Task 10.1) to the correct location in the Completed Work folder.

1. Using the Telephone Record from Task 10.1 schedule the requested appointments with Dr. Adams. All of the appointments are to be scheduled for today.

2. Print an Appointment List for April 18 and place it in your Completed Work folder behind Task 10.1.

Medical Transcription

SUPPLIES NEEDED (p. 551):
- Companion CD containing the medical transcription from April 17
- 5 Operative Report forms (located in the Supplies section)
- 1 Cardiology Report form (as illustrated in **Figure 10-1**)
- 1 Radiology Report form (as illustrated in **Figure 10-2**)

This is your last task of your internship with South Padre Medical Center.

1. Locate the "Medical Transcription" area on the companion CD.
   - This afternoon Gladys will cover the reception desk while you transcribe the medical dictation for surgeries performed Thursday, April 17.
   - There are five Operative Reports, one Cardiology Report, and one Radiology Report that were dictated. You are to key each on the correct form as indicated on the CD.

2. Once you have completed this task, place all reports in your Completed Work folder.

This concludes your tasks for all 10 days. You did a great job!

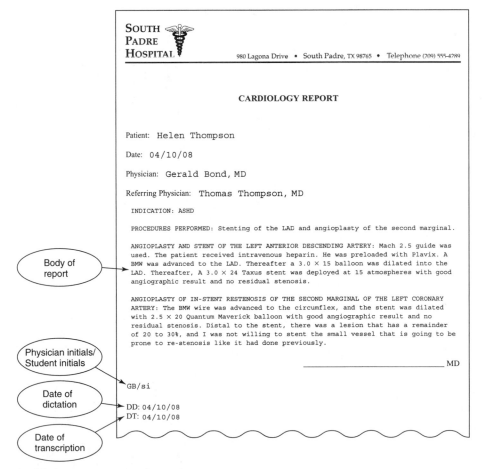

Figure **10-1** **Cardiology Report form.**

SOUTH PADRE HOSPITAL

980 Lagona Drive • South Padre, TX 98765 • Telephone (209) 555-4289

RADIOLOGY REPORT

Patient: Helen Thompson   DOB/Age: 05/10/80

Date: 04/10/08   Room/Bed/Surgery No.: 428

Physician: Larry Green, MD   X-ray No.: P1382

Requesting Physician: Gerald Bond, MD

PROCEDURE: Transesophageal echocardiogram

INDICATIONS: Evaluation of the aortic valve considering the stenosis that was not well-documented angiographically.

PROCEDURE: The patient received 2 mg of Versed, and a transesophageal probe was advanced to the lower part of the esophagus. We had good visualization of the heart. The mitral valve was thickened with slight prolapse, but there was no significant regurgitation noted. The LV displayed normal size and normal function. The aortic root is normal in size. The aortic valve is calcified with diffuse cusp excursions with still adequate opening. Valve area was variable in different incidents varying from 1 to even above 2.

CONCLUSION: This transesophaeal echo shows aortic valve disease but does not appear to be severe. It appeared to be moderately stenotic, and considering the angiography and the hemodynamics, this patient does not need valve surgery yet.

_____ MD

RT/si

DD: 04/10/08
DT: 04/10/08

Figure **10-2** **Radiology Report form.**

APPENDIX 1

Welcome

Welcome to the South Padre Medical Center. You will find the Center to be a busy, friendly place to work where your skills, knowledge, and abilities will be appreciated and used. As in every office, there are standard procedures that we all follow to ensure that the office operates smoothly. The Policies and Procedures located in Appendix 2 will familiarize you with the operating procedures that are standard for all employees of the Center.

The employees of the Center are here to help you put your education and training into action by performing the tasks that you learned in your educational program. We have been involved in the internship process for more than a decade and see the internship experience as a vital part of your education. We want to help you be successful. You can expect that all employees will treat you as a professional member of the health care team. Mutual respect is absolutely necessary to ensure South Padre Medical Center has an environment conducive to superior patient care. On behalf of each member of the team, we are glad you are here and hope you find your experience with us rewarding.

APPENDIX 1

APPENDIX 2

Make sure to check **evolve** for the latest content updates

Policies and Procedures

A. Introduction

You are ready to begin your 2-week internship as a medical office assistant in the South Padre Medical Center, a medical office located in South Padre, Texas. The Center is a partnership of four physicians affiliated with Texas Health Corporation, a managed care corporation located in Houston, Texas. **Figure A2-1** displays the organizational structure of the Center and the affiliation with Texas Health Corporation.

South Padre Medical Center is located at 9878 Palm Drive in South Padre in the South Padre Medical Complex. The one-story building houses several suites of professional offices. South Padre Medical Center is located in the middle of the building, just inside the front doors. The waiting room is the first area the patient enters. The front office area is separated from the patient waiting room by a registration desk.

There is a staff lounge located behind the lab area at the rear of the center. The lounge is used by all employees for breaks throughout the day. A picnic table is located outside the rear entrance and is also for employee use. There are lockers available in the lounge area, and all employees are required to place their personal items in a locker. Gladys Johnson, Medical Office Assistant, will assign you a locker and give you the combination to the lock located on the front of the locker. Personal items, such as purses and backpacks, are not allowed in the office area. Medically necessary items are, of course, allowed in the office area.

In consideration of our patients and employees with allergies and/or respiratory conditions, do not apply perfumes, colognes, or other fragrances. Use only unscented hairsprays, deodorants, and other personal care items.

Each of the physicians has a private office located a short distance from the seven patient examination rooms. When delivering mail or messages for the physicians, delivery is to be to the physician's private office. Never interrupt the physician in the patient examination rooms unless specifically told to do so by your supervisor.

A small lab is located in the Center and is used for a variety of laboratory procedures. Staff members collect specimens and some of the less complex analyses are conducted in the Center's laboratory by Center personnel. The

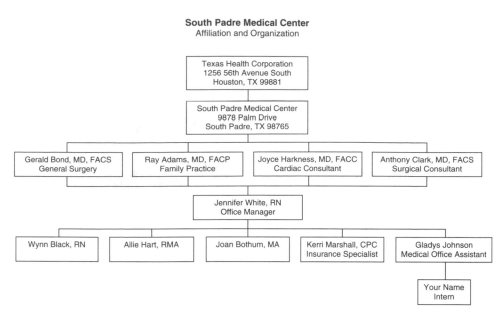

Figure **A2-1** **Affiliation and Organization of South Padre Medical Center.**

Center has contracted Island Express Labs to do all the Center's outside specimen analysis. The more complex analyses are sent to Island Express Labs, an outside laboratory. Each evening, a messenger from Island Express Labs delivers the results of previous analyses and picks up the specimens that are being sent to Island Express Labs for analysis. Island Express Labs also returns results using the U.S. mail system.

Minor surgical procedures are sometimes conducted in the Center, but the physicians are on staff at Island Hospital, where they admit patients for more major surgeries on either an inpatient or outpatient basis.

The South Padre Medical Complex building also houses offices of an independent radiologist; psychiatrist; and an ear, nose, and throat (ENT) specialist. The physicians from the Center often refer patients to these physicians for consultation. You will be receiving patient information from each of these offices regarding patients that have been referred for services, and you will be sending patient information to these offices while performing your office tasks.

B. About Our Physicians

South Padre Medical Center was established to meet the health needs of South Padre residents in general surgery and family practice, with consultation affiliates specializing in cardiology and surgery.

- Dr. Gerald Bond, a general surgeon, and Dr. Ray Adams, a family practitioner, founded the Center 20 years ago to provide health care to private patients and patients participating in Texas Health Corporation, a managed care organization.
- Dr. Joyce Harkness, a cardiologist, and Dr. Anthony Clark, a surgeon, serve as consultants to the Center. Dr. Harkness and Dr. Clark are from San Antonio and commute 2 days a week to see patients in the Center and at the hospital.

- All four physicians are registered with Texas Health Corporation as preferred providers. All physicians also have staff privileges at the South Padre Island Hospital and the South Padre Island Nursing Home.

C. Your Internship Duties

Your education has prepared you for this internship as a medical office assistant. Your internship will require you to do a variety of front office tasks in the areas of written correspondence, records management, telephone messages, patient appointments, mail, transcription, insurance claim, travel arrangements, banking services, bookkeeping, payroll, and arranging for meetings. Jennifer White is the office manager and has assigned Gladys Johnson, Medical Office Assistant, to provide your orientation, training, and supervision. You will also spend some time working for Kerri Marshall, who is the insurance specialist for the Center; however, Gladys will remain your supervisor throughout the duration of your internship.

D. Calendar and Work Hours

Your internship covers a 2-week period from April 7 to April 18, 2008.

April 2008						
S	M	T	W	T	F	S
		1	2	3	4	5
6	7	8	9	10	11	12
13	14	15	16	17	18	19
20	21	22	23	24	25	26
27	28	29	30			

Your work hours are from 7:45 AM to 4:45 PM each day. Gladys and you should arrive 15 minutes prior to the start of office hours to open the office and begin answering the telephones promptly at 8 AM. Kerri Marshall arrives at 8:15 AM and works until 5:15 PM and covers the reception desk from 4:45 PM until 5:15 PM The nursing personnel cover the reception desk from 5:15 PM until closing.

All staff take an hour lunch break, except on Wednesdays when all staff take a half-hour lunch break while three of the physicians are seeing office patients. All staff take a 15-minutue break in the morning and afternoon at various times to ensure continuous coverage of all Center services. Kerri Marshall covers the reception area for Gladys Johnson and you when both of you are on breaks.

E. Confidentiality

Every employee is required to read and sign a confidentiality statement. **Figure A2-2,** Confidentiality, is a critically important aspect of your position.

South Padre Medical Center
Confidentiality Agreement

All information regarding patients and their health care that is acquired during the course of employment at South Padre Medical Center shall be considered confidential.

Confidential information must never be disclosed for non-employment related purposes. Disclosure of confidential information outside of an employee's assigned duties will constitute unauthorized release of confidential information and can be grounds for dismissal.

By signing this document, I acknowledge that I understand this statement.

_____   _____

Employee name   Date

Figure **A2-2** **Confidentiality statement.** *(Modified from Potter BP: Medical office administration: a worktext, Philadelphia, 2003, Saunders.)*

The patients' names, addresses, telephone numbers, disorders, and financial information are all confidential information. Even the fact that the patient is a Center patient is confidential, as is *all* information about the patient. You will be allowed access to patient information on a need-to-know basis. You are not allowed to access patient information that you do not have a reason to access. Do not discuss patient information unless you need to do so to complete your assigned tasks. If you should need to discuss patient information please do so quietly, being cautious that other patients do not overhear your discussions.

When you receive a request for release of information, you are to verify that the release documentation has the signature of the patient, or in the case of a minor or incompetent patient, the signature of the legal guardian. As an intern or a new employee, you are to ask your supervisor/trainer to verify the correctness of the release documentation before releasing any information.

All documentation containing patient information, of any kind, is to be kept from public view. This includes, but is not limited to, appointment schedules, patient records, laboratory/pathology reports, surgery reports, insurance forms, financial information, and telephone logs. All patient medical documentation is to be kept on your desk in a location that will not allow others to view it.

The respect that you show for our patients by keeping their information confidential should also be extended to our physicians. You are a reflection of the Center in all you do and say, especially in what you say about the Center and the staff. Professionalism and respect for the privacy of the physicians and employees of the South Padre Medical Center is an expectation of all Center employees.

F. Telephone and Request for Inpatient Consultation Forms

The telephone is a vital business tool in the Center. When your responsibilities include this valuable task, answer the telephone with: "South Padre Medical Center, this is (your name)." You are to complete the following blocks of the Telephone Record **(Figure A2-3)** for each patient message (though not all messages will include all of the items of information listed here):

Left side

- **PRIORITY**—if patient/caller indicates an urgency, place a ✓ in the box.
- **Patient**—patient's first and last name.
- **Age**—note if patient/caller indicates the age.
- **Caller**—if the caller is not the patient, but is calling for the patient, indicate the relationship of the caller to the patient. For example, Jane Smith, mother of Carrie Smith.
- **Telephone**—the patient/caller's telephone number and area code if patient is calling from outside the local area code.
- **Referred to**—the physician or team member to whom you delivered the call.
- **Chart #**—if known.
- **Chart attached**—yes or no (for all tasks you will check "No" on all Chart Attached areas).
- **Date**—for this simulation, each patient/caller will state the date of the telephone call (MM/DD/YY).
- **Time**—for this simulation, each patient/caller will state the time called. Be sure to use AM or PM with all times.
- **Rec'd by**—your first name.

Right side

- **Message**—as precise and short as you can make it.
- **Temp**—if patient/caller indicates temperature, record it.

Figure **A2-3** **Telephone Record.**

- **Allergies**—if patient specifically states an allergy, record it; if not, leave blank.
- **Response**—note the day, date, and time you scheduled any tentative appointment. Use the MM/DD/YY format. For example 04/09/08.
- **PHY/RN Initials, Date, Time, Handled By**—located in lower right-hand corner of the form are *not* to be completed by you but rather the person who approves your response. For example, if the patient called on Saturday and requested an appointment for Monday, and you had an appropriate appointment time available, you would schedule the appointment and record the time of appointment in the "Response" section of the telephone record. Your supervisor would then review your suggested appointment time prior to the patient being contacted with the appointment time. Whoever calls the patient with the appointment time would complete this section of the Telephone Record.

The Telephone Records are printed four to a page.

REQUEST FOR INPATIENT CONSULTATION FORM

You are to complete the following items on the Request for Inpatient Consultation form **(Figure A2-4)**:

- **To**—check the physician from whom the consultation is requested.
- **ATTENDING**—record the name of the **requesting** physician.
- **TELEPHONE**—record the **requesting** physician's telephone number, if provided.
- **Request date and time**—complete with the date and time of the telephone call.
- **PATIENT**—the patient for whom the consultation is requested.
- **ADMIT DATE**—the date the patient was admitted to the hospital, also known as the admitting date or admission date. Provide this information if the requesting physician/caller indicates it (MM/DD/YY).
- **FACILITY**—the hospital or other inpatient facility that the patient was admitted to.

REQUEST FOR INPATIENT CONSULTATION

To: ❑ Gerald Bond, MD
❑ Ray Adams, MD
❑ Joyce Harkness, MD
❑ Anthony Clark, MD

ATTENDING: _____
TELEPHONE: _____
Request Date and Time: _____

PATIENT: _____   ADMIT DATE: _____

FACILITY: _____   FLOOR: _____   ROOM: _____

REASON FOR CONSULTATION: _____

_____

_____

_____

PLEASE COMPLETE BY: _____   RECEIVED BY: _____
(DATE)

Figure **A2-4**   **Request for Inpatient Consultation form.**

- **FLOOR**—the hospital floor number on which the patient is located.
- **ROOM**—the hospital room number in which the patient is located.
- **REASON FOR CONSULTATION**—record as stated by the requesting physician/caller.
- **PLEASE COMPLETE BY**—the date (MM/DD/YY) that the requesting physician has asked that the consultation be competed by.
- **RECEIVED BY**—your first name.

When a physician requests one of the Center physicians to provide a consultation at the hospital, place the consultation on the appointment schedule. For example, Dr. Thompson requests an inpatient consultation Monday afternoon by Dr. Bond. You would identify adequate time on the schedule, at either the requested time or a convenient time for the Center physician, and enter the information about the patient (i.e., name, room number, reason for consultation, requesting physician, and if the patient was a new or established patient) onto the schedule. Remember to schedule 15-minutes of travel time before the consultation.

G. Mail

The U.S. Postal Service delivers the mail each day between 9 AM and 10 AM. The front desk receptionist receives the mail and does the initial sorting. The mail should be sorted and handled as follows:

1. **Patients' laboratory or pathology results.**
   - Scan the results and write "rec'd" and the date (i.e., 04/08/08) received in the upper right-hand corner of each report as illustrated in **Figure A2-5.** Results that are positive are of the greatest priority.
   - Positive results are to be attached to the patient's medical record and placed on the top of the physician's incoming mail stack for immediate physician attention. If the physician is out of the office for more than a day, give the results and the medical record to the physician's nurse.
   - Negative results are to be placed in a file folder and placed in the physician's mail stack to be reviewed and initialed before the reports are filed into the medical records.

APPENDIX 2 F-G

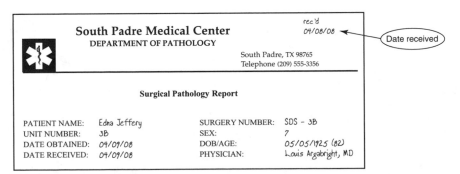

Figure **A2-5**   **Date received.**

2. **Mail marked "Personal" or "Confidential."**
   - These items are not to be opened by you, but placed on the mail stack as they were received with the date received (rec'd) on the front of the envelope in the lower left-hand corner as illustrated in **Figure A2-6.**

3. **Important letters, memos, documents.**
   - Open the mail and date stamp each item.
   - Review each item to ensure that it cannot be handled by another Center employee. When you are a new employee, you are to review these mail items with your supervisor/trainer until you are familiar with the office team and each employee's duties.

4. **Payments from patients or insurance companies.**
   - Sort the payments into two stacks—one for patient payments and the other for insurance company payments.
   - Payments are to be delivered to accounts receivable.
   - Place the envelope in which the payment was received behind each check or cash payment. Secure the envelope, payment, and any correspondence that accompanied the payment together with a paper clip. This step is especially important for payments that are made with cash and will ensure that all payments are credited to the correct accounts.

5. **Financial documents.**
   - Bank statements, invoices, statements, payroll forms, and state and federal tax information are to be dated and grouped together.

6. **Medical newsletters, journals, periodicals.**
   - These medical materials are to be delivered to the physician to whom they are addressed and are never to be placed in the patient waiting room.

7. **Reception room magazines and newspapers.**
   - People, Good Housekeeping, and other general reading magazines are to be placed in the waiting room.

Figure **A2-6** **Personal or confidential mail.**

- Some physicians have personal magazine subscriptions sent to the office. These personal magazines are to be delivered to the physician, not placed in the waiting room. Dr. Bond's personal subscriptions are RV World and Gold Prospector magazines. Dr. Adams subscribes to Money Monthly and Downhill Ski.

8. **Advertisements.**
   - Delivered to Gladys.

9. **Other**
   - Stationery, business cards, check blanks, and other items from a printer are to be delivered to Gladys, who will review and approve the items for distribution or storage.

H. Delivery Service Items

A variety of delivery services deliver packages and letters to the Center each day (e.g., Federal Express, United Parcel Service, private delivery services). The times for these deliveries vary; however, deliveries are usually made before 4 PM each day. When a service delivers an item, you are to follow the same procedures as outlined for U.S. mail service. Many of the supplies for the Center are delivered by the delivery service method and you should notify the department to whom the package is addressed immediately by telephone when a department item has been received. Write the department name on the top of the item so as to facilitate pickup by department personnel. Set these items under the reception counter for pickup by the receiving department's personnel.

I. Office Hours and Physicians' Schedules

Office hours are from 8 AM to 6 PM Monday through Friday. Hours for each of the physicians are as follows:

Physician	Monday	Tuesday	Wednesday	Thursday	Friday
Dr. Gerald Bond	10-6	9-5	9-12	9-12	8-5
Dr. Ray Adams	9-6	9-6	10-5	9-12	9-5
Dr. Joyce Harkness			2-6	2-6	
Dr. Anthony Clark			2-6	2-6	

NOTE: You are not to mark the following physician preferences on the appointment schedule at this time. You will be directed to mark the preferences in Task 1.1 when you begin working with the schedule. For now you are to only read about the preferences.

J. Physicians' Lunch Hours

Lunch breaks for physicians are 1 hour in length and should be scheduled from noon to 1 PM for physicians on days when his/her office hours begin at 8 AM or 9 AM and from 1 PM to 2 PM when his/her office hours begin at 10 AM. When a physician's office hours are only scheduled from 9 AM to noon or 10 AM to noon, you do not schedule a lunch break. Drs. Harkness and Clark request a 1 PM to 2 PM lunch break on the 2 days they are scheduled in the office. Should a physician change his/her office hours, you will change the lunch break accordingly.

K. Surgery Schedules

If the physician is scheduled in the office before a surgery is scheduled at the hospital, you are to block off the hour before the first surgery is scheduled. On days with a surgery schedule, you are to mark off as "Unavailable" any time following the last possible time to schedule surgery if the surgery schedule is in the afternoon. For example, Dr. Bond wants to have surgeries scheduled beginning at 1 PM, with the last starting time for a surgery no later than 4 PM. You would mark off the time periods from 12 PM through 12:45 PM, and label the 12:45 to 1 PM block "Surgery," with an arrow pointing to the surgery block of time. Refer to **Figure A2-7** for an illustration of marking off the surgery time. You outline the hours from 1 PM through 4 PM to set the surgery hours apart from the regular office scheduling time. You would also mark off the time blocks from 4:15 PM through 5:45 PM as "Unavailable" so no one schedules further surgeries or patients into this time for Dr. Bond. Dr. Harkness and Dr. Clark have morning surgery schedules followed by an hour of lunch, then begin seeing office patients at 2 PM on Wednesdays and Thursdays. See "M" for individual physician scheduling preferences.

L. Marking Off the End-of-Day Time Blocks

You are to mark off any time periods at the end of the day that the physician has indicated are not to be scheduled. For example, Dr. Bond wants to finish no later than 5 PM on Tuesdays; therefore, you would mark off the four 15-minute time blocks from 5 PM through 5:45 PM **(Figure A2-8).**

M. Other Physician Scheduling Preferences

DR. BOND
* Dr. Bond has a board meeting each Thursday from 7:30 AM to 8:45 AM and conducts inpatient rounds from 6 AM to 8:45 AM every Tuesday and Wednesday. He has requested a 15-minute travel time at the end of his

12:00	
12:15	
12:30	
12:45	Surgery
1:00	
1:15	
1:30	
1:45	
2:00	
2:15	
2:30	
2:45	
3:00	
3:15	
3:30	
3:45	
4:00	
4:15	Unavailable
4:30	
4:45	
5:00	
5:15	
5:30	
5:45	

Figure **A2-7** Surgery hours marked off on an appointment sheet.

4:30	
4:45	
5:00	Unavailable
5:15	
5:30	
5:45	

Figure **A2-8** End-of-day time marked off on appointment sheet.

rounds and board meeting to travel to the office but you do not need to write "travel" on the schedule, just block off the time as indicated.

- Dr. Bond has selected Wednesday and Thursday afternoons beginning at 1 PM as the preferred time for scheduling surgical procedures. He has requested that the last surgery never be scheduled later than a starting time of 4 PM. He has requested that an hour before surgery be marked off to provide desk, travel, and/or lunch time.

DR. ADAMS

- Dr. Adams has a board meeting the second Wednesday of each month from 8 AM to 9:45 AM and conducts rounds from 7 AM to 8:45 AM on Monday, Thursday, and Friday. He has requested that he have 15 minutes of travel time scheduled after the board meeting and rounds to travel to

Figure **A2-9** **Dr. Adams' schedule on Thursday.**

the office but you do not need to write "Travel" on the schedule, just block off the time because the physician is not leaving from the office or returning to the office.

- Dr. Adams also teaches a class at the local medical school from 1 PM to 3 PM each Thursday, and has requested 30 minutes "Travel" be written on his schedule (as illustrated in **Figure A2-9**). He has lunch from noon to 1 PM but wants the "travel" note as a reminder. Dr. Adams does not return to the office after the class is finished. Mark off his time from 3 PM and after as "Unavailable."

DR. HARKNESS AND DR. CLARK

- Drs. Harkness and Clark have selected 8 AM to 9 AM on Wednesday and Thursday for hospital rounds. They have requested that surgeries be scheduled from 9 AM and ending at or before 1 PM on Wednesdays and Thursdays. Mark off Monday, Tuesday, and Friday as "Unavailable".
- Both Dr. Harkness and Dr. Clark request patients be scheduled beginning at 2 PM on Wednesday and Thursday. Inpatient consultations are to be scheduled at the end of the day.

N. Appointment Scheduling Guidelines

For billing purposes, a **new patient** is defined as one who has not seen the physician or another physcian of the same specialty within the South Padre Medical Center within the past 3 years. An **established patient** is one who has seen any physician or another physician of the same specialty within the South Padre Medical Center within the past 3 years. Because the patient has seen a physician within the Center within 3 years means that the patient's medical record is available and only needs to be updated. Because updating requires less time than does development of a new patient record, physicians get paid more for a new patient office visit than they do for an established patient visit. But, for purposes of the schedule, if the patient has been seen in the Center by any of the Center physicians, he/she is considered an established patient because there is a medical record available for that patient.

When an established patient is scheduled for an appointment "Est" is to be placed on the appointment schedule behind the patient's name. When a new patient is scheduled, "New" is placed behind the name on the appointment schedule. In this way, you will know which patients need their medical records retrieved from storage and which patients need new medical records assembled.

It is your responsibility to schedule patient appointments and to ensure that the correct information is recorded on the appointment schedule. The physicians have developed a list of the length of time you are to allow for the most common patient complaints. The following are the scheduling guidelines you will use when scheduling both new and established patients:

15 MINUTES
- Allergies
- Burn
- Cast recheck
- Conjunctivitis
- Cough
- Ear pain or infection
- Ear wash
- Elevated temperature
- Flu symptoms
- Pharyngitis
- Rash, hives
- Recheck flu
- Recheck Pap
- Sinus
- Sore throat
- URI
- UTI
- Wart treatment

30 MINUTES
- Abdominal pain
- Asthma
- Bronchitis
- Cast change
- Chest congestion
- Chest pain
- Confusion

- Depression
- Diabetic new problem
- Diabetic recheck
- Dizziness
- Eye injury
- Foreign body removal (location)
- Headache
- Infection
- Ingrown toenail
- Lesion removal (1)
- Menstrual problems
- Muscle strain
- OB check
- Pap
- Postoperative visit
- Preop physical
- Shortness of breath (SOB)
- Sprain or suspected fracture
- STD
- Varicocele recheck

45 MINUTES
- Breast pain
- Dog bite
- Lump
- Varicose veins
- Postoperative complication or pain

15 to 60 MINUTES
- Pap included for female patients (over age 18)
- Physicals (px) and preoperatives (preop) (schedule by age)

Under 18	15 minutes
18-40	30 minutes
41-65	45 minutes
Over 65	60 minutes

CONSULTATION
Request for an inpatient consultation: Prefer an hour but can use 45 minutes. Note reason for consultation when placing inpatient consultation on schedule.

CARDIAC 1 HOUR
- New cardiac outpatient
- New inpatient consultation

SURGERY, ECHOCARDIOGRAM, AND MISCELLANEOUS 1 HOUR
- Pacemaker
- Surgical echocardiogram
- Lymphadenectomy

45 MINUTES

- Outpatient echocardiogram
- Hearing check
- Lesion removal (2 or more)
- Proctosigmoidoscopy (procto)
- Hernia repair, periumbilical

60 MINUTES

- Breast biopsy
- Initial (new) OB visit
- Kidney biopsy
- Liver biopsy
- Lymph biopsy
- Needle biopsy
- New surgical patient

90 MINUTES

- Diskectomy

If a patient requires an appointment for a complaint not listed, you are to use your judgment in making the appointment based on the similarity of the complaint to those on the scheduling guidelines.

O. Patient Lists

Prior to the physician's arrival for the day, a Patient List is prepared that displays all of the appointments for physicians for that day. **Figure A2-10** illustrates a previous Patient List prepared for Dr. Bond. Patient Lists are keyed onto blank paper. The Patient List has many purposes and is a necessary tool in the medical office:

PATIENT LIST
for
Monday, March 31, 2008

Gerald Bond, MD

8:00-10:00	Unavailable
10:00-10:30	McCormick, Matthew, New, Preop physical
10:30-11:00	Norman, Patty, New, Ulcer
11:00-11:30	Stout, Henry, New, Hernia
11:30-12:00	Meuler, Darrin, New, Preop physical
12:00-12:30	O'Leary, Corwin, New, Abdominal pain
12:30-1:00	Garcia, Manuel, New, Upper GI pain
1:00-2:00	Lunch
2:00-2:45	SPH Consultation, Lopez, Jesus, Room 522, pancreatic CA, Ref: Dr. Orlando
2:45-	Open

Figure **A2-10**   Sample Patient List.

- At the receptionist desk to mark off the patients as they arrive for their appointments and to ensure that the correct medical record is available for each patient.
- By the nursing staff to prepare the examination rooms and supplies needed for each patient's visit.
- By medical records personnel to pull from the filing shelves the records for the day's patients.
- By the physicians as their daily schedules.
- To check the daysheet of charges against the Patient List each day.

The Patient List is prepared the morning before the day represented on the list. The list is updated throughout the remainder of the day and the next morning before the first patient arrives. There are always changes to the schedule after the day begins, and it is the receptionist's responsibility to keep the master Patient List current throughout the day. At the end of the day the Patient Lists (one for each physician seeing patients in the office that day) are given to Gladys Johnson, who routes the updated lists to Kerri Marshall to ensure that all patients have been billed for services provided on that day. This extra step is a backup to the regular accounting system and a valuable reference in this busy office.

P. Patient Reception

When the patient arrives for his/her appointment, first cheerfully greet the patient. It is important to greet the patient quietly by name whenever possible. A simple greeting for an established patient could be: "Good morning, Mr. Wilson." (Don't forget to SMILE with your greeting.)

For an established patient, ask the patient to verify his/her address, telephone number, and insurance information as stated in the medical record, check the patient's name off the Patient List, and place the patient's medical record in the "Patients to Be Seen" inbox for the physician's nurse.

When a new patient arrives for his/her appointment, type a file folder label in capital letters with the last name, first name, middle initial. Secure the label to a file folder and place a blank Subsequent Findings form (see Figure 2-1) in the folder. Have the patient complete a Patient Information form (see Figure 2-2) and place the form in the folder. The newly created patient's medical record is then placed in the "Patients to Be Seen" inbox for the physician's nurse.

Ask the patient to be seated in the waiting area and assure him/her that the nurse will call his/her name when it is time to go into the examination room. For example, you could state, "Thank you, Mr. Wilson. Please be seated in the waiting room and the nurse will call you in about 5 minutes." If the appointments are running late, give the patient some idea of how long a wait to expect, with a brief explanation such as "The doctor is running a little behind today, so it will be about 15 minutes before the nurse will call you."

Q. Filing

There are two types of filing most commonly used in the medical setting—alphabetic and numeric. Numeric is often preferred because it provides anonymity to the patient. Numeric filing requires the use of an accession ledger that keeps track of each number that is assigned to a patient. The numbering system would begin with a higher number, such as 1000. The first patient assigned a number would be 1000 and the patient's name would be registered to that number by means of the accession ledger. Numbers are always assigned in consecutive order.

There are two commonly used numeric filing methods—consecutive and terminal digit filing. Consecutive number filing is when the charts are filed in order of the lowest to the highest number. For example, the following four file numbers are placed in consecutive order in a six-digit consecutive filing system:

004569
098122
560011
890103

Note that two zeros were added to 4569 and one zero to 98122 to maintain a six-digit consecutive filing system.

When using a terminal digit filing system, the numbers are separated into groups. For example, 890103 becomes 89 01 03. The 89 is the primary unit, 01 the secondary unit, and 03 the tertiary (third) unit. The 89 indicates that the record is filed in the "89" section of the medical records room, in the 01 section, with the record placed behind the "02" medical record. Using the terminal digit filing method, the file numbers used above would be filed as follows:

00	45	69
09	81	22
56	00	11
89	01	03

Color coding of the numbers in the filing system is often used to speed the filing process and reduce misfiles. For example, in an alphabetic filing system, the R would be orange and the I would be yellow. Ann Riggs's file would be have her name on the side of the file "RIGGS, ANN" and also along the side would be an orange R and a yellow I as illustrated in **Figure A2-11.** Another example is the letter **S** is yellow and the letter **A** is grey, Monica Sartori's file would appear as in **Figure A2-12.** As an added feature, note that at the top edge of Ann Riggs's file is 2000 to indicate she became a patient in the year 2000. Monica Sartori's file has a 99 to indicate she became a patient in 1999.

Color coding is used in a numeric filing system by having each number or a group of numbers assigned a certain color. The colored numbers are preprinted and come in rolls similar to file folder labels. The medical records clerk then applies the colored labels for each number. The following is an example of a color-coding system for a numeric system and an alphabetic system:

Figure **A2-11** **Example of color-coded file for Ann Riggs.**

Figure **A2-12** **Example of color-coded file for Monica Sartori.**

Number	Letter	Color
0	A, K, U	Grey
1	B, L, V	Pink
2	C, M, W	Purple
3	D, N, X	Green
4	E, O, Y	Red
5	F, P, Z	Tan
6	G, Q	White
7	H, R	Orange
8	I, S	Yellow
9	J, T	Blue

Using this color-coding system, chart number 004569 would have two grey zeros, a red 4, tan 5, white 6, and a blue 9. If the alphabetic filing system used color coding for the first two letters of the last name, Paul Smith's name would have a yellow **S** and a purple **M** on the medical record. You can see that these color-coding methods would certainly speed filing. It is also much easier to locate misfiled records when the added feature of color coding is used.

R. Inventory Management

The Center's Medical Office Assistant has established an inventory system that is used throughout the Center to inventory equipment and furniture in excess of $50. Items less than $50 are not inventoried using the inventory process; rather they are considered supplies. The inventory form contains the inventory number, product name, description, date purchased, and the room in which the item is located. Inventory checks are completed every 6 months in all rooms of the Center. Gladys assigns staff to various rooms in the Center, and those staff members are responsible for submitting a completed inventory form for the room(s) for which they are responsible. Gladys uses a computer program to manage the inventory and prints a copy of the items in each room and distributes the copies to the responsible employee. The employee is to determine that the equipment/furniture is in the assigned room and the inventory number is the same as is indicated on the equipment/furniture item. The inventory number is located on a tag that is glued to the back or underside of the item. When completing an inventory form, be certain the inventory number and the item are as listed on the form and then initial in the dated column (far right column). Your initials verify the item is located in the room indicated and that the inventory number is located on the item.

S. Referral

REFERRAL

FROM: Gerald Bond, MD   _____   TO: _____

         Ray Adams, MD   _____   TELEPHONE: _____

         Joyce Harkness, MD _____   ADDRESS: _____

         Anthony Clark, MD _____   Requested Date and Time: _____

PATIENT: _____   PATIENT'S PHONE NUMBER: _____

ADDRESS: _____

REASON FOR REFERRAL: _____

_____

_____

APPOINTMENT DATE AND TIME: _____

REFERRAL COMPLETED BY: _____ ARRANGEMENTS MADE BY: _____
                          (INITIAL AND DATE)   (INITIAL AND DATE)

Figure **A2-13** **Example of a Referral form.**

Figue A2-13 illustrates a Referral form that is used when one of the Centers' physicians wants a patient to be seen and/or treated by a physician who is not a member of our staff. In the "From" area of the form, place an "X" on the line indicating the referring physician. On the "To" line indicate the name of the physician to whom the patient is being referred. Indicate the telephone number and address of the physician to whom the patient is being referred. On the "Patient" line indicate the name of the patient being referred and the patient's telephone number on the "Patient's Phone Number" line. The "Address" line is for the patient's home address—street, city, state, and zip code. Indicate the reason the patient is being referred on the "Reason for Referral" line. The "Appointment Date and Time" line is left blank until a member of the office staff calls the physician to whom the patient is being referred and obtains a time and date. You will not be doing this, so leave the Appointment Date and Time area blank. Lastly, place your initials and date on the "Referral Completed By" line to indicate when you completed the Referral form. Leave the "Arrangements Made By" line blank as this area will be used by the staff member that obtains the time and date for the referral appointment.

APPENDIX 3

Third-Party Payer List and Directions

The CMS-1500 form is located on the data CD, in the Forms Library, and in the Supplies section of this text. The CMS-1500 is the universal insurance form used to submit charges to third-party payers or insurance companies. Some third-party payers have their own forms and require submission on those forms for claims made on behalf of patients covered by their insurance. Blocks 1 through 13 on the CMS-1500 contain patient information and blocks 14 through 33 contain provider information. Table 1 indicates the information that is to be placed in each block for the patient and provider information.

Assume that all patients have signed a previous authorization to submit insurance and receive payment directly from the payer. The insurance personnel enter "SOF" on the signature lines to indicate that the facility has the patient's signature on file.

The Center's Federal identification number is **00789200**.

By regulation, Medicare health care providers must obtain National Provider Identification (NPI) numbers. On the CMS-1500 (08/05), the referring provider's NPI is entered in 17b and the rendering provider's NPI is entered in 24J. The facility NPI is entered in 33a. The Center and each physician has an NPI number:

South Padre Medical Center	8866905213
Gerald Bond, MD	4682943911
Ray Adams, MD	7824443110
Anthory Clark, MD	8291458624
Joyce Harkness, MD	6894597377

Referring physicians' NPI numbers are:

Thomas Thompson, MD	1100986210
Bert Bethos, MD	3120981144
Clarence McDonald, MD	5925442862
Theodore Blackburn, MD	7739745986

The CMS-1500 is to be completed in capital letters with no punctuation. The following directions for completing the CMS-1500 are excerpts from the Medicare Claims Processing Manual, Chapter 26, Completing and Processing, 10.2, revised 02-24-06:

HEALTH INSURANCE CLAIM FORM

APPROVED BY NATIONAL UNIFORM CLAIM COMMITTEE 08/05

[ ][ ] PICA | PICA [ ][ ]

1. MEDICARE ☐ (Medicare #) MEDICAID ☐ (Medicaid #) TRICARE CHAMPUS ☐ (Sponsor's SSN) CHAMPVA ☐ (Member ID#) GROUP HEALTH PLAN ☐ (SSN or ID) FECA BLK LUNG ☐ (SSN) OTHER ☐ (ID) | 1a. INSURED'S I.D. NUMBER (For Program in Item 1)

2. PATIENT'S NAME (Last Name, First Name, Middle Initial) | 3. PATIENT'S BIRTH DATE MM DD YY SEX M☐ F☐ | 4. INSURED'S NAME (Last Name, First Name, Middle Initial)

5. PATIENT'S ADDRESS (No., Street) | 6. PATIENT RELATIONSHIP TO INSURED Self☐ Spouse☐ Child☐ Other☐ | 7. INSURED'S ADDRESS (No., Street)

CITY | STATE | 8. PATIENT STATUS Single☐ Married☐ Other☐ | CITY | STATE

ZIP CODE | TELEPHONE (Include Area Code) ( ) | Employed☐ Full-Time Student☐ Part-Time Student☐ | ZIP CODE | TELEPHONE (Include Area Code) ( )

9. OTHER INSURED'S NAME (Last Name, First Name, Middle Initial) | 10. IS PATIENT'S CONDITION RELATED TO: | 11. INSURED'S POLICY GROUP OR FECA NUMBER

a. OTHER INSURED'S POLICY OR GROUP NUMBER | a. EMPLOYMENT? (Current or Previous) YES☐ NO☐ | a. INSURED'S DATE OF BIRTH MM DD YY SEX M☐ F☐

b. OTHER INSURED'S DATE OF BIRTH MM DD YY SEX M☐ F☐ | b. AUTO ACCIDENT? PLACE (State) YES☐ NO☐ | b. EMPLOYER'S NAME OR SCHOOL NAME

c. EMPLOYER'S NAME OR SCHOOL NAME | c. OTHER ACCIDENT? YES☐ NO☐ | c. INSURANCE PLAN NAME OR PROGRAM NAME

d. INSURANCE PLAN NAME OR PROGRAM NAME | 10d. RESERVED FOR LOCAL USE | d. IS THERE ANOTHER HEALTH BENEFIT PLAN? YES☐ NO☐ If yes, return to and complete item 9 a-d.

READ BACK OF FORM BEFORE COMPLETING & SIGNING THIS FORM.
12. PATIENT'S OR AUTHORIZED PERSON'S SIGNATURE I authorize the release of any medical or other information necessary to process this claim. I also request payment of government benefits either to myself or to the party who accepts assignment below.

SIGNED _____ DATE _____

13. INSURED'S OR AUTHORIZED PERSON'S SIGNATURE I authorize payment of medical benefits to the undersigned physician or supplier for services described below.

SIGNED _____

14. DATE OF CURRENT: MM DD YY ◄ ILLNESS (First symptom) OR INJURY (Accident) OR PREGNANCY(LMP) | 15. IF PATIENT HAS HAD SAME OR SIMILAR ILLNESS. GIVE FIRST DATE MM DD YY | 16. DATES PATIENT UNABLE TO WORK IN CURRENT OCCUPATION FROM MM DD YY TO MM DD YY

17. NAME OF REFERRING PROVIDER OR OTHER SOURCE | 17a. 17b. NPI | 18. HOSPITALIZATION DATES RELATED TO CURRENT SERVICES FROM MM DD YY TO MM DD YY

19. RESERVED FOR LOCAL USE | 20. OUTSIDE LAB? YES☐ NO☐ $ CHARGES

21. DIAGNOSIS OR NATURE OF ILLNESS OR INJURY (Relate Items 1, 2, 3 or 4 to Item 24E by Line)
1. |___.___| 3. |___.___|
2. |___.___| 4. |___.___| | 22. MEDICAID RESUBMISSION CODE ORIGINAL REF. NO.

23. PRIOR AUTHORIZATION NUMBER

24. A. DATE(S) OF SERVICE			B. PLACE OF SERVICE	C. EMG	D. PROCEDURES, SERVICES, OR SUPPLIES (Explain Unusual Circumstances)		E. DIAGNOSIS POINTER	F. $ CHARGES	G. DAYS OR UNITS	H. EPSDT Family Plan	I. ID. QUAL.	J. RENDERING PROVIDER ID. #
From MM DD YY	To MM DD YY				CPT/HCPCS	MODIFIER						
1												NPI
2												NPI
3												NPI
4												NPI
5												NPI
6												NPI

25. FEDERAL TAX I.D. NUMBER SSN☐ EIN☐ | 26. PATIENT'S ACCOUNT NO. | 27. ACCEPT ASSIGNMENT? (For govt. claims, see back) YES☐ NO☐ | 28. TOTAL CHARGE $ | 29. AMOUNT PAID $ | 30. BALANCE DUE $

31. SIGNATURE OF PHYSICIAN OR SUPPLIER INCLUDING DEGREES OR CREDENTIALS (I certify that the statements on the reverse apply to this bill and are made a part thereof.)

SIGNED _____ DATE _____ | 32. SERVICE FACILITY LOCATION INFORMATION a. b. | 33. BILLING PROVIDER INFO & PH # ( ) a. b.

NUCC Instruction Manual available at: www.nucc.org | OMB APPROVAL PENDING

Figure **A3-1** Items shaded are to be left blank when patient has basic Medicare coverage.

1500

HEALTH INSURANCE CLAIM FORM

APPROVED BY NATIONAL UNIFORM CLAIM COMMITTEE 08/05

	PICA						PICA	

1. MEDICARE □ (Medicare #) MEDICAID □ (Medicaid #) TRICARE CHAMPUS □ (Sponsor's SSN) CHAMPVA □ (Member ID#) GROUP HEALTH PLAN □ (SSN or ID) FECA BLK LUNG □ (SSN) OTHER □ (ID)

1a. INSURED'S I.D. NUMBER (For Program in Item 1)

2. PATIENT'S NAME (Last Name, First Name, Middle Initial)

3. PATIENT'S BIRTH DATE MM DD YY   SEX M □ F □

4. INSURED'S NAME (Last Name, First Name, Middle Initial)

5. PATIENT'S ADDRESS (No., Street)

6. PATIENT RELATIONSHIP TO INSURED Self □ Spouse □ Child □ Other □

7. INSURED'S ADDRESS (No., Street)

CITY   STATE

8. PATIENT STATUS Single □ Married □ Other □

CITY   STATE

ZIP CODE   TELEPHONE (Include Area Code) ( )

Employed □ Full-Time Student □ Part-Time Student □

ZIP CODE   TELEPHONE (Include Area Code) ( )

9. OTHER INSURED'S NAME (Last Name, First Name, Middle Initial)

10. IS PATIENT'S CONDITION RELATED TO:

11. INSURED'S POLICY GROUP OR FECA NUMBER

a. OTHER INSURED'S POLICY OR GROUP NUMBER

a. EMPLOYMENT? (Current or Previous) □ YES □ NO

a. INSURED'S DATE OF BIRTH MM DD YY   SEX M □ F □

b. OTHER INSURED'S DATE OF BIRTH MM DD YY   SEX M □ F □

b. AUTO ACCIDENT? □ YES □ NO PLACE (State)

b. EMPLOYER'S NAME OR SCHOOL NAME

c. EMPLOYER'S NAME OR SCHOOL NAME

c. OTHER ACCIDENT? □ YES □ NO

c. INSURANCE PLAN NAME OR PROGRAM NAME

d. INSURANCE PLAN NAME OR PROGRAM NAME

10d. RESERVED FOR LOCAL USE

d. IS THERE ANOTHER HEALTH BENEFIT PLAN? □ YES □ NO If yes, return to and complete item 9 a-d.

READ BACK OF FORM BEFORE COMPLETING & SIGNING THIS FORM.

12. PATIENT'S OR AUTHORIZED PERSON'S SIGNATURE I authorize the release of any medical or other information necessary to process this claim. I also request payment of government benefits either to myself or to the party who accepts assignment below.

SIGNED _____ DATE _____

13. INSURED'S OR AUTHORIZED PERSON'S SIGNATURE I authorize payment of medical benefits to the undersigned physician or supplier for services described below.

SIGNED _____

14. DATE OF CURRENT: MM DD YY ◀ ILLNESS (First symptom) OR INJURY (Accident) OR PREGNANCY(LMP)

15. IF PATIENT HAS HAD SAME OR SIMILAR ILLNESS. GIVE FIRST DATE MM DD YY

16. DATES PATIENT UNABLE TO WORK IN CURRENT OCCUPATION FROM MM DD YY TO MM DD YY

17. NAME OF REFERRING PROVIDER OR OTHER SOURCE

17a.

17b. NPI

18. HOSPITALIZATION DATES RELATED TO CURRENT SERVICES FROM MM DD YY TO MM DD YY

19. RESERVED FOR LOCAL USE

20. OUTSIDE LAB? □ YES □ NO $ CHARGES

21. DIAGNOSIS OR NATURE OF ILLNESS OR INJURY (Relate Items 1, 2, 3 or 4 to Item 24E by Line)

1. ____.____   3. ____.____

2. ____.____   4. ____.____

22. MEDICAID RESUBMISSION CODE   ORIGINAL REF. NO.

23. PRIOR AUTHORIZATION NUMBER

24. A. DATE(S) OF SERVICE					B. PLACE OF SERVICE	C. EMG	D. PROCEDURES, SERVICES, OR SUPPLIES (Explain Unusual Circumstances)		E. DIAGNOSIS POINTER	F. $ CHARGES	G. DAYS OR UNITS	H. EPSDT Family Plan	I. ID. QUAL.	J. RENDERING PROVIDER ID. #
From MM DD YY			To MM DD YY				CPT/HCPCS	MODIFIER						
1													NPI	
2													NPI	
3													NPI	
4													NPI	
5													NPI	
6													NPI	

25. FEDERAL TAX I.D. NUMBER SSN □ EIN □

26. PATIENT'S ACCOUNT NO.

27. ACCEPT ASSIGNMENT? (For govt. claims, see back) □ YES □ NO

28. TOTAL CHARGE $

29. AMOUNT PAID $

30. BALANCE DUE $

31. SIGNATURE OF PHYSICIAN OR SUPPLIER INCLUDING DEGREES OR CREDENTIALS (I certify that the statements on the reverse apply to this bill and are made a part thereof.)

SIGNED _____ DATE _____

32. SERVICE FACILITY LOCATION INFORMATION

a.   b.

33. BILLING PROVIDER INFO & PH # ( )

a.   b.

NUCC Instruction Manual available at: www.nucc.org

OMB APPROVAL PENDING

Figure **A3-2** Items shaded are to be left blank when private insurance is the primary and only coverage.

1500
HEALTH INSURANCE CLAIM FORM
APPROVED BY NATIONAL UNIFORM CLAIM COMMITTEE 08/05

| | PICA | | | | | | | PICA | |

1. MEDICARE ☐ (Medicare #) MEDICAID ☐ (Medicaid #) TRICARE CHAMPUS ☐ (Sponsor's SSN) CHAMPVA ☐ (Member ID#) GROUP HEALTH PLAN ☐ (SSN or ID) FECA BLK LUNG ☐ (SSN) OTHER ☐ (ID)

1a. INSURED'S I.D. NUMBER (For Program in Item 1)

2. PATIENT'S NAME (Last Name, First Name, Middle Initial)

3. PATIENT'S BIRTH DATE MM DD YY   SEX M ☐ F ☐

4. INSURED'S NAME (Last Name, First Name, Middle Initial)

5. PATIENT'S ADDRESS (No., Street)

6. PATIENT RELATIONSHIP TO INSURED Self ☐ Spouse ☐ Child ☐ Other ☐

7. INSURED'S ADDRESS (No., Street)

CITY   STATE

8. PATIENT STATUS Single ☐ Married ☐ Other ☐

CITY   STATE

ZIP CODE   TELEPHONE (Include Area Code) (   )

Employed ☐ Full-Time Student ☐ Part-Time Student ☐

ZIP CODE   TELEPHONE (Include Area Code) (   )

9. OTHER INSURED'S NAME (Last Name, First Name, Middle Initial)

10. IS PATIENT'S CONDITION RELATED TO:

11. INSURED'S POLICY GROUP OR FECA NUMBER

a. OTHER INSURED'S POLICY OR GROUP NUMBER

a. EMPLOYMENT? (Current or Previous) YES ☐ NO ☐

a. INSURED'S DATE OF BIRTH MM DD YY   SEX M ☐ F ☐

b. OTHER INSURED'S DATE OF BIRTH MM DD YY   SEX M ☐ F ☐

b. AUTO ACCIDENT?   PLACE (State) YES ☐ NO ☐

b. EMPLOYER'S NAME OR SCHOOL NAME

c. EMPLOYER'S NAME OR SCHOOL NAME

c. OTHER ACCIDENT? YES ☐ NO ☐

c. INSURANCE PLAN NAME OR PROGRAM NAME

d. INSURANCE PLAN NAME OR PROGRAM NAME

10d. RESERVED FOR LOCAL USE

d. IS THERE ANOTHER HEALTH BENEFIT PLAN? YES ☐ NO ☐ If yes, return to and complete item 9 a-d.

READ BACK OF FORM BEFORE COMPLETING & SIGNING THIS FORM.
12. PATIENT'S OR AUTHORIZED PERSON'S SIGNATURE I authorize the release of any medical or other information necessary to process this claim. I also request payment of government benefits either to myself or to the party who accepts assignment below.

SIGNED _____ DATE _____

13. INSURED'S OR AUTHORIZED PERSON'S SIGNATURE I authorize payment of medical benefits to the undersigned physician or supplier for services described below.

SIGNED _____

14. DATE OF CURRENT: MM DD YY ◄ ILLNESS (First symptom) OR INJURY (Accident) OR PREGNANCY(LMP)

15. IF PATIENT HAS HAD SAME OR SIMILAR ILLNESS. GIVE FIRST DATE MM DD YY

16. DATES PATIENT UNABLE TO WORK IN CURRENT OCCUPATION FROM MM DD YY TO MM DD YY

17. NAME OF REFERRING PROVIDER OR OTHER SOURCE

17a.
17b. NPI

18. HOSPITALIZATION DATES RELATED TO CURRENT SERVICES FROM MM DD YY TO MM DD YY

19. RESERVED FOR LOCAL USE

20. OUTSIDE LAB? YES ☐ NO ☐ $ CHARGES

21. DIAGNOSIS OR NATURE OF ILLNESS OR INJURY (Relate Items 1, 2, 3 or 4 to Item 24E by Line)

1. |___.___| 3. |___.___|
2. |___.___| 4. |___.___|

22. MEDICAID RESUBMISSION CODE   ORIGINAL REF. NO.

23. PRIOR AUTHORIZATION NUMBER

24. A. DATE(S) OF SERVICE			B. PLACE OF SERVICE	C. EMG	D. PROCEDURES, SERVICES, OR SUPPLIES (Explain Unusual Circumstances)		E. DIAGNOSIS POINTER	F. $ CHARGES	G. DAYS OR UNITS	H. EPSDT Family Plan	I. ID. QUAL.	J. RENDERING PROVIDER ID. #
From MM DD YY	To MM DD YY				CPT/HCPCS	MODIFIER						
1												NPI
2												NPI
3												NPI
4												NPI
5												NPI
6												NPI

25. FEDERAL TAX I.D. NUMBER   SSN ☐ EIN ☐

26. PATIENT'S ACCOUNT NO.

27. ACCEPT ASSIGNMENT? (For govt. claims, see back) YES ☐ NO ☐

28. TOTAL CHARGE $

29. AMOUNT PAID $

30. BALANCE DUE $

31. SIGNATURE OF PHYSICIAN OR SUPPLIER INCLUDING DEGREES OR CREDENTIALS (I certify that the statements on the reverse apply to this bill and are made a part thereof.)

SIGNED _____ DATE _____

32. SERVICE FACILITY LOCATION INFORMATION

a.   b.

33. BILLING PROVIDER INFO & PH # (   )

a.   b.

NUCC Instruction Manual available at: www.nucc.org

OMB APPROVAL PENDING

Figure **A3-3** Items shaded are to be left blank when another insurance is the primary and Medicare is the secondary.

1500

HEALTH INSURANCE CLAIM FORM

APPROVED BY NATIONAL UNIFORM CLAIM COMMITTEE 08/05

☐☐☐ PICA ▮ ▮ PICA ☐☐☐

| 1. MEDICARE ☐ (Medicare #) | MEDICAID ☐ (Medicaid #) | TRICARE CHAMPUS ☐ (Sponsor's SSN) | CHAMPVA ☐ (Member ID#) | GROUP HEALTH PLAN ☐ (SSN or ID) | FECA BLK LUNG ☐ (SSN) | OTHER ☐ (ID) | 1a. INSURED'S I.D. NUMBER (For Program in Item 1) |

| 2. PATIENT'S NAME (Last Name, First Name, Middle Initial) | 3. PATIENT'S BIRTH DATE MM ┊ DD ┊ YY   SEX M ☐ F ☐ | 4. INSURED'S NAME (Last Name, First Name, Middle Initial) |

| 5. PATIENT'S ADDRESS (No., Street) | 6. PATIENT RELATIONSHIP TO INSURED Self ☐ Spouse ☐ Child ☐ Other ☐ | 7. INSURED'S ADDRESS (No., Street) |

| CITY | STATE | 8. PATIENT STATUS Single ☐ Married ☐ Other ☐ | CITY | STATE |

| ZIP CODE | TELEPHONE (Include Area Code) ( ) | Employed ☐ Full-Time Student ☐ Part-Time Student ☐ | ZIP CODE | TELEPHONE (Include Area Code) ( ) |

| 9. OTHER INSURED'S NAME (Last Name, First Name, Middle Initial) | 10. IS PATIENT'S CONDITION RELATED TO: | 11. INSURED'S POLICY GROUP OR FECA NUMBER |

| a. OTHER INSURED'S POLICY OR GROUP NUMBER | a. EMPLOYMENT? (Current or Previous) ☐ YES ☐ NO | a. INSURED'S DATE OF BIRTH MM ┊ DD ┊ YY   SEX M ☐ F ☐ |

| b. OTHER INSURED'S DATE OF BIRTH MM ┊ DD ┊ YY   SEX M ☐ F ☐ | b. AUTO ACCIDENT?   PLACE (State) ☐ YES ☐ NO | b. EMPLOYER'S NAME OR SCHOOL NAME |

| c. EMPLOYER'S NAME OR SCHOOL NAME | c. OTHER ACCIDENT? ☐ YES ☐ NO | c. INSURANCE PLAN NAME OR PROGRAM NAME |

| d. INSURANCE PLAN NAME OR PROGRAM NAME | 10d. RESERVED FOR LOCAL USE | d. IS THERE ANOTHER HEALTH BENEFIT PLAN? ☐ YES ☐ NO If yes, return to and complete item 9 a-d. |

READ BACK OF FORM BEFORE COMPLETING & SIGNING THIS FORM.

12. PATIENT'S OR AUTHORIZED PERSON'S SIGNATURE I authorize the release of any medical or other information necessary to process this claim. I also request payment of government benefits either to myself or to the party who accepts assignment below.

SIGNED _____ DATE _____

13. INSURED'S OR AUTHORIZED PERSON'S SIGNATURE I authorize payment of medical benefits to the undersigned physician or supplier for services described below.

SIGNED _____

| 14. DATE OF CURRENT: MM ┊ DD ┊ YY ◀ ILLNESS (First symptom) OR INJURY (Accident) OR PREGNANCY(LMP) | 15. IF PATIENT HAS HAD SAME OR SIMILAR ILLNESS. GIVE FIRST DATE MM ┊ DD ┊ YY | 16. DATES PATIENT UNABLE TO WORK IN CURRENT OCCUPATION FROM MM ┊ DD ┊ YY TO MM ┊ DD ┊ YY |

| 17. NAME OF REFERRING PROVIDER OR OTHER SOURCE | 17a. | 18. HOSPITALIZATION DATES RELATED TO CURRENT SERVICES FROM MM ┊ DD ┊ YY TO MM ┊ DD ┊ YY |
| | 17b. NPI | |

| 19. RESERVED FOR LOCAL USE | 20. OUTSIDE LAB? $ CHARGES ☐ YES ☐ NO |

21. DIAGNOSIS OR NATURE OF ILLNESS OR INJURY (Relate Items 1, 2, 3 or 4 to Item 24E by Line)	22. MEDICAID RESUBMISSION CODE ORIGINAL REF. NO.
1. └___ . ___ 3. └___ . ___	23. PRIOR AUTHORIZATION NUMBER
2. └___ . ___ 4. └___ . ___	

24. A. DATE(S) OF SERVICE From MM DD YY To MM DD YY	B. PLACE OF SERVICE	C. EMG	D. PROCEDURES, SERVICES, OR SUPPLIES (Explain Unusual Circumstances) CPT/HCPCS ┊ MODIFIER	E. DIAGNOSIS POINTER	F. $ CHARGES	G. DAYS OR UNITS	H. EPSDT Family Plan	I. ID. QUAL.	J. RENDERING PROVIDER ID. #
1								NPI	
2								NPI	
3								NPI	
4								NPI	
5								NPI	
6								NPI	

| 25. FEDERAL TAX I.D. NUMBER   SSN ☐ EIN ☐ | 26. PATIENT'S ACCOUNT NO. | 27. ACCEPT ASSIGNMENT? (For govt. claims, see back) ☐ YES ☐ NO | 28. TOTAL CHARGE $ | 29. AMOUNT PAID $ | 30. BALANCE DUE $ |

| 31. SIGNATURE OF PHYSICIAN OR SUPPLIER INCLUDING DEGREES OR CREDENTIALS (I certify that the statements on the reverse apply to this bill and are made a part thereof.) SIGNED _____ DATE _____ | 32. SERVICE FACILITY LOCATION INFORMATION a.   b. | 33. BILLING PROVIDER INFO & PH # ( ) a.   b. |

NUCC Instruction Manual available at: www.nucc.org   OMB APPROVAL PENDING

Figure **A3-4**   Items shaded are to be left blank when Medicaid is the only coverage.

Item 1	Check the appropriate box for the patient's insurance.
Item 1a	Enter insured's identification number.
Item 2	Enter the patient's last name, first name, and middle initial, if any, as shown on the patient's Medicare card.
Item 3	Enter the patient's 8-digit birth date (MM/DD/CCYY) and sex.
Item 4	If there is insurance primary to Medicare, from any source, list the name of the insured here. When the insured and the patient are the same, enter the word SAME. If Medicare is primary, leave blank.
Item 5	Enter the patient's mailing address and telephone number. On the first line enter the street address; the second line, the city and state; the third line, the ZIP code and phone number.
Item 6	Check the appropriate box for patient's relationship to insured when item 4 is completed.
Item 7	Enter the insured's address and telephone number. When the address is the same as the patient's, enter the word SAME. Complete this item only when items 4, 6, and 11 are completed.
Item 8	Check the appropriate box for the patient's marital status and whether employed or a student.
Item 9a through 9d	Leave blank unless covered by Medigap.
Items 10a through 10c	Check "YES" or "NO" to indicate whether employment, auto liability, or other accident involvement applies to one or more of the services described in item 24.
Item 10d	Use this item exclusively for Medicaid (MCD) information. If the patient is entitled to Medicaid, enter the patient's Medicaid number preceded by MCD.
Item 11	By completing this item, the physician/supplier acknowledges having made a good faith effort to determine whether Medicare is the primary or secondary payer. If there is insurance primary to Medicare, enter the insured's policy or group number and proceed to items 11a, 11c. Items 4, 6, and 7 must also be completed. Enter the appropriate information in item 11c if insurance primary to Medicare is indicated in item 11. If there is no insurance primary to Medicare, enter the word "NONE" and proceed to item 12.
Item 11a	Enter the insured's 8-digit birth date (MM/DD/CCYY) and sex if different from item 3.
Item 11b	Enter employer's name, if applicable.
Item 11c	Enter the 9-digit PAYERID number of the primary insurer. If no PAYERID number exists, then enter the **complete** primary payer's program or plan name. If the primary payer's EOB does not contain the claims processing address, record the primary payer's claims processing address directly on the EOB. This is required if there is insurance primary to Medicare that is indicated in item 11.
Item 11d	Leave blank. Not required by Medicare.
Item 12	The patient or authorized representative must sign and enter either a 6-digit date (MM/DD/YY), 8-digit date (MM/DD/CCYY), or an alpha-numeric date (e.g., January 1, 1998) unless the signature is on file. In lieu of signing the claim, the patient may sign a statement to be retained in the provider, physician, or supplier file in accordance with Chapter 1, "General Billing Requirements." This can be "Signature on File" (SOF) and/or a computer-generated signature. The patient's signature authorizes release of medical information necessary to process the claim. It also authorizes payment of benefits to the provider of service or supplier when the provider of service or supplier accepts assignment on the claim.
Item 13	The signature in this item authorizes payment of benefits to the participating physician or supplier. This can be "Signature on File" signature and/or a computer-generated signature.

Item 14	Enter either an 8-digit (MM/DD/CCYY) or 6-digit (MM/DD/YY) date of current illness, injury, or pregnancy.
Item 15	Leave blank. Not required by Medicare.
Item 16	If the patient is employed and is unable to work in his/her current occupation, enter an 8-digit (MM/DD/CCYY) or 6-digit (MM/DD/YY) date when patient is unable to work.
Item 17	Enter the name of the referring or ordering physician if the service or item was ordered or referred by a physician.
Item 17a	Enter the NPI of the referring/ordering physician listed in item 17. This field is required when a service was ordered or referred by a physician.
Item 18	Enter either an 8-digit (MM/DD/CCYY) or a 6-digit (MM/DD/YY) date when a medical service is furnished as a result of, or subsequent to, a related hospitalization.
Item 19	Leave blank. Reserved for local use.
Item 20	Leave blank. Reserved for local use.
Item 21	Enter the patient's diagnosis/condition.
Item 22	Leave blank. Not required by Medicare.
Item 23	Enter any prior authorization number for procedures requiring prior approval.
Item 24A	Enter a 6-digit or 8-digit (MM/DD/CCYY) date for each procedure, service, or supply. When "from" and "to" dates are shown for a series of identical services, enter the number of days or units in column G.
Item 24B	Enter the appropriate place of service code(s) from the list provided *(partial list)*: *11 Office* *12 Home* *21 Inpatient hospital* *22 Outpatient hospital* *23 ED hospital*
Item 24C	Medicare providers are not required to complete this item.
Item 24D	Enter the CPT/HCPCS codes for the procedures, services, or supplies. When applicable, show modifiers with the code.
Item 24E	Enter the diagnosis code reference number as shown in item 21 to relate the date of service and the procedures performed to the primary diagnosis.
Item 24F	Enter the charge for each listed service.
Item 24G	Enter the number of days or units. This field is most commonly used for multiple visits, units of supplies, anesthesia minutes, or oxygen volume. If only one service is performed, the numeral 1 must be entered.
Item 24H	Leave blank. Not required by Medicare.
Item 24I	Leave blank. Not required by Medicare.
Item 24J	Leave blank. Not required by Medicare.
Item 24K	Enter the NPI of the performing provider of service/supplier if the provider is a member of a group practice.
Item 25	Enter the provider of service or supplier Federal Tax ID (Employer Identification Number) or Social Security Number. *The Federal tax identification number for the South Padre Medical Center is 00789200.*
Item 26	Enter the patient's account number assigned by the provider's of service.
Item 27	Check the appropriate block to indicate whether the provider of service accepts assignment of Medicare benefits.

APPENDIX 3

Item 28	Enter total charges for the services.
Item 29	Enter the total amount the patient paid on the covered services only.
Item 30	Leave blank. Not required by Medicare.
Item 31	Enter the signature of provider of service or supplier, or his/her representative, and either the 6-digit date (MM/DD/YY), 8-digit date (MM/DD/CCYY), or alpha-numeric date (e.g., January 1, 1998) the form was signed.
Item 32	Enter the name and address, and ZIP code of the facility if the services were furnished in a hospital, clinic, laboratory, or facility other than the patient's home or physician's office. Effective for claims received on or after April 1, 2004, the name, address, and zip code of the service location for all services other than those furnished in place of service home—12.
Item 33	Enter the provider of service/supplier's billing name, address, ZIP code, and telephone number. This is a required field. Enter the group NPI, for the performing provider of service/supplier who is a member of a group practice.

TABLE 1:   CMS-1500 (08/05) Medicare Claims

Item Number	Patient Information
	Left printer alignment block
	Right printer alignment block
1	Medicare
1	Medicaid
1	Tricare Champus
1	Champva
1	Group Health Plan
1	FECA Blk Lung
1	Other
1a	Insured's ID Number
2	Patient's Name (Last, First, MI)
3	Patient's Birth Date (Month)
3	Patient's Birth Date (Day)
3	Patient's Birth (Year)
3	Sex-Male
3	Sex-Female
4	Insured Name (Last, First, MI)
5	Patient's Address
6	Patient Relationship to Insured (Self)
6	Patient Relationship to Insured (Spouse)
6	Patient Relationship to Insured (Child)
6	Patient Relationship to Insured (Other)
7	Insured's Address
5	Patient's City
5	Patient's State
8	Patient Status (Single)

TABLE 1: cont'd

Item Number	Patient Information
8	Patient Status (Married)
8	Patient Status (Other)
7	Insured's City
7	Insured's State
5	Patient's Zip Code
5	Patient's Area Code
5	Patient's Phone Number
8	Patient Status (Employed)
8	Patient Status (Full Time Student)
8	Patient Status (Part Time Student)
7	Insured's Zip Code
7	Insured's Area Code
7	Insured's Phone Number
9	Other Insured's Name (Last, First, MI)
11	Insured's Policy, Group or FECA Number
9a	Other Insured's Policy or Group Number
10a	Condition Related (Employment C/P, Yes)
10a	Condition Related (Employment C/P, No)
11a	Insured's Date of Birth (Month)
11a	Insured's Date of Birth (Day)
11a	Insured's Date of Birth (Year)
11a	Sex-Male
11a	Sex-Female
9b	Other Insured's Date of Birth (Month)
9b	Other Insured's Date of Birth (Day)
9b	Other Insured's Date of Birth (Year)
9b	Sex-Male
9b	Sex-Female
10b	Condition Related To: (Auto Accident-Yes)
10b	Condition Related To: (Auto Accident-No)
10b	Condition Related To: (Auto Accident-State)
11b	Insured's Employer's Name or School Name
9c	Other Insured's Employer's Name or School Name
10c	Other Accident (Yes)
10c	Other Accident (No)
11c	Insured's Insurance Plan or PayerID
9d	Other Insured's Insurance Plan Name or PayerID
10d	(Reserved for Local Use)
11d	Another Benefit Health Plan (Yes)
11d	Another Benefit Health Plan (No)

TABLE **1:** cont'd

Item Number	Patient Information
12	Left Blank for Patient's Signature & Date
13	Left Blank for Insured's Signature
14	Date of Current Illness, Injury, Pregnancy (Month)
14	Date of Current Illness, Injury, Pregnancy (Day)
14	Date of Current Illness, Injury, Pregnancy—(Year)
15	First Date Has Had Same or Similar Illness (Month)
15	First Date Has Had Same or Similar Illness (Day)
15	First Date Has Had Same or Similar Illness—(Year)
16	Dates Patient Unable to Work (From Month)
16	Dates Patient Unable to Work (From Day)
16	Dates Patient Unable to Work (From Year)
16	Dates Patient Unable to Work (To Month)
16	Dates Patient Unable to Work (To Day)
16	Dates Patient Unable to Work (To Year)
17a	Legacy Qualifier/Provider Number of Referring Physician
17	Name of Referring Physician or Other Source
17b	NPI Number of Referring Physician
18	Hospitalization Related Current Svcs (From Month)
18	Hospitalization Related Current Svcs (From Day)
18	Hospitalization Related Current Svcs (From Year)
18	Hospitalization Related Current Svcs (To Month)
18	Hospitalization Related Current Svcs (To Day)
18	Hospitalization Related Current Svcs (To Year)
19	Reserved for Local Use
19	Reserved for Local Use
20	Outside Lab (Yes)
20	Outside Lab (No)
20	$ Charges
21.1	Diagnosis or Nature of Illness or Injury (Code)
21.3	Diagnosis or Nature of Illness or Injury (Code)
22	Medicaid Resubmission Code
22.2	Original Reference Number
21.2	Diagnosis or Nature of Illness or Injury (Code)
21.4	Diagnosis or Nature of Illness or Injury (Code)
23	Prior Authorization Number
24	Line Detail Narrative
24.1i	Legacy Qualifier Rendering Provider
24.1j	Legacy Provider Number Rendering Provider
24.1a	Date(s) of Service—(From Month)
24.1a	Date(s) of Service—(From Day)

TABLE 1: cont'd

Item Number	Patient Information
24.1a	Date(s) of Service—(From Year)
24.1a	Date(s) of Service—(To Month)
24.1a	Date(s) of Service—(To Day)
24.1a	Date(s) of Service—(To Year)
24.1b	Place of Service
24.1c	EMG
24.1d	Procedures, Svcs or Supplies (CPT/HCPCS)
24.1d	Procedures, Svcs or Supplies (Modifier 1)
24.1d	Procedures, Svcs or Supplies (Modifier 2)
24.1d	Procedures, Svcs or Supplies (Modifier 3)
24.1d	Procedures, Svcs or Supplies (Modifier 4)
24.1e	Diagnosis Pointer
24.1f	$ Charges
24.1g	Days or Units
24.1h	EPSDT Family Plan
24.1i	Legacy Qualifier Rendering Provider (Leave Bank)
24.1j	Legacy Provider Number Rendering Provider
24	Line Detail Narrative
24.2i	Legacy Qualifier Rendering Provider
24.2j	Legacy Provider Number Rendering Provider
24.2a	Date(s) of Service—(From Month)
24.2a	Date(s) of Service—(From Day)
24.2a	Date(s) of Service—(From Year)
24.2a	Date(s) of Service—(To Month)
24.2a	Date(s) of Service—(To Day)
24.2a	Date(s) of Service—(To Year)
24.2b	Place of Service
24.2c	EMG
24.2d	Procedures, Svcs or Supplies (CPT/HCPCS)
24.2d	Procedures, Svcs or Supplies (Modifier 1)
24.2d	Procedures, Svcs or Supplies (Modifier 2)
24.2d	Procedures, Svcs or Supplies (Modifier 3)
24.2d	Procedures, Svcs or Supplies (Modifier 4)
24.2e	Diagnosis Pointer
24.2f	$ Charges
24.2g	Days or Units
24.2h	EPSDT Family Plan
24.2i	Legacy Qualifier Rendering Provider (Leave Blank)
24.2j	Legacy Provider Number Rendering Provider
24	Line Detail Narrative

APPENDIX 3

TABLE 1: cont'd

Item Number	Patient Information
24.3i	Legacy Qualifier Rendering Provider
24.3j	Legacy Provider Number Rendering Provider
24.3a	Date(s) of Service—(From Month)
24.3a	Date(s) of Service—(From Day)
24.3a	Date(s) of Service—(From Year)
24.3a	Date(s) of Service—(To Month)
24.3a	Date(s) of Service—(To Day)
24.3a	Date(s) of Service—(To Year)
24.3b	Place of Service
24.3c	EMG
24.3d	Procedures, Svcs or Supplies (CPT/HCPCS)
24.3d	Procedures, Svcs or Supplies (Modifier 1)
24.3d	Procedures, Svcs or Supplies (Modifier 2)
24.3d	Procedures, Svcs or Supplies (Modifier 3)
24.3d	Procedures, Svcs or Supplies (Modifier 4)
24.3e	Diagnosis Pointer
24.3f	$ Charges
24.3g	Days or Units
24.3h	EPSDT Family Plan
24.3i	Legacy Qualifier Rendering Provider (Leave Blank)
24.3j	Legacy Provider Number Rendering Provider
24	Line Detail Narrative
24.4i	Legacy Qualifier Rendering Provider
24.4j	Legacy Provider Number Rendering Provider
24.4a	Date(s) of Service—(From Month)
24.4a	Date(s) of Service—(From Day)
24.4a	Date(s) of Service—(From Year)
24.4a	Date(s) of Service—(To Month)
24.4a	Date(s) of Service—(To Day)
24.4a	Date(s) of Service—(To Year)
24.4b	Place of Service
24.4c	EMG
24.4d	Procedures, Svcs or Supplies (CPT/HCPCS)
24.4d	Procedures, Svcs or Supplies (Modifier 1)
24.4d	Procedures, Svcs or Supplies (Modifier 2)
24.4d	Procedures, Svcs or Supplies (Modifier 3)
24.4d	Procedures, Svcs or Supplies (Modifier 4)
24.4e	Diagnosis Pointer
24.4f	$ Charges
24.4g	Days or Units

TABLE 1: cont'd

Item Number	Patient Information
24.4h	EPSDT Family Plan
24.4i	Legacy Qualifier Rendering Provider (Leave Blank)
24.4j	Legacy Provider Number Rendering Provider
24	Line Detail Narrative
24.5i	Legacy Qualifier Rendering Provider
24.5j	Legacy Provider Number Rendering Provider
24.5a	Date(s) of Service—(From Month)
24.5a	Date(s) of Service—(From Day)
24.5a	Date(s) of Service—(From Year)
24.5a	Date(s) of Service—(To Month)
24.5a	Date(s) of Service—(To Day)
24.5a	Date(s) of Service—(To Year)
24.5b	Place of Service
24.5c	EMG
24.5d	Procedures, Svcs or Supplies (CPT/HCPCS)
24.5d	Procedures, Svcs or Supplies (Modifier 1)
24.5d	Procedures, Svcs or Supplies (Modifier 2)
24.5d	Procedures, Svcs or Supplies (Modifier 3)
24.5d	Procedures, Svcs or Supplies (Modifier 4)
24.5e	Diagnosis Pointer
24.5f	$ Charges
24.5g	Days or Units
24.5h	EPSDT Family Plan
24.5i	Legacy Qualifier Rendering Provider (Leave Blank)
24.5j	Legacy Provider Number Rendering Provider
24	Line Detail Narrative
24.6i	Legacy Qualifier Rendering Provider
24.6j	Legacy Provider Number Rendering Provider
24.6a	Date(s) of Service—(From Month)
24.6a	Date(s) of Service—(From Day)
24.6a	Date(s) of Service—(From Year)
24.6a	Date(s) of Service—(To Month)
24.6a	Date(s) of Service—(To Day)
24.6a	Date(s) of Service—(To Year)
24.6b	Place of Service
24.6c	EMG
24.6d	Procedures, Svcs or Supplies (CPT/HCPCS)
24.6d	Procedures, Svcs or Supplies (Modifier 1)
24.6d	Procedures, Svcs or Supplies (Modifier 2)
24.6d	Procedures, Svcs or Supplies (Modifier 3)

TABLE 1: cont'd

Item Number	Patient Information
24.6d	Procedures, Svcs or Supplies (Modifier 4)
24.6e	Diagnosis Pointer
24.6f	$ Charges
24.6g	Days or Units
24.6h	EPSDT Family Plan
24.6i	Legacy Qualifier Rendering Provider (Leave Blank)
24.6j	Legacy Provider Number Rendering Provider
25	Federal Tax ID Number
25	Federal Tax ID Number (SSN)
25	Federal Tax ID Number (EIN)
26	Patient's Account Number
27	Accept Assignment (Yes)
27	Accept Assignment (No)
28	Total Charge
29	Amount Paid
30	Balance Due
33	Billing Provider Phone Number Area Code
33	Billing Provider Phone Number
32	Name of Facility Where Svcs Rendered
33	Physician/Supplier Billing Name
32	Address of Facility Where Svcs Rendered
33	Physician/Supplier Address
31	Left Blank for Signature Physician/Supplier
32	City, State and Zip Code of Facility
33	City, State and Zip Code of Billing Provider
32a	Facility NPI Number
32b	Facility Qualifier and Legacy Number
33a	Billing Provider NPI Number
33b	Billing Provider Qualifier and Legacy Number

Modified from Department of Health and Human Services (DHHS), Centers for Medicare and Medicaid Services (CMS): *CMS manual system: Pub 100-04 Medicare claims processing* (Transmittal 899), March 31, 2006, Change Request 4293.

APPENDIX 4

Software Instructions

The Instructor will guide you in the installation of your software prior to doing the following steps.

Adding South Padre Medical Center Data to Medisoft Program

Begin by opening the **companion** CD, and locating the mwBaseData.mbk file. Copy this file by right-clicking on it and selecting "Copy" from the drop down menu. Open the C drive and locate the MediData file. Place the curser over the MediData file and right click. From the drop down menu select Paste. Open the MediData file and verify that the mwBaseData.mbk file is now located in the MediData file. Close any open windows and return to the desktop. Open the Medisoft Advanced Patient Accounting program. In the Medisoft software main menu screen toolbar, select File (located in the upper left corner of the screen). Next, select Restore Data from the drop down menu. Click "OK" in the Warning window. In the Restore window—Backup File Path and Name, enter C:\MediData. The Existing Backup window will populate with the wmBaseData.mbk file. Click on this file to complete the Backup File Path and Name field. Next, click the Start Restore button located in the Restore window. Click OK in the Confirm window. Once the restoration is complete, Click OK in the Information window. You will need to sign into the MediSoft program again before beginning the first task of creating a Login Name and Password.

Using the Medisoft Advanced Patient Accounting Software

Once you have opened the Medisoft software program a User Login window will open and require that you enter Login Name and Password **(Figure A4-1).**

For this time only, you will log on as Jennifer White, as you will be adding yourself to the Security Setup Users list. In the Login Name field enter JW. The Password is 1. Click the "OK" button. You should now be at the Medisoft Advanced Patient Account Software Main Menu **(Figure A4-2).**

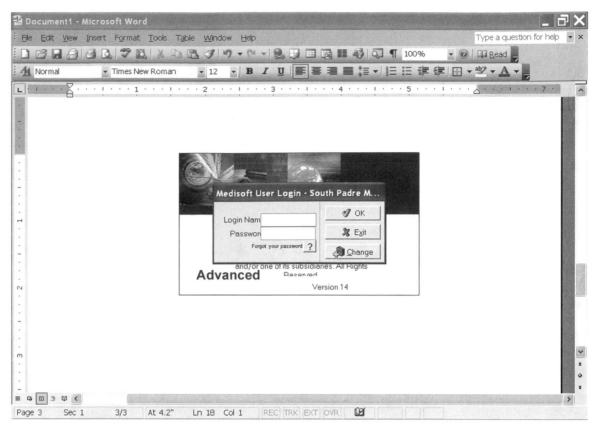

Figure **A4-1** Medisoft screenshot—User Log-in.

Figure **A4-2** Medisoft screenshot.

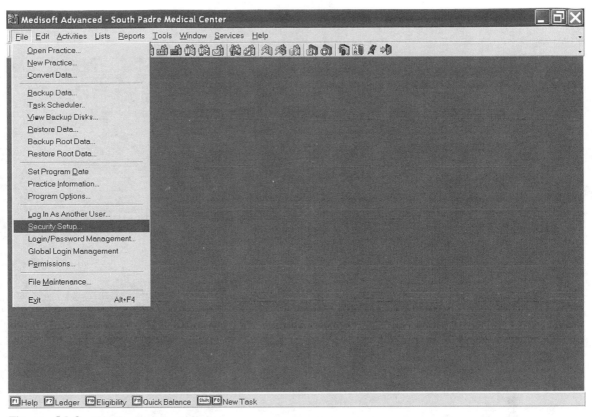

Figure **A4-3** **Medisoft screenshot.**

From the tool bar located at the top of the screen, select File. On this drop down menu, click on Security Setup **(Figure A4-3)**. In the Security Setup window **(Figure A4-4)**, click the New button. In the User Entry window Main tab **(Figure A4-5)** enter your first and last initial in the Login Name field. Complete the Full Name and Password fields.

Enter a 1 in the Access Level field. Reconfirm your password but do not complete the remaining fields or tabs. Click the Save button. You should now be returned to the Security Setup window. Verify that you have been added to the Security Setup Users list and click the Close button located at the bottom of the window.

You should now be back at the Main Menu. From the tool bar again, select File. From the drop down menu, select Login In As Another User **(Figure A4-6)**. Login in again using your Login Name and Password. You need to use this login each time you log on to the Medisoft program.

DATA BACK-UP

Begin by creating your back-up file. While in the Medisoft software main menu screen, click the X located in the top right corner of the screen. In the Backup Reminder window **(Figure A4-7)** click the Backup Data Now button located at the bottom of this window. In the next window, Backup Warning, click the OK button located in this window **(Figure A4-8).** Now you will create your individual backup file in the backup window **(Figure A4-9).** You will need to know the drive (i.e., A:, C:, or E:) where your storage device is located to begin this step. If you do not have this information you will need

Figure **A4-4** **Medisoft screenshot.**

Figure **A4-5** **Medisoft screenshot.**

Figure **A4-6**   Medisoft screenshot.

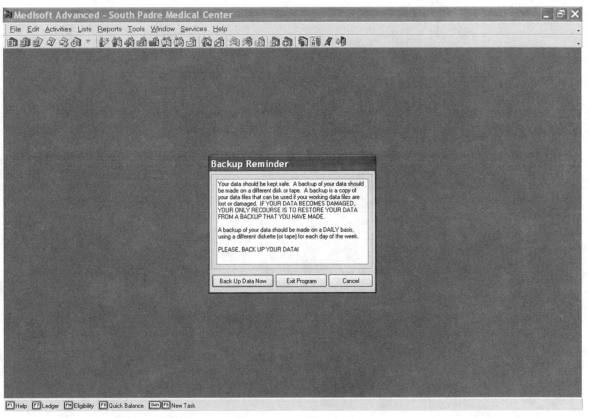

Figure **A4-7**   Medisoft screenshot.

137

Figure **A4-8**   **Medisoft screenshot.**

Figure **A4-9**   **Medisoft screenshot.**

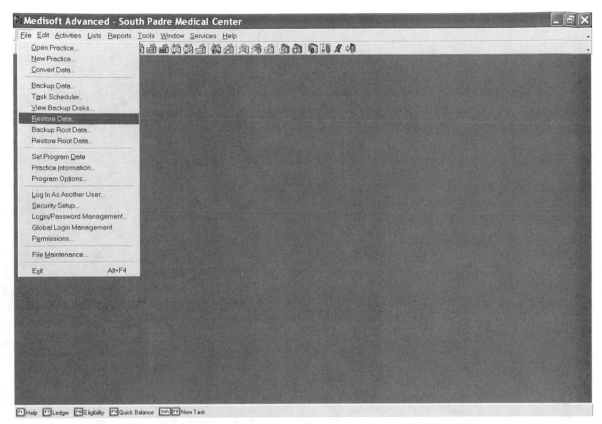

Figure **A4-10**　**Medisoft screenshot.**

to get it now. In the Destination File Path and Name window, enter the location of where the backup data is to be stored followed by a back slash and your initials. For example, E:\MOPS, and click the Start Backup button located in the Backup window. Write down your backup file path and name as you will need this to restore your data later. Once the backup is complete, the Medisoft software program will close. You will need to back up your data after completing your assignments each day before exiting the Medisoft software. Likewise, you will need to restore this data to the Medisoft software before beginning each day's tasks. The steps to restore your data are listed below.

DATA RESTORATION

In the Medisoft software main menu screen toolbar, select File. Next, select Restore Data from the drop down menu **(Figure A4-10).** Click OK in the Warning window. In the Restore window Backup File Path and Name, enter your backup file's path and name (i.e., E:\MOPS) followed by .mbk. The .mbk was attached to your backup file by the software on completion of your first backup. You will need to attach it to your backup file path and name each time you restore your data **(Figure A4-11).** Next, click the Start Restore button located in the Restore window. Click OK in the Confirm window. Once the restoration is complete, Click OK in the Information window. You are now ready to begin the your daily assignments.

APPENDIX 4

Figure **A4-11**   **Medisoft screenshot.**

Scheduling Window

From the Main Menu, click on the Activities button located on the tool bar at the top of the screen. From the drop down menu, choose Appointment Book **(Figure A4-12).** The Appointment Book can also be opened by clicking on the Appointment Book (sixth) icon on the icon tool bar **(Figure A4-13).** This will open the Office Hours appointment scheduling program **(Figure A4-14).**

   To select the physician whose schedule you wish to view/edit, click on the search button (magnifying glass) beside the information field located on the icon toolbar.

   From the Provider Search Window, click on the name of the physician whose schedule you wish to view/edit **(Figure A4-15).** Click the OK button located at the bottom of the Provider Search Window. To change the date of the schedule shown, click on the date in the calendar located to the left of the appointment schedule. Click on the forward or back scroll arrows beside the Day, Week, Month, and Year choices located below the calendar to change the calendar to the month needed for scheduling/viewing.

A. Matrixing the Calendar/ Blocking Time

To block times when the physician is not available for scheduling of patient visits or to indicate times reserved for surgery, a break in the schedule is

Figure **A4-12** Medisoft screenshot.

Figure **A4-13** Medisoft screenshot.

Figure **A4-14** Medisoft screenshot.

Figure **A4-15** Medisoft screenshot.

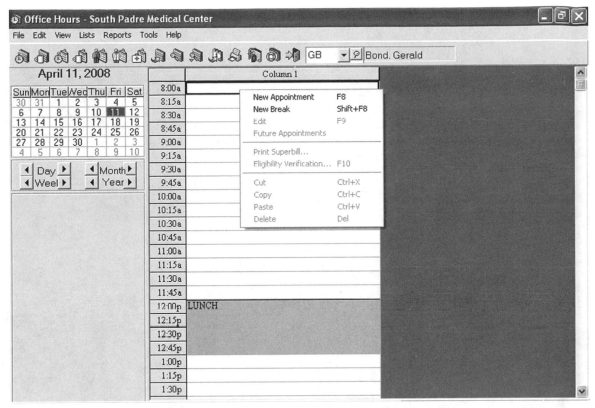

Figure **A4-16** **Medisoft screenshot.**

created. Each break is labeled and highlighted according to the reason for the block. Labels and colors are assigned as follows:

UNAVAILABLE   Red

HOSPITAL ROUNDS   Teal

BOARD MEETING   Fuchsia

LUNCH   Lime

SURGERY   Aqua

MEDICAL SCHOOL   Olive

NURSING HOME VISITS   Purple

Begin by opening the schedule window. Select the correct physician and the beginning date for which you are matrixing. Once you have the indicated the physician and date, you should begin blocking times during which the physician is unavailable.

Select the correct time slot for the block to begin by clicking on the time's appointment line. With the appointment timeframe highlighted, right click to open scheduling menu. Select and click on New Break **(Figure A4-16).** Using the New Break Entry window you will provide the information needed to schedule the time blocked **(Figure A4-17).** In the Description field enter, in capital letters, the reason for the block from the labels listed above. Once scheduled, this label will appear in the first time slot of the block.

Verify that the information in the Date and Time fields is correct for the scheduling block you are entering. To enter the Length of the scheduled

APPENDIX 4

Figure **A4-17** Medisoft screenshot.

block, you may either enter the amount of time needed in the Length field or use the up/down arrows located to the right until the amount of time needed appears in the Length box. Each time the up/down arrow is used the time will increase or decrease in increments of 15 minutes. If the block being scheduled is a repeating one (weekly, daily, monthly, or yearly), click on the Change button located on the left side of the New Break Entry window. In the Repeat Change window **(Figure A4-18)** select the frequency for which the break is being scheduled by clicking on the radio button located before either Daily, Weekly, Monthly, or Yearly. Once the frequency is selected, the Repeat Change window will be modified to reflect the frequency interval selected. As you will be scheduling breaks at weekly intervals, you should have selected Weekly from the Repeat Change Frequency window **(Figure A-19).** In the modified window indicate the frequency of weeks and days the break is to be repeated. In the End On field enter the date for which the repeating break will end. Clicking on the drop down arrow to the right of the End On field will open a calendar to assist with this process.

From the matrixing list chose the color of the block by using the search button located next to the color window. Click on the appropriate color from the color menu. If not already checked, check the All Columns box and the Current Provider(s) radio button. After all scheduling block information has been entered and verified to be correct, click the Save button located on the right side of the New Break Entry window. The blocked time now appears on the physician's schedule.

Figure **A4-18** Medisoft screenshot.

Figure **A4-19** Medisoft screenshot.

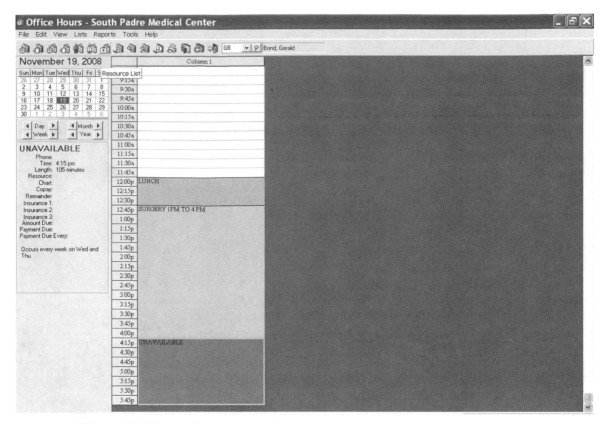

Figure **A4-20**   **Medisoft screenshot.**

All blocks except SURGERY time slots are scheduled in this manner. When scheduling blocks for SURGERY, the Label and available surgery times are placed in the time slot before the first available surgery slot **(Figure A4-20).**

B. Scheduling Patient Visits

Begin scheduling office visits from the scheduling window. Select the physician and date needed for scheduling by using the provider search window and calendar. Click on the available time slot for which you are scheduling the appointment. Open the drop down menu and select New Appointment **(Figure 4A-21)** to open the New Appointment Entry window **(Figure A4-22).**

SCHEDULING ESTABLISHED PATIENTS
In the New Appointment Entry window, use the search button (magnifying glass) located next to the Patient field to search for the established patient's information. (This step should also be performed before scheduling a new patient to verify the patient's status as new or established.) In the Patient Search window, Search for field and enter the patient's last name **(Figure A4-23).** Select the patient from the list by clicking on the patient's name. Click the OK button. The patient's name and identification number now populate the Chart fields. Using the drop down arrow to the right of the Resource field indicate the location in which the patient will be seen **(Figure A4-24).** In the Note field enter the reason for the encounter, the referring physician, patient's

Figure **A4-21** Medisoft screenshot.

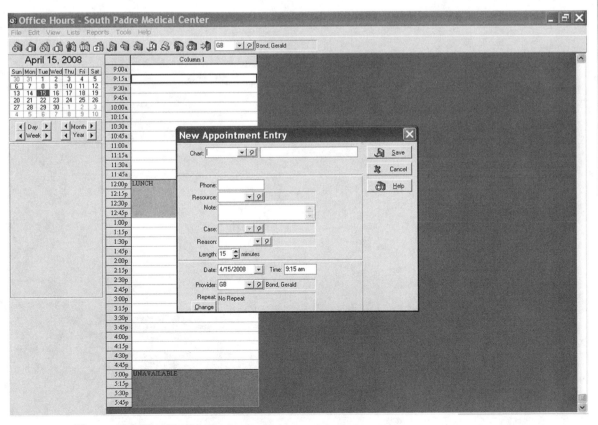

Figure **A4-22** Medisoft screenshot.

APPENDIX 4

Figure **A4-23**   Medisoft screenshot.

Figure **A4-24**   Medisoft screenshot.

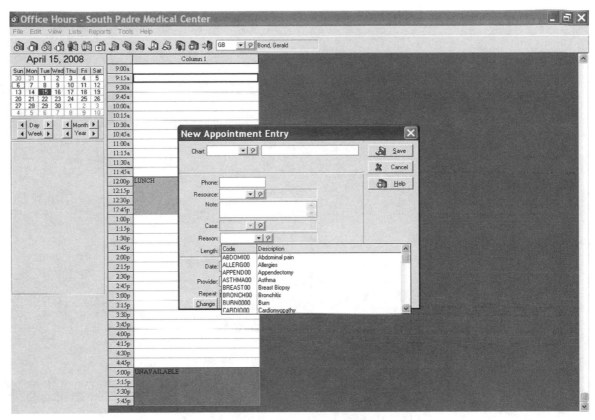

Figure **A4-25** **Medisoft screenshot.**

age (if necessary), and any other information important to this patient's appointment. If the case field is blank, click on the drop down arrow located in this field and select the patient's available case. Next, click on the drop down arrow located in the Reason field. Enter the reason for the encounter by selecting it from this list **(Figure A4-25).** The Length field will be populated once a reason for the encounter is selected; however, it should be verified for correctness and may be altered by using the up and down arrows in this field. Verify the information in the Date and Time and Provider fields is correct for the appointment being scheduled. Once you have verified that the information you have entered for this appointment is correct, click the Save button. The created appointment now appears on the appointment schedule.

SCHEDULING NEW PATIENTS
In the New Appointment Entry window, enter the new patient's name (Last, First) in the field located to the right of the Chart field. If available, enter the patient's phone number in the Phone field in this field **(Figure A4-26).** Do not enter the dashes; the software will do this. As this is a new patient and no case yet exists for this patient, the Case field will not be available to be completed. Complete the remaining fields in the same manner as completed for an established patient (see above Scheduling Established Patients). Once you have verified that the information you have entered for this appointment is correct, click the Save button. The created appointment now appears on the Schedule Report.

APPENDIX 4

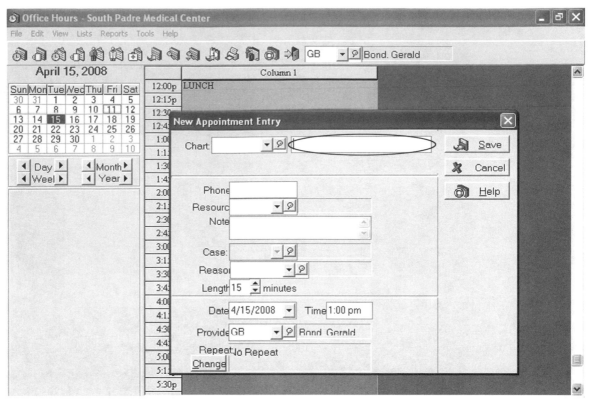

Figure **A4-26** **Medisoft screenshot.**

C. Editing/Deleting Breaks or Appointments

To reschedule an existing appointment, locate the appointment or break to be rescheduled in the scheduling window. Select the appointment or break by clicking on the patient's name or break description. With the appointment or break highlighted, right click to open the scheduling menu. Select Edit from the scheduling menu **(Figure A4-27).** In the Edit Break window or Edit Appointment window **(Figures A4-28** and **A4-29)** edit or correct the field in which the error is located. If changing the information in the Provider field, be sure to verify that the appointment time to which the break or patient appointment is to be moved is available. Verify that the information is correct and click on the Save button.

To delete an existing break or appointment, select the break or appointment and open the scheduling menu. From the scheduling menu select Delete **(Figure A4-30).** A prompt will appear asking "Delete this appointment?". Clicking on the yes button will delete the break or appointment.

D. Appointment List

An Appointment List prints a list, by provider, of all breaks and patients scheduled, each patient's phone number, and the time, length, reason of the

Figure **A4-27**   Medisoft screenshot.

Figure **A4-28**   Medisoft screenshot.

Figure **A4-29**   Medisoft screenshot.

Figure **A4-30**   Medisoft screenshot.

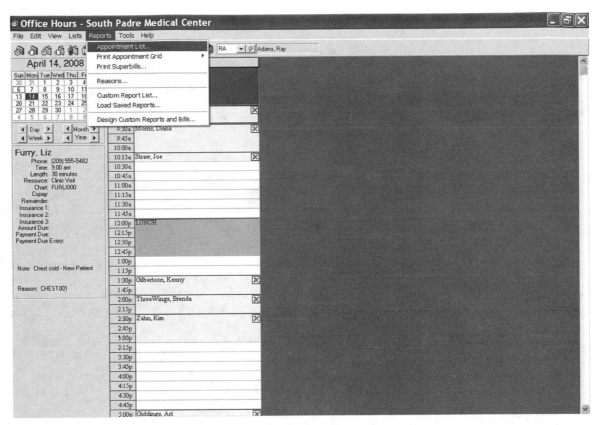

Figure **A4-31** Medisoft screenshot.

visit, and any notes added in the Appointment Schedule window for the selected date(s) or provider(s). To print this report, on the Office Hours software program toolbar click on Reports. From the drop down menu select Appointment List **(Figure A4-31).** The Report Setup Print Selection window allows you to either print the list or view it first on screen before printing the list. To print the list, select the radio button for Print the report on the printer and click the Start button **(Figure A4-32).** In the Data Selection window, use the up and down arrows in the date fields to select a date or range of dates for which the list is being generated. Use the drop down arrows or search button in the Provider fields to select an individual or range of providers for which the list is being generated **(Figure A4-33).** Verify the information requested is correct and Click the OK button located in the Select Data window.

E. Patient Demographic Entry

From the Medisoft program main menu toolbar, click on the Patient icon located on the icon toolbar at the top of the screen, or you can click on the Lists menu and select Patient/Guarantors and Cases **(Figure A4-34).** At the top of the Patient List window, click on the radio button for Patient. Click on the New Patient button **(Figure A4-35).** The Patient/Guarantor (New) window is now open.

Beginning on the Name, Address tab, Last Name field, enter the patient's demographic information **(Figure A4-36).** On the Other Information tab, use the drop down arrow in the Type field to indicate if this record is for a

Figure **A4-32** Medisoft screenshot.

Figure **A4-33** Medisoft screenshot.

Figure **A4-34** Medisoft screenshot.

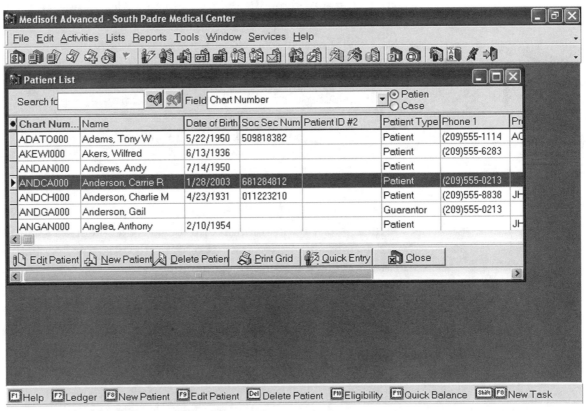

Figure **A4-35** Medisoft screenshot.

Figure **A4-36**   **Medisoft screenshot.**

patient or guarantor **(Figure A4-37).** For a patient record, use the drop down arrow in the Assigned Provider field to indicate the patient's provider and complete the Emergency Contact fields. The search buttons located to the right of the Employer fields may be used to find the information needed to populate these fields. If this information is not available, leave these fields blank as they will be reviewed by Kerri Marshall, Insurance Specialist, before a claim is submitted. When entering a Guarantor's record, this information does not need to be completed.

Review the completed Patient Information form for the patient's or guarantor's signature for assignment of benefits and release of information. If completed on this form, check the Signature on File box on the Other Information tab and enter the date of the signature. The remaining fields and tab have been populated by default or should remain blank. Once you have verified that the information entered is correct, click the Save button located on the right side of the Patient/Guarantor window to save the patient record and return to the Patient List window.

Now click on the radio button for Case, located at the top of the Patient List window. Select and highlight the patient being added and click on the New Case button located at the bottom of the Patient List window **(Figure A4-38).** In the Case entry window, Personal tab, Description field, enter **New Patient (Figure A4-39).** Using the drop down arrows located in the Marital and Student fields complete each of these fields. With the information available from the Patient Information forms or additional source documents complete the Employment fields.

Figure **A4-37** Medisoft screenshot.

Figure **A4-38** Medisoft screenshot.

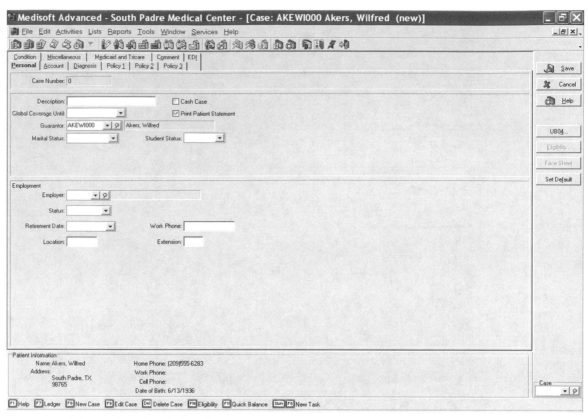

Figure **A4-39**   **Medisoft screenshot.**

On the Account tab, using the drop down arrows located in each field and the source document information available, complete the Assigned, Referring, and Operating Provider fields **(Figure A4-40).** Leave the remaining fields blank; these will be completed by Kerri Marshal at a later date.

Next, click on the Policy 1 tab. Using the drop down arrow in the Insurance 1 field, select the patient's primary insurance. If the patient is a minor or the patient is not the policy holder of the insurance, use the drop down arrow located in the Policy Holder field to select the policy holder from the Patient/Guarantor list. The Relationship to Insured field defaults to Self. If the patient is not the policy holder, use the drop down arrow located in this field to enter the correct relationship **(Figure A4-41).** Enter the Policy and Group numbers in each of these fields and check the Accept Assignment/Assignment of Benefits box. The remaining fields will be completed by Kerri Marshall.

F. Printing Patient Face Sheets

From the main menu, click on Reports located on the toolbar at the top of the screen. On the Reports menu select Custom Reports List **(Figure A4-42).** In the Open Report menu, scroll to and select Patient Face Sheet. Click the OK button located in the Open Reports menu. In the Print Reports Where window, click on the radio button for Print the report on the printer. In the Patient Face Sheet: Data Selection Questions window **(Figure A4-43)** use the

Figure **A4-40** **Medisoft screenshot.**

Figure **A4-41** **Medisoft screenshot.**

Figure **A4-42** **Medisoft screenshot.**

Figure **A4-43** **Medisoft screenshot.**

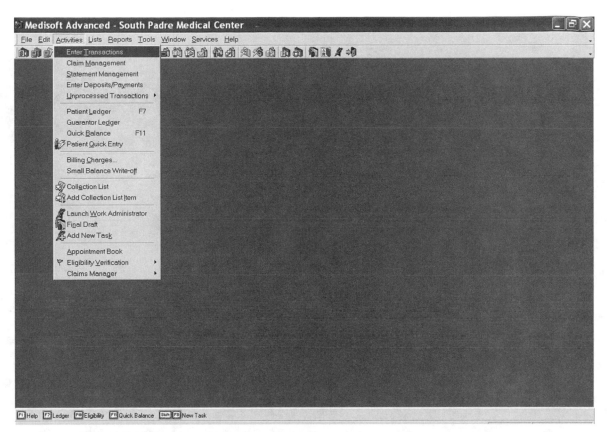

Figure **A4-44** **Medisoft screenshot.**

search button located in the Chart Number Range field to open the Patient Search widow. Enter the patient last name in the Search for field. Select and highlight the patient from the list and click the OK button located at the bottom of the Patient Search window. You will need to complete this step for both Chart Number Range fields. Click the OK button located in the Patient Face Sheet: Data Selection Questions window.

G. Charge Entry

From the main menu, click on Activities, located on the toolbar at the top of the main menu Medisoft program. From the dropdown menu, select Enter Transactions **(Figure A4-44).** The Transaction Entry window is now available **(Figure A4-45).** Using the search button located in the Chart field, open the Patient search window and select the patient for which you are entering charges. Use the dropdown arrow in the Case field to select the case for this patient. The software program will populate the Chart field with the ID number of the patient. Clicking in each field of the Charges portion of the Transaction Entry window will activate a drop down list for each field. Enter the date of the service(s) in the Date field. For example, clicking on the drop down arrow in the Date field will open a calendar on which you may indicate the date of service for the transaction being entered **(Figure A4-46).** Using the drop down arrows in each field, enter the Procedure and Diagnosis fields from the patient's superbill. Repeat these steps until all services and diagnoses have been entered. Tab or enter past the remaining charge entry fields; Kerri Marshall will review and, if needed, complete these fields.

Figure **A4-45** **Medisoft screenshot.**

Figure **A4-46** **Medisoft screenshot.**

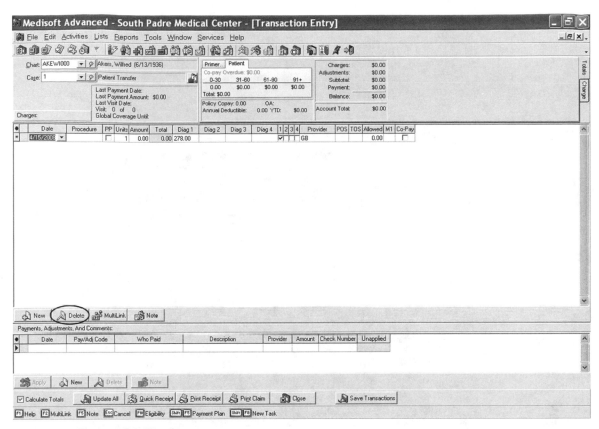

Figure **A4-47** **Medisoft screenshot.**

Verify that the date, procedure, and diagnosis fields have been completed correctly. If any errors have occurred, the charge line may be deleted while in the Transaction Entry window. Select and highlight the date of service for the charge line to be deleted. With the charge line highlighted click on the Delete button located at the bottom of the Transaction Entry, Charges window **(Figure A4-47).** If all charges are correct as entered, payments received and included on the superbill may also be entered while in the Transaction Entry window. To enter payments, see Payment Entry below. If no payments are to be entered at this time, click on the Update All button located at the bottom of the Charge Entry window. Next, close the Transaction window by clicking on the Close button located at the bottom of this window.

H. Payment Entry

From the main menu click on Activities located on the toolbar at the top of the main menu Medisoft program. From the drop down menu, select Enter Transactions **(Figure A4-44).** The Transaction Entry window is now available **(Figure A4-45).** Using the search button located in the Chart field, open the Patient search window and select the patient for which you are entering charges. Use the drop down arrow in the Case field to select the case for this patient. The software program will populate the Chart field with the ID number of the patient. Clicking in each field of the Payments, Adjustments, and Comments portion of the Transaction Entry window will activate a drop down list for each field **(Figure A4-46).** Enter the date the payment was received in the Date field. Using the drop down arrows in the Pay/Adj Code

Figure **A4-48** **Medisoft screenshot.**

and Who Paid complete these fields with the information from each source document (superbill, EOB, etc.) Enter the amount received in the Amount field.

Verify that all information entered is correct. Next, the payment will need to be applied to the patient's account. Click on the Apply button located at the bottom of the Payments, Adjustments, And Comments portion of the Transaction Entry window. In the Apply Payments to Charges window **(Figure A4-47),** click this Payment field to enter the amount to be applied to each charge. Verify that all funds have been applied by reviewing the Unapplied field located at the top of the Apply Payments to Charges window **(Figure A4-48).** If all funds have been applied, the Unapplied field should be 0.00. Once all information has been verified as correct, click the Close button located at the bottom of the Apply Payments to Charges window. In the Transaction Entry window, click the Update All and then Close button located at the bottom of the window.

DELETING OR EDITING CHARGES/PAYMENTS

Once applied, charges and/or payments may be deleted from the patient's account by accessing each patient's ledger. From the Activities menu, select Patient Ledger **(Figure A4-49).** In the Quick Ledger window use the search button in the Chart field to locate and select the patient **(Figure A4-50).** Select and highlight the transaction line to be edited or deleted and right click to open the Quick Ledger menu. Selecting Edit from this menu will return to the Transaction Entry window for the charge/payment. (See Charge/Payment Entry above). To delete the charge/payment, select Delete Transaction from

Figure **A4-49**   Medisoft screenshot.

Figure **A4-50**   Medisoft screenshot.

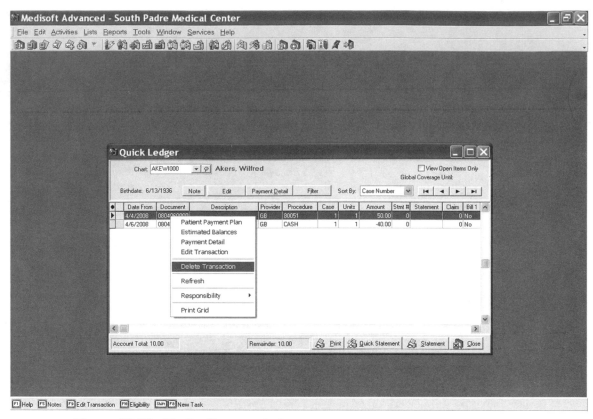

Figure **A4-51**   **Medisoft screenshot.**

the Quick Ledger menu **(Figure A4-51).** A confirmation window will open. Confirm the deletion by clicking the Yes button in this window. Once all transactions have been deleted, close the Quick Ledger window.

I. Patient Ledger

To print a patient ledger, select Activities from the main menu toolbar. From the Activities menu, select Patient Ledger **(Figure A4-49).** In the Quick Ledger window use the search button in the Chart field to locate and select the patient **(Figure A4-50).** Click on the Print button located at the bottom of the Quick ledger window. The patient ledger will appear in the Preview Report window. Verify the ledger is correct and click the print button located at the top of the Preview Report window.

J. Day Sheet with Transaction Detail

From the main menu, click on Reports located on the toolbar at the top of the screen. Click on Day Sheets in the drop down menu, then Patient Day Sheet from the next drop down menu **(Figure A4-52).** In the Data Selection Question—Patient Day Sheet User Match window, enter the date the charges were posted in the Date Created Range fields. Enter the date of the charges and payments in the Date From Range fields **(Figure A4-53).** Once you have verified the information requested is correct, click the Print button located at the bottom of the Data Selection Question—Patient Day Sheet User Match window.

Figure **A4-52**   **Medisoft screenshot.**

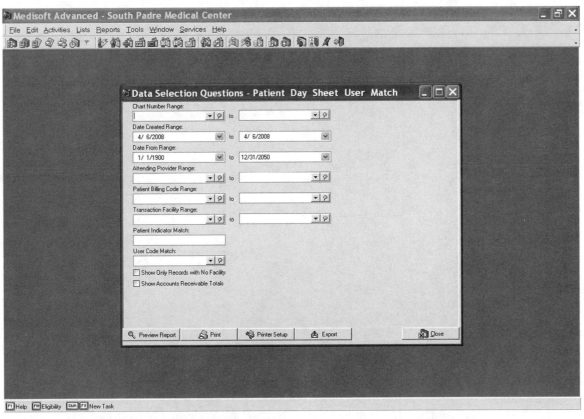

Figure **A4-53**   **Medisoft screenshot.**

APPENDIX 5

Forms Library

South Padre Medical Center
9878 Palm Drive
SOUTH PADRE, TX 98765

FIRST NATIONAL BANK
100 FIRST STREET
SOUTH PADRE, TX 98765

98-95
—––
1251

N⁰   999

PAY _____   DOLLARS

	DATE	CHECK NO.	AMOUNT	

TO THE
ORDER OF _____

_____   _____

_____   _____

⑈0⑈0123⑈ ⑆4567⑈8901⑆ ⑈1234567890⑈

1500

HEALTH INSURANCE CLAIM FORM

APPROVED BY NATIONAL UNIFORM CLAIM COMMITTEE 08/05

| | PICA | | | | | | | | PICA | | |

1. MEDICARE ☐ (Medicare #)　MEDICAID ☐ (Medicaid #)　TRICARE CHAMPUS ☐ (Sponsor's SSN)　CHAMPVA ☐ (Member ID#)　GROUP HEALTH PLAN ☐ (SSN or ID)　FECA BLK LUNG ☐ (SSN)　OTHER ☐ (ID)

1a. INSURED'S I.D. NUMBER　(For Program in Item 1)

2. PATIENT'S NAME (Last Name, First Name, Middle Initial)

3. PATIENT'S BIRTH DATE MM DD YY　SEX M ☐ F ☐

4. INSURED'S NAME (Last Name, First Name, Middle Initial)

5. PATIENT'S ADDRESS (No., Street)

6. PATIENT RELATIONSHIP TO INSURED　Self ☐　Spouse ☐　Child ☐　Other ☐

7. INSURED'S ADDRESS (No., Street)

CITY　STATE

8. PATIENT STATUS　Single ☐　Married ☐　Other ☐

CITY　STATE

ZIP CODE　TELEPHONE (Include Area Code) ( )

Employed ☐　Full-Time Student ☐　Part-Time Student ☐

ZIP CODE　TELEPHONE (Include Area Code) ( )

9. OTHER INSURED'S NAME (Last Name, First Name, Middle Initial)

10. IS PATIENT'S CONDITION RELATED TO:

11. INSURED'S POLICY GROUP OR FECA NUMBER

a. OTHER INSURED'S POLICY OR GROUP NUMBER

a. EMPLOYMENT? (Current or Previous)　YES ☐　NO ☐

a. INSURED'S DATE OF BIRTH MM DD YY　SEX M ☐ F ☐

b. OTHER INSURED'S DATE OF BIRTH MM DD YY　SEX M ☐ F ☐

b. AUTO ACCIDENT?　PLACE (State)　YES ☐　NO ☐

b. EMPLOYER'S NAME OR SCHOOL NAME

c. EMPLOYER'S NAME OR SCHOOL NAME

c. OTHER ACCIDENT?　YES ☐　NO ☐

c. INSURANCE PLAN NAME OR PROGRAM NAME

d. INSURANCE PLAN NAME OR PROGRAM NAME

10d. RESERVED FOR LOCAL USE

d. IS THERE ANOTHER HEALTH BENEFIT PLAN?　YES ☐　NO ☐　If yes, return to and complete item 9 a-d.

READ BACK OF FORM BEFORE COMPLETING & SIGNING THIS FORM.

12. PATIENT'S OR AUTHORIZED PERSON'S SIGNATURE I authorize the release of any medical or other information necessary to process this claim. I also request payment of government benefits either to myself or to the party who accepts assignment below.

SIGNED _____ DATE _____

13. INSURED'S OR AUTHORIZED PERSON'S SIGNATURE I authorize payment of medical benefits to the undersigned physician or supplier for services described below.

SIGNED _____

14. DATE OF CURRENT: MM DD YY　◄ ILLNESS (First symptom) OR INJURY (Accident) OR PREGNANCY(LMP)

15. IF PATIENT HAS HAD SAME OR SIMILAR ILLNESS. GIVE FIRST DATE MM DD YY

16. DATES PATIENT UNABLE TO WORK IN CURRENT OCCUPATION FROM MM DD YY　TO MM DD YY

17. NAME OF REFERRING PROVIDER OR OTHER SOURCE

17a.
17b. NPI

18. HOSPITALIZATION DATES RELATED TO CURRENT SERVICES FROM MM DD YY　TO MM DD YY

19. RESERVED FOR LOCAL USE

20. OUTSIDE LAB?　YES ☐　NO ☐　$ CHARGES

21. DIAGNOSIS OR NATURE OF ILLNESS OR INJURY (Relate Items 1, 2, 3 or 4 to Item 24E by Line)

1. |___.___
2. |___.___
3. |___.___
4. |___.___

22. MEDICAID RESUBMISSION CODE　ORIGINAL REF. NO.

23. PRIOR AUTHORIZATION NUMBER

24. A. DATE(S) OF SERVICE From MM DD YY	To MM DD YY	B. PLACE OF SERVICE	C. EMG	D. PROCEDURES, SERVICES, OR SUPPLIES (Explain Unusual Circumstances) CPT/HCPCS	MODIFIER	E. DIAGNOSIS POINTER	F. $ CHARGES	G. DAYS OR UNITS	H. EPSDT Family Plan	I. ID. QUAL.	J. RENDERING PROVIDER ID. #
1										NPI	
2										NPI	
3										NPI	
4										NPI	
5										NPI	
6										NPI	

25. FEDERAL TAX I.D. NUMBER　SSN ☐ EIN ☐

26. PATIENT'S ACCOUNT NO.

27. ACCEPT ASSIGNMENT? (For govt. claims, see back)　YES ☐　NO ☐

28. TOTAL CHARGE $

29. AMOUNT PAID $

30. BALANCE DUE $

31. SIGNATURE OF PHYSICIAN OR SUPPLIER INCLUDING DEGREES OR CREDENTIALS (I certify that the statements on the reverse apply to this bill and are made a part thereof.)

SIGNED _____ DATE _____

32. SERVICE FACILITY LOCATION INFORMATION

a.　b.

33. BILLING PROVIDER INFO & PH # ( )

a.　b.

NUCC Instruction Manual available at: www.nucc.org

OMB APPROVAL PENDING

172

CONTINUATION

APPENDIX 5

DEPOSIT TICKET

SOUTH PADRE MEDICAL CENTER
9878 PALM DRIVE
SOUTH PADRE, TX 98765

FIRST NATIONAL BANK
100 FIRST STREET
SOUTH PADRE, TX 98765

DATE _____

DEPOSITS MAY NOT BE AVAILABLE FOR IMMEDIATE WITHDRAWAL

	DOLLARS	CENTS
CURRENCY		
COIN		
CHECKS LIST EACH SEPARATELY		
1		
2		
3		
4		
5		
6		
7		
8		
9		
10		
11		
12		
13		
14		
15		
16		
17		
18		
19		
20		
21		
22		
23		
24		
25		
26		
27		
28		
TOTAL FROM OTHER SIDE OR ATTACHED LIST		
PLEASE RE-ENTER TOTAL HERE TOTAL		

00001001002005

$

Checks and other items are received for deposit subject to the provisions of the Uniform Commercial Code or any applicable colllection agreement.

174

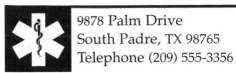

Gerald Bond, MD
Ray Adams, MD
Joyce Harkness, MD
Anthony Clark, MD

South Padre Medical Center

9878 Palm Drive
South Padre, TX 98765
Telephone (209) 555-3356

HISTORY AND PHYSICAL EXAMINATION

APPENDIX 5

South Padre Medical Center

Interoffice Memo

JOURNAL OF DAILY CHARGES & PAYMENTS

	DATE	PROFESSIONAL SERVICE	FEE	PAYMENT	ADJUST-MENT	NEW BALANCE	OLD BALANCE	PATIENTíS NAME	
1									1
2									2
3									3
4									4
5									5
6									6
7									7
8									8
9									9
10									10
11									11
12									12
13									13
14									14
15									15
16									16
17									17
18									18
19									19
20									20
21									21
22									22
23									23
24									24
25									25
26									26
27									27
28									28
29									29
30									30
31								TOTALS THIS PAGE	31
32								TOTAL PREVIOUS PAGE	32
33								TOTALS MONTH TO DATE	33

COLUMN A   COLUMN B   COLUMN C   COLUMN D   COLUMN E

MEMO _____

_____

_____

_____

_____

DAILY - FROM LINE 31

ARITHMETIC POSTING PROOF	
Column E	$
Plus Column A	
Sub-Total	
Minus Column B	
Sub-Total	
Minus Column C	
Equals Column D	

MONTH - FROM LINE 31

ACCOUNTS RECEIVABLE PROOF	
Accts. Receivable Previous Day	$
Plus Column A	
Sub-Total	
Minus Column B	
Sub-Total	
Minus Column C	
Accts. receivable End of Day	

YEAR TO DATE - FROM LINE 33

ACCOUNTS RECEIVABLE PROOF		
Accts. Receivable beginning of Month		$
Plus Column A	MONTH TO DATE	
Sub-Totaln C		
Minus Column B	MONTH TO DATE	
Sub-Total		
Minus Column C	MONTH TO DATE	
Accts. receivable End of Month	MONTH TO DATE	

APPENDIX 5

South Padre Medical Center

Gerald Bond, MD
Ray Adams, MD
Joyce Harkness, MD
Anthony Clark, MD

9878 Palm Drive
South Padre, TX 98765
Telephone (209) 555-3356

South Padre Medical Center

Gerald Bond, MD
Ray Adams, MD
Joyce Harkness, MD
Anthony Clark, MD

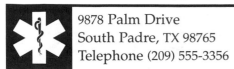

9878 Palm Drive
South Padre, TX 98765
Telephone (209) 555-3356

PATIENT INFORMATION

Please Print

Today's Date _____

Last Name _____ First Name _____ Initial _____

Date of Birth _____ Age _____ Sex _____ SS# _____-_____-_____

Home Address   Street _____ City _____

State _____ Zip_____ Home Phone (_____)_____

Occupation _____ Employer _____

Employer Address   Street _____ City_____

State _____ Zip _____ Work Phone (_____)_____

Are you currently a student?   Yes   No   Name of School _____

Spouse's Name _____ Marital Status   M   S   D   W   SEP

Spouse's SS# _____-_____-_____ Spouse's Employer _____

In case of emergency, notify _____ Relationship_____

Home Phone (____) _____ Work Phone (____) _____

If you are a minor: Parent's _____SS# _____-_____-_____

Street _____ City _____ State _____ Zip_____

Home Phone (____) _____ Work Phone (____) _____

Reason for Visit _____

Work related injury?   Yes   No   Date of injury_____

Automobile accident?   Yes   No   Date of injury_____

Other injury?   Yes   No   Date of injury_____

Insurance (Primary)   Company Name: _____

Street _____ City _____ State _____ Zip_____

Subscriber's Name _____

Relationship to Subscriber: _____

Policy #_____ Group #_____

Insurance (Secondary)   Company Name: _____

Street _____ City _____ State _____ Zip_____

Subscriber's Name _____

Relationship to Subscriber: _____

Policy #_____ Group #_____

Assignment of Benefits:

I directly assign all medical/surgical benefits, including major medical benefits and Medicare, to South Padre Medical Center. I understand that this authorization for assignment remains in effect until I revoke it in writing. A photocopy of this assignment will be considered as valid as this original assignment. I further understand that I am responsible for my indebtedness no matter what charges the insurance pays for.

Insured or Guardian's Signature _____ Date _____

APPENDIX 5

SOUTH PADRE MEDICAL CENTER
PETTY CASH JOURNAL

Beginning Balance: _____

DATE	STAFF	PURPOSE	AMOUNT	BALANCE

PRIORITY ☐

Telephone Record

Patient _____ Age _____

Caller _____

Telephone _____

Referred to _____

Chart # _____

Chart Attached ☐ YES ☐ NO

Date ___/___/___ Time _____ Rec'd By _____

Message _____

Temp	Allergies

Response _____

PHY/RN Initials	Date ___/___/___	Time	Handled By

PRIORITY ☐

Telephone Record

Patient _____ Age _____

Caller _____

Telephone _____

Referred to _____

Chart # _____

Chart Attached ☐ YES ☐ NO

Date ___/___/___ Time _____ Rec'd By _____

Message _____

Temp	Allergies

Response _____

PHY/RN Initials	Date ___/___/___	Time	Handled By

PRIORITY ☐

Telephone Record

Patient _____ Age _____

Caller _____

Telephone _____

Referred to _____

Chart # _____

Chart Attached ☐ YES ☐ NO

Date ___/___/___ Time _____ Rec'd By _____

Message _____

Temp	Allergies

Response _____

PHY/RN Initials	Date ___/___/___	Time	Handled By

PRIORITY ☐

Telephone Record

Patient _____ Age _____

Caller _____

Telephone _____

Referred to _____

Chart # _____

Chart Attached ☐ YES ☐ NO

Date ___/___/___ Time _____ Rec'd By _____

Message _____

Temp	Allergies

Response _____

PHY/RN Initials	Date ___/___/___	Time	Handled By

APPENDIX 5

REFERRAL

FROM: Gerald Bond, MD   _____   TO: _____

            Ray Adams, MD   _____

            Joyce Harkness, MD _____

            Anthony Clark, MD   _____   TELEPHONE: _____

                                                ADDRESS: _____

                                              Requested Date and Time: _____

PATIENT: _____ PATIENT'S PHONE NUMBER: _____

ADDRESS: _____

REASON FOR REFERRAL: _____

_____

_____

APPOINTMENT DATE AND TIME: _____

REFERRAL COMPLETED BY: _____ ARRANGEMENTS MADE BY: _____
                     (INITIAL AND DATE)   (INITIAL AND DATE)

REQUEST FOR INPATIENT CONSULTATION

To: ❏ Gerald Bond, MD   ATTENDING: _____
       ❏ Ray Adams, MD   TELEPHONE: _____
       ❏ Joyce Harkness, MD   Request Date and Time: _____
       ❏ Anthony Clark, MD

PATIENT: _____ ADMIT DATE: _____

FACILITY: _____ FLOOR: _____ ROOM: _____

REASON FOR CONSULTATION: _____

_____

_____

_____

PLEASE COMPLETE BY: _____ RECEIVED BY: _____
                            (DATE)

APPENDIX 5

REQUEST FOR PREAUTHORIZATION FOR SURGERY

Surgeon: Gerald Bond, MD
(circle one)   Ray Adams, MD
               Joyce Harkness, MD
               Anthony Clark, MD

PATIENT NAME: _____   FACILITY: _____

DATE OF BIRTH: _____   ADMIT DATE: _____

ACCOUNT #: _____   SURGERY DATE: _____

INSURANCE: _____   POLICY#: _____

PROCEDURE: _____

DIAGNOSIS: _____

AUTHORIZATION: _____

COMPLETED BY: _____

DATE COMPLETED: _____

SOUTH PADRE MEDICAL CENTER
9878 Palm Drive
South Padre, TX 98765

Gerald Bond, MD
Ray Adams, MD
Joyce Harkness, MD
Anthony Clark, MD

Affiliated with:
Texas Health Corporation
1256 56th Avenue South
Houston, TX 99881

STATEMENT TO:

- -

TEAR OFF AND RETURN UPPER PORTION WITH PAYMENT

Balance Forward

DATE	PROFESSIONAL?SERVICE	FEE	PAYMENT	ADJUST-MENT	NEW BALANCE

APPENDIX 5

South Padre Medical Center

Patient's Name _____ Age _____ Sex _____ Marital Status S M W D

Address _____ _____ Insurance _____

Telephone _____ Referred _____

Date	Subsequent Findings

186

South Padre Medical Center

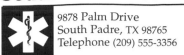

9878 Palm Drive
South Padre, TX 98765
Telephone (209) 555-3356

Gerald Bond, MD
Ray Adams, MD
Joyce Harkness, MD
Anthony Clark, MD

PATIENT'S LAST NAME	FIRST	ACCOUNT #	BIRTHDATE / /	SEX ☐ MALE ☐ FEMALE	TODAY'S DATE / /

INSURANCE COMPANY	SUBSCRIBER	GROUP/PLAN #	SUB. #	TIME

ASSIGNMENT: I hereby assign my insurance benefits to be paid directly to the undersigned physician. I am financially responsible for non-covered services.
SIGNED: (Patient,
Or parent, if Minor)_____ DATE: / /

RELEASE: I hereby authorize the physician to release to my insurance carriers any information required to process this claim.
SIGNED: (Patient,
Or Parent, if Minor) _____ DATE: / /

√	DESCRIPTION	CPT	Diag.	FEE	√	DESCRIPTION	CPT	Diag.	FEE	√	DESCRIPTION	CPT	Diag.	FEE
	OFFICE VISIT					**IMMUNIZATIONS/INJECTIONS**					**PROCEDURES**			
	NEW PATIENT					Admin of Vaccine 1	90471				Inhalation treatment	94640		
	Problem Focused					Admin of Vac 2+	90472				Demo/eval treatment	94664		
	Exp Problem Focused	99202				TB Tine, skin	86486				Vital Capacity	94150		
	Detailed	99203				Pneumococcal	90732				Spirometry	94010		
	Comp/ Mod MDM	99204				Medicare code	G0009				EKG w/interpretation	93000		
	Comp/ High MDM	99205				Influenza <3	90657				I&D abscess	10060		
	ESTABLISHED PATEINT					Influenza 3 and >	90658				Remove skin tag <15	11200		
	Minimal/Nurse Visit	99211				Medicare code	G0008				**EXCISION BENIGN LESIONS (inc. margins)**			
	Problem Focused	99212				Varicella	90716				Trunk, arms, legs			
	Exp Problem Forcused	99213				DPT	90701				0.5 cm or less	11400		
	Detailed	99214				DT children	90702				0.6 to 1.0 cm	11401		
	Comprehensive	99215				Td adult	90718				1.1 to 2.0 cm	11402		
	CONSULTATION					DtaP	90700				2.1 to 3.0 cm	11403		
	Problem Focused	99241				IPV	90713				Scalp, neck, hand, ft			
	Exp Problem Focused	99242				Rubella	90706				0.5 cm or less	11420		
	Detailed	99243				MMR	90707				0.6 to 1.0 cm	11421		
	Comp/ Mod MDM	99244				Hep B Child	90744				1.1 to 2.0 cm	11422		
	Comp/High MDM	99245				Hep B Adult	90746				2.1 to 3.0 cm	11423		
						IM Administration	96372				Face, ears, eyelids, lip			
	Requesting Provider _____					Compazine	J0780				0.5 cm or less	11440		
	Post-op Exam	99024	0.00			Demerol	J2175				0.6 to 1.0 cm	11441		
	PREVENTIVE MEDICINE					Depo-Provera	J1055				1.1 to 2.0 cm	11442		
	NEW PATIENT					Dexamethasone	J1100				2.1 to 3.0 cm	11443		
	Infant – 1 yr	99381				Solumedrol	J1720				**EXCISION MALIGNANT LESIONS (inc. margins)**			
	1 yr – 4 yr	99382				Antigen admin 1	95115				Trunk, arms, legs			
	5 yr – 11 yr	99383				Antigen admin 2+	95117				0.5 cm or less	11600		
	12 yr – 17 yr	99384				**LABORATORY**					0.6 to 1.0 cm	11601		
	18 yr – 39 yr	99385				Blood collect Vein	36415				1.1 to 2.0 cm	11602		
	40 yr – 64 yr	99386				Capillary	36416				2.1 to 3.0 cm	11603		
	65 yr and over	99387				Hemoglobin	85018				Scalp, neck, hand, ft			
	ESTABLISHED PATIENT					Glucose, reagent	82948				0.5 cm or less	11620		
	Infant – 1 yr	99391				Pregnancy, Serum	84702				0.6 to 1.0 cm	11621		
	1 yr – 4 yr	99392				Pregnancy, Urine	81025				1.1 to 2.0 cm	11622		
	5 yr – 11 yr	99393				Health panel	80050				2.1 to 3.0 cm	11623		
	12 yr – 17 yr	99394				B Met Pan Cal ion	80047				Face, ears, eyelids, lip			
	18 yr – 39 yr	99395				B Met Pan Cal tot	80048				0.5 cm or less	11640		
	40 yr – 64 yr	99396				C Metabolic panel	80053				0.6 to 1.0 cm	11641		
	65 yr and over	99397				Ob panel	80055				1.1 to 2.0 cm	11642		
	SUPPLIES					Lipid panel	80061				2.1 to 3.0 cm	11643		
	Take home burn kit	99070				UA Auto w/o micro	81003				***Awaiting path report***	☐ Yes		☐ No
	Take home wound kit	99070				UA dip stck	81000				Wart destruction < 14	17110		
	Miscellaneous					Strep test	87880				Cerumen removal	69210		
						Hemoccult	82270				Endometrial biopsy	58100		
	MODIFIERS					Lab Handling	99000							
	Significant/Sep EM provided with other service	-25				30 DAYS					60 DAYS		90 DAYS	
	Unrelated EM in post op period	-24												
	Repeat procedure, same physician, same day	-76												

DIAGNOSIS:	RETURN APPOINTMENT:	TODAY'S TOTAL	
1) _____	(days) (wks) (mos) (PRN)		
2) _____	NEXT APPOINTMENT:	PREVIOUS BALANCE	
3) _____	M - T - W - TH - F - S		
	DATE / / TIME	AMOUNT REC'D TODAY	
4) _____		REC'D BY _____	
	Provider's Signature:	BALANCE DUE	

APPENDIX 5

South Padre Medical Center

SURGICAL REQUEST AND INFORMATION

This portion is to be completed by requesting surgeon.

Surgeon:
❑ Gerald Bond, MD
❑ Ray Adams, MD
❑ Joyce Harkness, MD
❑ Anthony Clark, MD

Schedule: ❑ URGENT ❑ IMMEDIATE ❑ PATIENT CONVENIENCE

Date Requested: _____ Time Requested: _____

Patient Name: _____

Procedure: _____

Procedure Code(s): _____

Diagnosis(es): _____

Diagnosis(es) Code(s): _____

Estimated Surgery Time: _____

Surgical Assistant Requested: _____

Additional Information: _____

This portion is to be completed by scheduling personnel.

Surgery Date: _____ Time: _____
     Day   Date

Authorization Obtained: ❑ YES ❑ NO ❑ REQUESTED

If authorization has been requested and response is pending, list date and contact information from the initial request.

Requested From: _____ Date: _____
      (Carrier and person)

Telephone: _____ Ext: _____

Completed By: _____

Date Completed: _____

South Padre Medical Center

Patient Health History

Today's Date: _____

Name: _____ Date of Birth: _____

Marital Status:　　S　　M　　D　　W

Reason for today's visit: _____

Nutrition and Activity

Diet (check one):　❑ Good　❑ Poor

Level of Physical Activity (check one):

　❑ Very Active　　❑ Active　　❑ Sedentary　　❑ Inactive

Medical History (Please list any you currently have or have had in the past)

Allergies: _____

Significant illnesses or conditions: _____

_____

Current medications: _____

Hospitalizations or Surgery: _____

Injuries requiring medical treatment: _____

Family History

Have any members of your family had any of the following (check one):

❑ Asthma　　　　　　❑ Diabetes　　　　　❑ Bleeding Disorder

❑ Glaucoma　　　　　❑ Heart Disease　　　❑ Drug/Alcohol Addiction

❑ Hypertension　　　❑ Mental Illness　　　❑ Strokes

❑ Cancer (list) _____　❑ Other (list) _____

Family relationship for any of the above condition(s) checked: _____

_____

Social History

Occupation: _____

Are you sexually active?　❑ Yes　　❑ No

Have you ever had a sexually transmitted infection (STI)?　❑ Yes　　❑ No

If yes, please list the STI type(s) and treatment(s) used _____

Do you consume alcohol?　❑ Yes　　❑ No

Do you smoke?　❑ Yes　　❑ No

If yes, average weekly consumption and drink of choice _____

If yes, check all that apply:　❑ Cigarettes　❑ Pipe tobacco　❑ Cigars

Do you chew tobacco?　❑ Yes　　❑ No

How much tobacco do you consume on average per day? _____

How long have you used tobacco? _____

Do you or have you used illegal substance(s)?　❑ Yes　　❑ No

If yes, please list _____

APPENDIX 5

SOUTH PADRE HOSPITAL

980 Lagona Drive • South Padre, TX 98765 • Telephone (209) 555-4289

CARDIOLOGY REPORT

SOUTH PADRE HOSPITAL

980 Lagona Drive • South Padre, TX 98765 • Telephone (209) 555-4289

OPERATIVE REPORT

SOUTH PADRE HOSPITAL

980 Lagona Drive • South Padre, TX 98765 • Telephone (209) 555-4289

RADIOLOGY REPORT

APPENDIX 6

Make sure to check
evolve
for the latest
content updates

Other Physician, Business, Third-Party Payer Directory

Physicians

Dr. John Andrews
Louis Argabright, MD
Bert Bethos, MD
  (209)555-8231
Dr. Blackburn
Dr. Evans
Dr. Green
Dr. Greggory
Dr. McDonald
  (209)555-8292
Dr. Morgan
Dr. Peters
Dr. Smith, Fort Worth
Morton Samson, MD
  1256 56th Avenue South
  Houston TX 99881
  (956)934-6120
Thomas Thompson, MD
  (209)555-0090

Business Information

First National Bank
South Padre TX 98765
100 First Street

South Padre Medical Center
9878 Palm Drive
South Padre TX 98765
(209)555-3356

APPENDIX 6

South Padre Hospital
980 Lagona Drive
South Padre TX 98765
(209)555-4289

South Padre Surgery Center
(209)555-8247

Texas Health Corporation
1256 56th Avenue South
Houston TX 99881

Texas Health Corporation
884 Worthington Rd
San Antonio TX 99784

Third-Party Payers

BC/BS of Texas
1514 West Road
Houston TX 99881

Delta of New York
8119 Tower
New York NY 59800

Medicare/Medicaid
402 Main Street
South Padre TX 98765

Primer Mutual
897 Wayland Rd
Boston MA 82643

Primer West
4200 Douglas St
San Diego CA 98110

Prudential
86410 Worldum Avenue
St. Louis MO 88488

South Padre Insurance Company
2702 Oak Line Drive
South Padre TX 98765

Traveler's Insurance
42110 West Road
Houston TX 99881

Workers' Compensation Claims
10 State Highway
Houston TX 99881

SUPPLIES

Make sure to check **evolve** for the latest content updates

Equipment Maintenance and Desk Security

INTERN: _____

INTERNSHIP DATES: _____ April 7-April 18, 2008 _____

SUPERVISOR: _Gladys Johnson_____

DATE	MAINTAINED EQUIPMENT	SECURED DESK
April 7		
April 8		
April 9		
April 10		
April 11		
April 14		
April 15		
April 16		
April 17		
April 18		

South Padre Medical Center
Confidentiality Agreement

All information regarding patients and their health care that is acquired during the course of employment at South Padre Medical Center shall be considered confidential.

Confidential information must never be disclosed for non-employment related purposes. Disclosure of confidential information outside of an employee's assigned duties will constitute unauthorized release of confidential information and can be grounds for dismissal.

By signing this document, I acknowledge that I understand this statement.

_____   _____

Employee name   Date

SUPPLIES

PRIORITY ☐   Telephone Record

Patient   Age   Message
_____   _____
Caller   _____
_____   _____
Telephone
_____   Temp   │ Allergies
Referred to   _____ │_____
_____   Response
Chart #   _____
_____   _____
Chart Attached   ☐ YES   ☐ NO
                                              PHY/RN Initials │ Date / / │ Time │ Handled By
Date / /   Time   Rec'd By

PRIORITY ☐   Telephone Record

Patient   Age   Message
_____   _____
Caller   _____
_____   _____
Telephone
_____   Temp   │ Allergies
Referred to   _____ │_____
_____   Response
Chart #   _____
_____   _____
Chart Attached   ☐ YES   ☐ NO
                                              PHY/RN Initials │ Date / / │ Time │ Handled By
Date / /   Time   Rec'd By

PRIORITY ☐   Telephone Record

Patient   Age   Message
_____   _____
Caller   _____
_____   _____
Telephone
_____   Temp   │ Allergies
Referred to   _____ │_____
_____   Response
Chart #   _____
_____   _____
Chart Attached   ☐ YES   ☐ NO
                                              PHY/RN Initials │ Date / / │ Time │ Handled By
Date / /   Time   Rec'd By

PRIORITY ☐   Telephone Record

Patient   Age   Message
_____   _____
Caller   _____
_____   _____
Telephone
_____   Temp   │ Allergies
Referred to   _____ │_____
_____   Response
Chart #   _____
_____   _____
Chart Attached   ☐ YES   ☐ NO
                                              PHY/RN Initials │ Date / / │ Time │ Handled By
Date / /   Time   Rec'd By

SUPPLIES

PRIORITY ☐   Telephone Record

Patient _____ Age _____

Caller _____

Telephone _____

Referred to _____

Chart # _____

Chart Attached ☐ YES   ☐ NO

Date __/__/__ Time _____ Rec'd By _____

Message _____
_____

Temp	Allergies

Response _____
_____

PHY/RN Initials	Date __/__/__	Time	Handled By

PRIORITY ☐   Telephone Record

Patient _____ Age _____

Caller _____

Telephone _____

Referred to _____

Chart # _____

Chart Attached ☐ YES   ☐ NO

Date __/__/__ Time _____ Rec'd By _____

Message _____
_____

Temp	Allergies

Response _____
_____

PHY/RN Initials	Date __/__/__	Time	Handled By

PRIORITY ☐   Telephone Record

Patient _____ Age _____

Caller _____

Telephone _____

Referred to _____

Chart # _____

Chart Attached ☐ YES   ☐ NO

Date __/__/__ Time _____ Rec'd By _____

Message _____
_____

Temp	Allergies

Response _____
_____

PHY/RN Initials	Date __/__/__	Time	Handled By

PRIORITY ☐   Telephone Record

Patient _____ Age _____

Caller _____

Telephone _____

Referred to _____

Chart # _____

Chart Attached ☐ YES   ☐ NO

Date __/__/__ Time _____ Rec'd By _____

Message _____
_____

Temp	Allergies

Response _____
_____

PHY/RN Initials	Date __/__/__	Time	Handled By

SUPPLIES

TASK **1.3**   201

REQUEST FOR INPATIENT CONSULTATION

To: ❏ Gerald Bond, MD   ATTENDING: _____
       ❏ Ray Adams, MD   TELEPHONE: _____
       ❏ Joyce Harkness, MD   Request Date and Time: _____
       ❏ Anthony Clark, MD

PATIENT: _____ ADMIT DATE: _____

FACILITY: _____ FLOOR: _____ ROOM: _____

REASON FOR CONSULTATION: _____

_____

_____

_____

PLEASE COMPLETE BY: _____ RECEIVED BY: _____
                              (DATE)

SUPPLIES

REQUEST FOR INPATIENT CONSULTATION

To: ❏ Gerald Bond, MD   ATTENDING: _____

❏ Ray Adams, MD   TELEPHONE: _____

❏ Joyce Harkness, MD   Request Date and Time: _____

❏ Anthony Clark, MD

PATIENT: _____ ADMIT DATE: _____

FACILITY: _____ FLOOR: _____ ROOM: _____

REASON FOR CONSULTATION: _____

_____

_____

_____

PLEASE COMPLETE BY: _____ RECEIVED BY: _____
                              (DATE)

SUPPLIES

REQUEST FOR INPATIENT CONSULTATION

To: ❏ Gerald Bond, MD   ATTENDING: _____

           ❏ Ray Adams, MD   TELEPHONE: _____

           ❏ Joyce Harkness, MD   Request Date and Time: _____

           ❏ Anthony Clark, MD

PATIENT: _____   ADMIT DATE: _____

FACILITY: _____   FLOOR: _____ ROOM: _____

REASON FOR CONSULTATION: _____

_____

_____

_____

PLEASE COMPLETE BY: _____   RECEIVED BY: _____
                        (DATE)

SUPPLIES

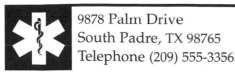

South Padre Medical Center

Gerald Bond, MD
Ray Adams, MD
Joyce Harkness, MD
Anthony Clark, MD

9878 Palm Drive
South Padre, TX 98765
Telephone (209) 555-3356

HISTORY AND PHYSICAL EXAMINATION

PATIENT: Gloria Hydorn
DATE: Thursday, April 3, 2008
PHYSICIAN: Ray Adams, MD

This 68-year-old female presents to the office today requesting a complete physical examination. She has recently moved to our area and states she would like to establish with a family practitioner. She has a history of coronary artery disease, status post coronary artery bypass x 3 in 1978. She has been doing well. Gravid 3, para 3, postmenopausal x 20 years. History is also significant for hypertension, controlled by diet. Otherwise no complaints.

Past Medical History: Remarkable for conditions stated above.

Operations: 1. Hysterectomy with bladder repair, 1973

                2. Bilateral blepharoplasty

                3. D&C x 4

Allergies: None.

Medications: Digoxin in 0.25 mg, Lasix 40 mg p.o.q.d. Estrogen.

Tobacco: Does not smoke. Alcohol: Occasional.

Social History: Homemaker, mother of three. Husband recently deceased.

Family History: Mother deceased from heart disease. Father has multiple strokes. Two brothers, one with polio. Three children, health is good. One sister, died of breast cancer at age 35.

Review of systems: Denies nausea, vomiting, headaches, dysuria, incontinence; dyspnea. Occasional bouts of atrial fibrillation, always converts spontaneously.

SUPPLIES

Hydorn, Gloria

2

HEENT: Wears glasses. Otherwise negative.

Respiratory: Negative.

Cardiovascular: Negative except as discussed above.

GI/GU: Postmenopausal, on estrogen.

Endocrine: No diabetes or thyroid problems.

Musculoskeletal: Some arthritis, both hands.

Psychiatric: Negative.

Physical examination: Reveals a very pleasant elderly female, in no distress.

Vitals: Blood pressure is 140/84; pulse 90 and regular, right arm sitting position. 150/90 left arm sitting position.

Weight: 115 pounds.

Skin: No skin lesions are present.

Nodes: No lymphadenopathy.

ENT: Negative.

Chest: Clear to auscultation.

Cardiac: Reveals a regular rhythm. I did not hear any murmurs or gallops.

Breast exam: Right side free from lumps or masses. Small lump noted in left breast upon examination which is painless, without discharge, without retraction.

Assessment and plan:

1. History of coronary artery disease, status post coronary artery bypass. No complaints at present, no abnormal findings. Continue medications as previously prescribed.
2. Breast mass on examination. Suggest mammography. If positive, consultation will be requested from surgery.
3. Postmenopausal, continue on estrogen therapy.

SUPPLIES

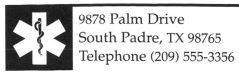

South Padre Medical Center

Gerald Bond, MD
Ray Adams, MD
Joyce Harkness, MD
Anthony Clark, MD

9878 Palm Drive
South Padre, TX 98765
Telephone (209) 555-3356

HISTORY AND PHYSICAL EXAMINATION

SUPPLIES

CONTINUATION

PATIENT: Gloria Hydorn

DATE: Friday, April 4, 2008

Patient has bilateral diagnostic mammography that shows normal finding on the right, but dense, suspicious area on the left. Suggestion by radiologist is further clinical study. Referred to Dr. Gerald Bond for evaluation of left breast lump.

Ray Adams, MD

SUPPLIES

CONTINUATION

SUPPLIES

South Padre Medical Center

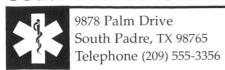

Gerald Bond, MD
Ray Adams, MD
Joyce Harkness, MD
Anthony Clark, MD

9878 Palm Drive
South Padre, TX 98765
Telephone (209) 555-3356

PATIENT INFORMATION
Please Print

Today's Date **April 3, 2008**

Last Name **Hydorn**   First Name **Gloria**   Initial **J**

Date of Birth **02/02/40**   Age **68**   Sex **F**   SS# **010-88-9321**

Home Address   Street **862 Oceanside Way**   City **South Padre**

State **TX**   Zip **98765**   Home Phone (**209**) **555-8694**

Occupation **Retired teacher**   Employer **—**

Employer Address   Street _____   City _____

State **—**   Zip **—**   Work Phone (**—**)_____

Are you currently a student?   Yes   (No)   Name of School _____

Spouse's Name **Ronald**   Marital Status   M   S   D   (W)   SEP

Spouse's SS# __-__-__   Spouse's Employer _____

In case of emergency, notify **Elizabeth Johnson** Relationship **Daughter**

Home Phone (**210**) **548-9341**   Work Phone (**—**)_____

If you are a minor: Parent's **—**   SS# __-__-__

Street **—**   City _____   State ____ Zip____

Home Phone (**—**)_____   Work Phone (____)_____

Reason for Visit **Establish a family practice doctor**

Work related injury?   Yes   (No)   Date of injury_____

Automobile accident?   Yes   (No)   Date of injury_____

Other injury?   Yes   (No)   Date of injury_____

Insurance (Primary)   Company Name: **Primer mutual**

Street **897 Wayland Rd** City **Boston** State **MA** Zip **82643**

Subscriber's Name **Self**

Relationship to Subscriber: **—**

Policy # **KLI 5000**   Group # **SP4652**

Insurance (Secondary) Company Name: **Medicare**

Street _____   City _____   State ____ Zip____

Subscriber's Name _____

Relationship to Subscriber: _____

Policy # **010889321 A**   Group # _____

Assignment of Benefits:

I directly assign all medical/surgical benefits, including major medical benefits and Medicare, to South Padre Medical Center. I understand that this authorization for assignment remains in effect until I revoke it in writing. A photocopy of this assignment will be considered as valid as this original assignment. I further understand that I am responsible for my indebtedness no matter what charges the insurance pays for.

Insured or Guardian's Signature **Gloria Hydorn**   Date **04/03/08**

SUPPLIES

TASK **1.5**   219

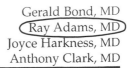

Gerald Bond, MD
Ray Adams, MD
Joyce Harkness, MD
Anthony Clark, MD

South Padre Medical Center

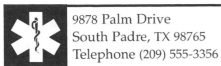

9878 Palm Drive
South Padre, TX 98765
Telephone (209) 555-3356

PATIENT INFORMATION
Please Print

Today's Date **11/01/07**

Last Name **Anderson**   First Name **Carrie**   Initial **R**

Date of Birth **01/28/03**   Age **4**   Sex **F**   SS# **681-28-4812**

Home Address   Street **590 West Ward**   City **South Padre**

                 State **TX**   Zip **98765**   Home Phone **(209) 555-0213**

Occupation **N/A**   Employer **N/A**

Employer Address   Street **N/A**   City **N/A**

                     State **N/A**   Zip **N/A**   Work Phone (___) **N/A**

Are you currently a student?   Yes   ⊘No   Name of School _____

Spouse's Name **none**   Marital Status   M   Ⓢ   D   W   SEP

Spouse's SS# ___-___-___   Spouse's Employer **N/A**

In case of emergency, notify **Gail Anderson**   Relationship **Mother**

          Home Phone **(209) 555-0213**   Work Phone (___) **N/A**

If you are a minor: Parent's **Gail Anderson**   SS# ___-___-___

                        Street **590 West Ward** City **South Padre** State **TX** Zip **98765**

          Home Phone **(209) 555-0213**   Work Phone (___) **N/A**

Reason for Visit **Stomach and chest pain**

          Work related injury?   Yes   ⓃNo   Date of injury _____

          Automobile accident?   Yes   ⓃNo   Date of injury _____

          Other injury?   Yes   ⓃNo   Date of injury _____

Insurance (Primary)   Company Name: **Medicaid**

          Street **402 Main Street** City **South Padre** State **TX** Zip **98765**

          Subscriber's Name **Carrie Anderson**

          Relationship to Subscriber: _____

          Policy # **HYH892210199**   Group # _____

Insurance (Secondary)   Company Name: **None**

          Street _____ City _____ State _____ Zip _____

          Subscriber's Name _____

          Relationship to Subscriber: _____

          Policy # _____   Group # _____

Assignment of Benefits:

I directly assign all medical/surgical benefits, including major medical benefits and Medicare, to South Padre Medical Center. I understand that this authorization for assignment remains in effect until I revoke it in writing. A photocopy of this assignment will be considered as valid as this original assignment. I further understand that I am responsible for my indebtedness no matter what charges the insurance pays for.

Insured or Guardian's Signature **Gail Anderson**   Date **11/01/07**

SUPPLIES

South Padre Medical Center

Patient's Name ___Carrie R. Anderson___ Age __4__ Sex __F__ Marital Status ⓢ M W D

Address ___590 West Ward___ Insurance ___Medicaid___

Telephone ___209-555-0213___ Referred ___Self___

Date	Subsequent Findings
11/01/07	CHIEF COMPLAINT: Abdominal and chest pain.
	HISTORY OF PRESENT ILLNESS: This is a 4-year-old female who presents complaining of
	abdominal pain. She has had some urinary-type symptoms. No fever. Appetite has been
	fair. No vomiting or diarrhea. She has also had some left-sided chest pain. No cough. No
	allergies. No medications. No particular exacerbating or relieving factors. This has been
	going on over the past one-and one-half hours. She denies hurting herself.
	PAST MEDICAL HISTORY: Is negative.
	CURRENT MEDICATIONS: None.
	ALLERGIES: None.
	FAMILY HISTORY: Noncontributory.
	SOCIAL HISTORY: Noncontributory.
	REVIEW OF SYSTEMS: Remarkable for the absence of fever and positive for abdominal
	pain. No vomiting, diarrhea, constipation, fever, cough.
	OBJECTIVE: On physical examination, vital signs are stable. The patient appears well. No
	rashes are noted. The tympanic membranes are normal. Throat is benign. Neck is without
	adenopathy. Lungs are clear. Abdomen is soft. Bowel sounds are active. No masses,
	rebound or rigidity.
	ASSESSMENT: Abdominal pain of undetermined etiology.
	PLAN: Reassurance. I do not feel she has any evidence of an acute surgical abdomen.
	Obviously, if this is a surgical abdomen it is very early in its course. If there is any change
	or worsening over the next 24 hours they need to return or go to the emergency room.
	Their questions were answered.
	Ray Adams, MD

SUPPLIES

South Padre Medical Center

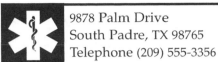

9878 Palm Drive
South Padre, TX 98765
Telephone (209) 555-3356

PATIENT INFORMATION

Please Print

Today's Date __Dec 11, 01__

Last Name __Oakland__   First Name __David__   Initial __T__

Date of Birth __12/04/51__   Age __50__   Sex __M__   SS# __500-21-1144__

Home Address   Street __4001 Western Road__   City __South Padre__

     State __TX__   Zip __98765__   Home Phone __(209) 555-5453__

Occupation __Bus Driver__   Employer __Greyhound__

Employer Address   Street __43 Circle Drive__   City __South Padre__

     State __TX__   Zip __98765__   Work Phone __(209) 555-5000__

Are you currently a student?   Yes   (No)   Name of School _____

Spouse's Name __Susan__   Marital Status   (M)   S   D   W   SEP

Spouse's SS# __504-88-2104__   Spouse's Employer __none__

In case of emergency, notify __Susan__   Relationship __Wife__

     Home Phone __(209) 555-5453__   Work Phone (___) __none__

If you are a minor: Parent's _____   SS# ___-___-___

     Street _____   City _____   State _____   Zip _____

     Home Phone (___) _____   Work Phone (___) _____

Reason for Visit __Bites on the back of right leg__

     Work related injury?   Yes   (No)   Date of injury_____

     Automobile accident?   Yes   (No)   Date of injury_____

     Other injury?   Yes   (No)   Date of injury_____

Insurance (Primary)   Company Name: __Prudential__

     Street __86410 Wordum Ave__   City __St. Louis__   State __MO__   Zip __88488__

     Subscriber's Name __David Oakland__

     Relationship to Subscriber: __Self__

     Policy # __JKH4090__   Group # __HE220__

Insurance (Secondary)   Company Name: _____

     Street _____   City _____   State _____   Zip _____

     Subscriber's Name _____

     Relationship to Subscriber: _____

     Policy # _____   Group # _____

Assignment of Benefits:

I directly assign all medical/surgical benefits, including major medical benefits and Medicare, to South Padre Medical Center. I understand that this authorization for assignment remains in effect until I revoke it in writing. A photocopy of this assignment will be considered as valid as this original assignment. I further understand that I am responsible for my indebtedness no matter what charges the insurance pays for.

Insured or Guardian's Signature __David Oakland__   Date __Dec 11, 01__

SUPPLIES

South Padre Medical Center

Patient's Name ___David T. Oakland___ Age __50__ Sex __M__ Marital Status S (M) W D
Address ___4001 Western Road___ Insurance ___Prudential___
Telephone ___209-555-5453___ Referred ___Self___

Date	Subsequent Findings
12/11/07	Patient presents with three day history of "bites on the back of his right leg." The patient awakened one morning and noticed what appeared to be several bites on his right posterior thigh. These were somewhat sore and had become more so over the past few days with surrounding redness and tiredness. Patient has otherwise been feeling well. He has not noted any fever, chills or systemic symptoms.
	On examination he has four regions on his right posterior thigh with surrounding redness and slight warmth to the area. No other skin abnormalities are noted and a prominent right superficial varicosity is noted on the right posterior thigh, but the remainder of his leg exam is negative.
	IMPRESSION: Probable insect bite to the right posterior thigh with secondary cellulitis.
	PLAN: Patient will be treated with Erythromycin 400 mg t.i.d. times ten days. I have also given him a prescription for 0.1% Triamcinolone cream to be used b.i.d. to the inflamed area. Should he note any worsening of the affected area, he should call in to be seen. Otherwise, follow-up p.r.n.
	Ray Adams, MD

SUPPLIES

Gerald Bond, MD
Ray Adams, MD
Joyce Harkness, MD
Anthony Clark, MD

South Padre Medical Center

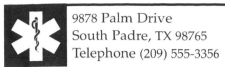

9878 Palm Drive
South Padre, TX 98765
Telephone (209) 555-3356

PATIENT INFORMATION
Please Print

Today's Date **01/04/08**

Last Name **Forest**   First Name **Kathy**   Initial **F.**

Date of Birth **08/04/73**   Age **34**   Sex **F**   SS# **891-00-0181**

Home Address   Street **118 Willow Way**   City **South Padre**

          State **TX**   Zip **98765** Home Phone **(209) 555-0107**

Occupation **unemployed**   Employer **(209) 555-1110 (Cell)**

Employer Address   Street _____   City _____

          State _____   Zip _____   Work Phone (___) _____

Are you currently a student?   Yes   (No)   Name of School _____

Spouse's Name **none**   Marital Status   M   (S)   D   W   SEP

Spouse's SS# ___-___-___ Spouse's Employer _____

In case of emergency, notify **George Forest**   Relationship **Father**

          Home Phone **(209) 555-0102**   Work Phone (___) _____

If you are a minor: Parent's _____ SS# ___-___-___

          Street _____   City _____   State _____ Zip_____

          Home Phone (___) _____ Work Phone (___) _____

Reason for Visit **Sores on mouth**

          Work related injury?   Yes   (No)   Date of injury _____

          Automobile accident?   Yes   (No)   Date of injury _____

          Other injury?   Yes   (No)   Date of injury _____

Insurance (Primary)   Company Name: **none**

          Street _____   City _____ State _____ Zip_____

          Subscriber's Name _____

          Relationship to Subscriber: _____

          Policy # _____ Group # _____

Insurance (Secondary)   Company Name: _____

          Street _____   City _____ State _____ Zip_____

          Subscriber's Name _____

          Relationship to Subscriber: _____

          Policy # _____ Group # _____

Assignment of Benefits:

I directly assign all medical/surgical benefits, including major medical benefits and Medicare, to South Padre Medical Center. I understand that this authorization for assignment remains in effect until I revoke it in writing. A photocopy of this assignment will be considered as valid as this original assignment I further understand that I am responsible for my indebtedness no matter what charges the insurance pays for.

Insured or Guardian's Signature **Kathy Forest**   Date **01/04/08**

SUPPLIES

South Padre Medical Center

Patient's Name __Kathy F. Forest__ Age __34__ Sex __F__ Marital Status ⓈM W D

Address __118 Willow Way__ Insurance __None__

Telephone __209-555-0102__ Referred __Self__

Date	Subsequent Findings
01/04/08	SUBJECTIVE: Comes in and had cold sore about 1 1/2 weeks. It just gets progressively worse. The whole left side of her mouth now has a crusted, erythematous area.
	OBJECTIVE: Nodes: increased left anterior cervical and submandibular. There is about a 2 cm crusted area on the left lateral lip margin.
	ASSESSMENT: Impetigo.
	PLAN:
	1. Cephalexin 250/5 cc, 1 tsp. q.i.d.
	2. Bacitracin to the area.
	3. Use some wet heat.
	4. Will see back if need be.
	Ray Adams, MD

SUPPLIES

South Padre Medical Center

Gerald Bond, MD
Ray Adams, MD
Joyce Harkness, MD
Anthony Clark, MD

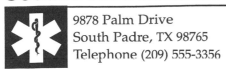

9878 Palm Drive
South Padre, TX 98765
Telephone (209) 555-3356

PATIENT INFORMATION
Please Print

Today's Date __4/4/08__

Last Name __Scott__ First Name __Silvia__ Initial __S.__

Date of Birth __12/25/35__ Age __72__ Sex __F__ SS# __101 - 31 - 0411__

Home Address Street __46 Western Road__ City __South Padre__

State __TX__ Zip __98765__ Home Phone (__209__) __555 - 7894__

Occupation __Retired__ Employer __—__

Employer Address Street __—__ City __—__

State __—__ Zip __—__ Work Phone (__—__) __—__

Are you currently a student? Yes (No) Name of School __—__

Spouse's Name __Ray__ Marital Status (M) S D W SEP

Spouse's SS# __421 - 11 - 8193__ Spouse's Employer __—__

In case of emergency, notify __Ray Scott__ Relationship _____

Home Phone (__209__) __555 - 7894__ Work Phone (___) _____

If you are a minor: Parent's Name _____ SS# __-__-__

Street _____ City _____ State ____ Zip____

Home Phone (___) _____ Work Phone (___) _____

Reason for Visit __Establish a doctor__

Work related injury? Yes (No) Date of injury_____

Automobile accident? Yes (No) Date of injury_____

Other injury? Yes (No) Date of injury_____

Insurance (Primary) Company Name: __Medicare__

Street __402 Main St.__ City __South Padre__ State __TX__ Zip __98765__

Subscriber's Name __Silvia__

Relationship to Subscriber: __Self__

Policy # __101 - 310411A__ Group #_____

Insurance (Secondary) Company Name: _____

Street _____ City _____ State ____ Zip____

Subscriber's Name _____

Relationship to Subscriber: _____

Policy #_____ Group #_____

Assignment of Benefits:

I directly assign all medical/surgical benefits, including major medical benefits and Medicare, to South Padre Medical Center. I understand that this authorization for assignment remains in effect until I revoke it in writing. A photocopy of this assignment will be considered as valid as this original assignment. I further understand that I am responsible for my indebtedness no matter what charges the insurance pays for.

Insured or Guardian's Signature __Silvia Scott__ Date __4/04/08__

SUPPLIES

South Padre Medical Center

Patient's Name   __Silvia S. Scott__   Age __72__ Sex __F__ Marital Status   S (M) W D

Address   __46 Western Road__   Insurance __Medicare__

Telephone   __209-555-7894__   Referred __Self__

Date	Subsequent Findings
04/04/08	SUBJECTIVE: The patient is a 72-year-old female who presents to establish primary care. She is a previous patient of Dr. Minor, who has now left practice.
	HISTORY OF PRESENT ILLNESS: The patient states that she has had burning pain occurring between her shoulders. This started back in July but has been getting progressively worse. The pain radiates laterally around to the sides of her chest on both sides. She also gets a tingling sensation in this area. The pain occurs when she is doing strenuous activity such as cleaning or extensive use of her arms. No shortness of breath. She denies productive cough. No fever or chills.
	PAST MEDICAL HISTORY:
	1. Hypertension.
	2. Hypercholesterolemia with hypertriglyceridemia.
	3. Impaired glucose tolerance.
	4. Atypical chest pain.
	5. Left carotid bruit without evidence of high-grade stenosis on carotid ultrasound in May 2000.
	6. Diverticulosis.
	7. Asymptomatic cystorectocele.
	8. History of right pulmonary nodule, diagnosed in 1987 with benign bronchoscopy.
	9. Positive family history of ovarian cancer, coronary artery disease, hypertension, thyroid disease, and diabetes.
	PREVIOUS SURGERIES: None.
	CURRENT MEDICATIONS:
	1. Procardia 60 mg, 2 tablets daily.
	2. Atenolol 50 mg daily.
	3. Baby aspirin 1 daily.
	4. Niacin 500 mg daily.
	5. Vitamin D 500,000 units biweekly.
	6. Calcium 500 mg t.i.d.
	7. Vitamin E supplement, 1 daily.
	ALLERGIES: No known drug allergies.

SUPPLIES

Continuation
Scott, Sylvia S.
2

FAMILY HISTORY: Mother died of ovarian cancer. Father died at age 89 from cancer of the abdomen. The primary source was felt to be the colon. He also had a myocardial infarction while in his 80s. The patient has five brothers, two of them died in infancy. The oldest brother is healthy. She has another brother who has heart disease and has had a CABG. Her youngest brother has hypertension. She has three sisters, two of them had benign colon polyps removed.

SOCIAL/OCCUPATIONAL: The patient is married. Her and her husband reside in South Padre. They are both retired. She is gravida 8, para 8. Two sons died in infancy. She has no previous smoking history. She denies use of alcohol. She does exercise by walking on the treadmill 15 minutes each day.

REVIEW OF SYSTEMS: Limited to her chief complaint as she had her complete annual physical performed in June of last year.

OBJECTIVE: On physical exam, weight is 139 pounds. Blood pressure 142/52. Oxygen saturation is 99%. Pulse is 46. Patient is alert and oriented and in no acute distress.
HEENT: Head normocephalic. Face is symmetrical. Eyes clear. EOMs intact.
PERRLA. Oropharynx is clear without erythema. Neck is soft and supple without lymphadenopathy. No thyromegaly. No JVD. Carotid upstrokes are normal bilaterally. She has a faint left carotid bruit which was noted on previous examination. Chest: Heart rate and rhythm are regular; no murmurs. No S3. Lungs are clear to auscultation without adventitious sounds. She has normal chest to percussion. There is no adenopathy of the chest. She has no trigger point tenderness in the neck, shoulders, or around the scapular regions. She has normal range of motion of both shoulders. There is no evidence of any vesicular lesions or erythema to the back. No palpable tenderness. There is no tenderness palpable along the spine.

IMPRESSION:
1. Mid-back pain in the thoracic region, described as burning with paresthesias without evidence of any palpable pain or vesicular lesions on examination.
2. Hypertension, controlled.
3. History of hypercholesterolemia and hypertriglyceridemia.
4. History of coronary artery disease with abnormal stress test with recent cardiac catheterization showing 30% blockage of one artery and 60% blockage of another artery per patient description.
5. Left carotid bruit without evidence of high-grade stenosis on carotid ultrasound in May 1998.
6. Remainder of stable problem list.

PLAN:
1. Will start the patient on Vioxx 12.5 mg to take 1 tablet daily. If this does not control the pain, then I will ask her to take 2 tablets daily. She was also instructed to avoid any Advil, Motrin, or Ibuprofen while on this medication.
2. Instructed the patient to have her husband check her back at least once a day. If she starts to break out in any lesions, she needs to return for evaluation. I suspect that she may be developing some shingles that have not surfaced as of yet.
3. I will await to hear from the patient to see if there is any change in her status. Otherwise, we will see her back when she is due for her annual physical.

Ray Adams, MD

RA/gj
DD: 04/04/08
DT: 04/04/08

SUPPLIES

South Padre Medical Center

Gerald Bond, MD
Ray Adams, MD
Joyce Harkness, MD
Anthony Clark, MD

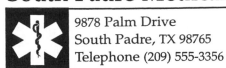

9878 Palm Drive
South Padre, TX 98765
Telephone (209) 555-3356

PATIENT INFORMATION
Please Print

Today's Date __Sept 4, 07__

Last Name __Burthold__ First Name __Kara__ Initial __J.__

Date of Birth __12/17/94__ Age __12__ Sex __F__ SS# __001-13-4982__

Home Address Street __1816 Gulfstream Drive__ City __South Padre__

State __TX__ Zip __98765__ Home Phone (__209__) __555-0809__

Occupation ____—____ Employer _____

Employer Address Street ____—____ City ____—____

State ____—____ Zip ____—____ Work Phone (__—__) ____—____

Are you currently a student? (Yes) No Name of School __South Padre Public__

Spouse's Name ____—____ Marital Status M (S) D W SEP

Spouse's SS# __—-—-—__ Spouse's Employer _____

In case of emergency, notify __Carol Burthold__ Relationship __Mother__

Home Phone (__209__) __555-0809__ Work Phone (__209__) __555-4444__

If you are a minor: Parent's Name _____ SS# _____

Street _____ City _____ State _____ Zip _____

Home Phone (___) _____ Work Phone (___) _____

Reason for Visit _____

Work related injury? Yes (No) Date of injury _____

Automobile accident? Yes (No) Date of injury _____

Other injury? Yes (No) Date of injury _____

Insurance (Primary) Company Name: __Texas Health Corporation__

Street __1258 56th Ave S__ City __Houston__ State __TX__ Zip __99881__

Subscriber's Name __Don__

Relationship to Subscriber: __Daughter__

Policy # __MYT 8822__ Group # __P2 900__

Insurance (Secondary) Company Name: _____

Street _____ City _____ State _____ Zip _____

Subscriber's Name _____

Relationship to Subscriber: _____

Policy # _____ Group # _____

Assignment of Benefits:

I directly assign all medical/surgical benefits, including major medical benefits and Medicare, to South Padre Medical Center. I understand that this authorization for assignment remains in effect until I revoke it in writing. A photocopy of this assignment will be considered as valid as this original assignment. I further understand that I am responsible for my indebtedness no matter what charges the insurance pays for.

Insured or Guardian's Signature __Carol Burthold__ Date __Sept 4, 07__

SUPPLIES

South Padre Medical Center

Patient's Name __Karra J. Burthold__   Age __12__ Sex __F__ Marital Status Ⓢ M W D
Address __1816 Gulfstream Drive__   Insurance __Texas Health Corporation__
Telephone __209-555-0809__   Referred __Self__

Date	Subsequent Findings
09/04/07	SUBJECTIVE: Karra is a 12-year-old who presents today to receive approval for her participation in her school's sports program.
	OBJECTIVE: On general appearance, Karra is alert and does not appear in acute distress. Temperature 96.6 degrees. Weight is 45.6 kg, this places her right at the 50th percentile and she is actually up 6 pounds from where she was last month. Height is 62 inches, places her right at that 50th percentile. HEENT: Eyes are clear. Reflex is seen bilaterally, both TMs are nice and clear. Disks are sharp. Oropharynx is unremarkable. Neck, supple. Heart reveals a regular rate and rhythm without murmur. Lungs are clear to auscultation bilaterally, her abdomen is soft. She is stage II to III, Tanner stage development II to III, and pubic hair development. Screening musculoskeletal exam: She is able to perform all maneuvers without difficulty. Her back reveals a straight spine. She does have a little bit of lipohypertrophy in her right arm and left arm areas. No other place noted. Peripheral pulses are intact.
	IMPRESSION: A 12-year-old girl with insulin-dependent diabetes mellitus, okay to participate in sports.
	PLAN:
	1. We will give her tetanus and first hepatitis, we can repeat the second when she returns.
	2. I would like to see her back in five to six weeks.
	3. I did recommend going down on her Humolog in the evenings to 6. I also recommended going down on her Humolog in the morning to 6. Recommended about using her legs in the morning.
	4. We reviewed where we wanted her hemoglobin A1c to be, the last time it was 11.9. Told her about not thinking of sugars as good or bad. I told her that is was much more important for her to have those high numbers down in her books, so we can make adjustments. She was in agreement with this plan.
	5. We talked about high risk behaviors as well.
	Ray Adams, MD

SUPPLIES

South Padre Medical Center

Gerald Bond, MD
Ray Adams, MD
Joyce Harkness, MD
Anthony Clark, MD

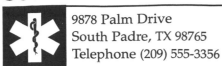

9878 Palm Drive
South Padre, TX 98765
Telephone (209) 555-3356

PATIENT INFORMATION

Please Print

Today's Date _September 3, 2007_

Last Name _Kennedy_   First Name _Sylvia_   Initial _P._

Date of Birth _04/01/1946_   Age _61_   Sex _F_   SS# _550-14-3211_

Home Address   Street _642 Terrace Drive_   City _South Padre_

          State _TX_   Zip _98765_   Home Phone (_209_)_555-1415_

Occupation _Retired Cook_   Employer _____

Employer Address   Street _____   City _____

          State _____   Zip _____   Work Phone (_____)_____

Are you currently a student?   Yes   No   Name of School _____

Spouse's Name _John_   Marital Status (M) S D W SEP

Spouse's SS# _210-13-4451_ Spouse's Employer _Retired_

In case of emergency, notify _John_   Relationship _____

          Home Phone (_____)_____   Work Phone (_____)_____

If you are a minor: Parent's Name _____   SS# _____-_____-_____

          Street _____   City _____   State _____   Zip_____

          Home Phone (_____)_____   Work Phone (_____)_____

Reason for Visit _Physical_

          Work related injury?   Yes   (No)   Date of injury _____

          Automobile accident?   Yes   (No)   Date of injury _____

          Other injury?   Yes   (No)   Date of injury _____

Insurance (Primary)   Company Name: _Prune West_

          Street _4200 Douglas St_ City _San Diego_ State _CA_ Zip _98110_

          Subscriber's Name _John_

          Relationship to Subscriber: _Wife_

          Policy # _MHI 222335_   Group # _P202X1_

Insurance (Secondary) Company Name: _____

          Street _____ City _____ State _____ Zip_____

          Subscriber's Name _____

          Relationship to Subscriber: _____

          Policy #_____   Group #_____

Assignment of Benefits:

I directly assign all medical/surgical benefits, including major medical benefits and Medicare, to South Padre Medical Center. I understand that this authorization for assignment remains in effect until I revoke it in writing. A photocopy of this assignment will be considered as valid as this original assignment. I further understand that I am responsible for my indebtedness no matter what charges the insurance pays for.

Insured or Guardian's Signature _Sylvia Kennedy_   Date _9/3/2007_

SUPPLIES

TASK **1.5**   243

South Padre Medical Center

Patient's Name __Sylvia P. Kennedy__   Age __61__ Sex __F__ Marital Status   S Ⓜ W D
Address __642 Terrace Drive__   Insurance __Primer West__
Telephone __209-555-1415__   Referred __Self__

Date	Subsequent Findings
09/03/07	SUBJECTIVE: Sylvia comes in for a general checkup. She is 61 years old. She has hypertension, hypothyroidism, and she is postmenopausal on estrogen replacement. Recently she was started on Prozac. She has been struggling with a lot of stress in her life. Her husband has colon cancer and is under treatment. She lost her business.
	Earlier this year she had a cardiac evaluation. A regular stress test was nondiagnostic, so she had a Cardiolite stress, which showed no evidence of ischemia. She has had some trouble lately with heartburn. She takes an occasional Tagamet for that.
	OBJECTIVE: On exam today, Sylvia is alert and pleasant. Blood pressure is 160/74. Neck is supple. She has kind of a prominence of her right lobe of her thyroid gland; no nodularity; no carotid bruits. Chest is clear. Heart is regular without murmur. Abdomen is obese; no organomegaly. Breasts are without masses or nipple discharge. I did not do a pelvic examination.
	We have some labs pending.
	She had a mammogram this year, which was normal.
	IMPRESSION: General physical with the following diagnoses:
	1. Hypertension.
	2. Hypothyroidism.
	3. Postmenopausal, on estrogen replacement.
	4. Depression.
	5. Hiatal hernia with gastresophageal reflux.
	PLAN: She feels the Prozac is helping her mood. She is able to concentrate better and is less down about things. I suggested she take the Prozac for at least three months and perhaps six months. I gave her prescriptions for Prozac and all her other medications, including Synthroid 0.2 mg, Prinivil 10 mg, and Premarin 0.625 mg. She has had a mammogram recently, which showed no evidence of breast cancer.
	Ray Adams, MD

SUPPLIES

South Padre Medical Center

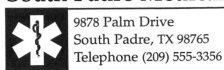

Gerald Bond, MD
Ray Adams, MD
Joyce Harkness, MD
Anthony Clark, MD

9878 Palm Drive
South Padre, TX 98765
Telephone (209) 555-3356

PATIENT INFORMATION
Please Print

Today's Date __8-1-07__

Last Name __Carlisle__ First Name __Aggy__ Initial __P__

Date of Birth __8-8-36__ Age __70__ Sex __F__ SS# __218-49-8444__

Home Address Street __1101 SouthView__ City __South Padre__

State __TX__ Zip __98765__ Home Phone __(209) 555-7890__

Occupation __Retired__ Employer __Baker__

Employer Address Street __n/a__ City _____

State _____ Zip _____ Work Phone (___) _____

Are you currently a student? Yes (No) Name of School _____

Spouse's Name __Ralph__ Marital Status M S D (W) SEP

Spouse's SS# ___-___-___ Spouse's Employer _____

In case of emergency, notify __Mary Godfrey__ Relationship __daughter__

Home Phone (__811__) __1049-8220__ Work Phone (___) _____

If you are a minor: Parent's Name _____ SS#___-___-___

Street _____ City _____ State _____ Zip _____

Home Phone (___) _____ Work Phone (___) _____

Reason for Visit __Pap and physical__

Work related injury? Yes (No) Date of injury _____

Automobile accident? Yes (No) Date of injury _____

Other injury? Yes (No) Date of injury _____

Insurance (Primary) Company Name: __Delta of New York__

Street __8119 Tower__ City __New York__ State __NY__ Zip __59800__

Subscriber's Name __Aggy Carlisle__

Relationship to Subscriber: __Self__

Policy # __XRT0126__ Group # __PS 220021__

Insurance (Secondary) Company Name: __none__

Street _____ City _____ State _____ Zip _____

Subscriber's Name _____

Relationship to Subscriber: _____

Policy # _____ Group # _____

Assignment of Benefits:

I directly assign all medical/surgical benefits, including major medical benefits and Medicare, to South Padre Medical Center. I understand that this authorization for assignment remains in effect until I revoke it in writing. A photocopy of this assignment will be considered as valid as this original assignment. I further understand that I am responsible for my indebtedness no matter what charges the insurance pays for.

Insured or Guardian's Signature __Aggy Carlisle__ Date __8-1-07__

SUPPLIES

South Padre Medical Center

Patient's Name ___Aggy P. Carlisle___ Age __70__ Sex __F__ Marital Status S M Ⓦ D

Address ___1101 South View___ Insurance ___Delta of NY___

Telephone ___209-555-7890___ Referred ___Self___

Date	Subsequent Findings
08/01/07	CHIEF COMPLAINT: Pap and physical.
	SUBJECTIVE: This 70-year-old widowed Caucasian female presents for an annual examination
	and Pap smear. She voices no new concerns.
	PAST MEDICAL HISTORY: History is significant for chronic positional vertigo and numerous
	seborrheic keratoses, some of which have been frozen in the past. She had a TAH in 1997
	because of dysfunctional uterine bleeding. She is currently on Premarin 0.65 mg one every other
	day. She has three grown children—two sons living in South Padre and a daughter in Austin.
	FAMILY HISTORY: Brother died at age 72 from heart disease. Mom died at age 73 from a
	cerebral hemorrhage.
	SOCIAL/OCCUPATIONAL HISTORY: She is a retired baker. She lost her home to a
	hurricane and has moved into a new house which is keeping her busy.
	HABITS: Tobacco: None. Alcohol: Occasional. Diet: Watches fat, cholesterol and sweets. She is a
	milk drinker along with four cups of coffee daily. She tries to walk for exercise. Sleeping well.
	Seat belts used consistently. Last mammogram March 2004. Flexible sigmoidoscopy was done
	March 2001.
	OBJECTIVE: Weight is 128 pounds. Blood pressure is 128/64. General: Well-developed and
	well-nourished elderly female who appears younger than her stated age. Skin is negative, with
	the exception of scattered seborrheic keratoses. ENT is unremarkable. Neck is supple with no
	palpable nodes. Thyroid is not enlarged. Breasts are symmetric and nontender with no palpable
	mass or discharge. Heart has a regular rate without murmurs. Lungs are clear to auscultation.
	Abdomen is benign. No CVA tenderness. Pelvic: Normal external female genitalia. No odor or
	discharge. Uterus is absent. No adnexal mass or tenderness. Rectal confirms bimanual; no
	tenderness, mass or stool. Good peripheral pulses; no edema.
	IMPRESSION:
	1. Postmenopausal female on estrogen replacement therapy.
	2. Seborrheic keratoses.
	3. History of benign positional vertigo.
	PLAN: We will send Pap report. Three seborrheic keratoses are frozen with liquid nitrogen. This
	includes one behind the left ear and two on the back. We will monitor for signs of infection.
	Reinforced monthly breast self exam, annual mammogram, and positive lifestyle behaviors. Sent
	with hemoccult cards. Recommend screening flexible sigmoid; the patient indicates that she will
	call back to get this scheduled. Will also return for a fasting lipid panel and blood sugar. Return
	to the clinic as noted/annually/p.r.n.
	Ray Adams, MD

SUPPLIES

South Padre Medical Center

Gerald Bond, MD
Ray Adams, MD
Joyce Harkness, MD
Anthony Clark, MD

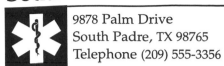

9878 Palm Drive
South Padre, TX 98765
Telephone (209) 555-3356

PATIENT INFORMATION
Please Print

Today's Date __11/20/2007__

Last Name __Meires__   First Name __anne__   Initial __R__

Date of Birth __05/14/1965__   Age __42__   Sex __F__   SS# __506-91-4551__

Home Address   Street __14 Western Way__   City __South Padre__

State __TX__   Zip __98765__   Home Phone __(209) 555-1213__

Occupation __Secretary__   Employer __Texas Power__

Employer Address   Street __1814 main__   City __South Padre__

State __TX__   Zip __98765__   Work Phone __(209) 555-9191__

Are you currently a student?   Yes   (No)   Name of School _____

Spouse's Name __none__   Marital Status   M   (S)   D   W   SEP

Spouse's SS# ___-___-___   Spouse's Employer _____

In case of emergency, notify __Morrisa Welch__   Relationship __niece__

Home Phone __(012) 450-2213__   Work Phone (___) __none__

If you are a minor: Parent's Name _____   SS# ___-___-___

Street _____   City _____   State ___   Zip _____

Home Phone (___) _____   Work Phone (___) _____

Reason for Visit __Flu__

Work related injury?   Yes   (No)   Date of injury _____

Automobile accident?   Yes   (No)   Date of injury _____

Other injury?   Yes   (No)   Date of injury _____

Insurance (Primary)   Company Name: __Texas Health Corporation__

Street __1256 56th Ave. S__   City __Houston__   State __TX__   Zip __99881__

Subscriber's Name __self__

Relationship to Subscriber: __Self__

Policy # __TRG8731__   Group # __P840__

Insurance (Secondary)   Company Name: _____

Street _____   City _____   State ___   Zip _____

Subscriber's Name _____

Relationship to Subscriber: _____

Policy #_____   Group #_____

Assignment of Benefits:

I directly assign all medical/surgical benefits, including major medical benefits and Medicare, to South Padre Medical Center. I understand that this authorization for assignment remains in effect until I revoke it in writing. A photocopy of this assignment will be considered as valid as this original assignment. I further understand that I am responsible for my indebtedness no matter what charges the insurance pays for.

Insured or Guardian's Signature __anne Meires__   Date __11/20/2007__

SUPPLIES

TASK **1.5**   251

South Padre Medical Center

Patient's Name ___Anne R. Meires___ Age __42__ Sex __F__ Marital Status Ⓢ M W D

Address ___14 Western Way___ Insurance ___TX Health Corporation___

Telephone ___209-555-1213___ Referred ___Self___

Date	Subsequent Findings
11/20/07	PROBLEM: Flu.
	SUBJECTIVE: Anne is a 42-year-old female, new patient who presents with the "flu." She
	has been throwing up off and on since last Saturday, which is about four days ago. She
	has had a little temperature off and on. No complaint of sore throat. No earache. No
	cough or cold. She has had one little episode of diarrhea and that is it. She disclaims
	any urinary tract symptoms. She has had a bladder infection in the past. Some
	decrease in voiding and then this morning she threw up. Because of this, she came in.
	OBJECTIVE: She is alert and awake. Ears: TMs are clear. Nose is clear. Throat looks
	okay. Neck is supple. Chest is clear. Abdomen is soft; slightly tender on the left side—just
	more of a generalized tenderness. No rebound. Normal bowel sounds. No masses can be
	delineated. No CVA tenderness. Heart is nice and regular. Urinalysis is done. This is just
	lightly cloudy. Specific gravity of 1.030 but negative for nitrite. Negative for leukocyte
	and 2-6 white cells. It does not look anything significant. Her white count is 11,780 with a
	hemoglobin of 14.6 and with it being predominantly neutrophils 85.2%.
	ASSESSMENT: Gastroenteritis.
	PLAN: Give her some Phenergan suppositories, 12.5 #4. Insert one four to six hours p.r.n. for
	nausea and vomiting. Continue with fluids. Take some Tylenol, if tolerated.
	Ray Adams, MD

SUPPLIES

South Padre Medical Center

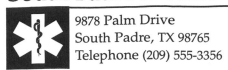

Gerald Bond, MD
Ray Adams, MD
Joyce Harkness, MD
Anthony Clark, MD

9878 Palm Drive
South Padre, TX 98765
Telephone (209) 555-3356

PATIENT INFORMATION
Please Print

Today's Date **06/02/2007**

Last Name **Socorri** First Name **Anthony** Initial **N**

Date of Birth **08/23/1973** Age **33** Sex **M** SS# **482-44-0001**

Home Address Street **333 Breezy Point Drive** City **South Padre**

State **TX** Zip **98765** Home Phone **(209) 555-7778**

Occupation **Painter** Employer **Self-employed**

Employer Address Street _____ City _____

State _____ Zip _____ Work Phone (___)_____

Are you currently a student? Yes (No) Name of School _____

Spouse's Name **N/A** Marital Status M (S) D W SEP

Spouse's SS# ___-___-___ Spouse's Employer ___

In case of emergency, notify **Harold Socorri** Relationship **Father**

Home Phone **(209) 555-7778** Work Phone (___) **N/A**

If you are a minor: Parent's Name _____ SS#___-___-___

Street _____ City _____ State _____ Zip_____

Home Phone (___)_____ Work Phone (___)_____

Reason for Visit **back ache**

Work related injury? Yes (No) Date of injury_____

Automobile accident? Yes (No) Date of injury_____

Other injury? Yes (No) Date of injury_____

Insurance (Primary) Company Name: **Traveler's Insurance**

Street **42110 West Rd** City **Houston** State **TX** Zip **99881**

Subscriber's Name **Anthony Socorri**

Relationship to Subscriber: **self**

Policy # **KUI 0974** Group # **TSP 008**

Insurance (Secondary) Company Name: **NONE**

Street _____ City _____ State _____ Zip_____

Subscriber's Name _____

Relationship to Subscriber: _____

Policy #_____ Group #_____

Assignment of Benefits:

I directly assign all medical/surgical benefits, including major medical benefits and Medicare, to South Padre Medical Center. I understand that this authorization for assignment remains in effect until I revoke it in writing. A photocopy of this assignment will be considered as valid as this original assignment. I further understand that I am responsible for my indebtedness no matter what charges the insurance pays for.

Insured or Guardian's Signature **Anthony Socorri** Date **06/02/2007**

SUPPLIES

TASK **1.5** 255

South Padre Medical Center

Patient's Name __Anthony N. Socorri__   Age __33__ Sex __M__ Marital Status Ⓢ M W D

Address __333 Breezy Point Drive__   Insurance __Traveler's__

Telephone __209-555-7778__   Referred __Self__

Date	Subsequent Findings
06/02/07	Patient presents with low back pain of seven days duration. Denies radiation of pain to
	legs. Pn is aggravated by sneezing or coughing. No redness, tenderness, swelling or heat.
	Well-developed 33-year-old. Height, 5'6"; weight, 158; BP 130/70; gait normal. Pulses 2+1.
	Range of motion of all joints within normal limits. L5 spine flexation to 70° and extension
	14°. Ambulates without assistance.
	Advised limited bed rest with aspirin for pn, to return if condition shows no improvement. He
	has a back brace from earlier episode. Advised to use brace sparingly so as not to
	further weaken his back muscles.
	Ray Adams, MD

SUPPLIES

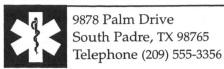

South Padre Medical Center

Gerald Bond, MD
Ray Adams, MD
Joyce Harkness, MD
Anthony Clark, MD

9878 Palm Drive
South Padre, TX 98765
Telephone (209) 555-3356

PATIENT INFORMATION
Please Print

Today's Date 12/01/2007

Last Name Larson First Name Bridget Initial G.

Date of Birth 01/08/2004 Age 3 Sex F SS# 862-90-4111

Home Address Street 9820 Bold View City South Padre

State TX Zip 98765 Home Phone (209) 555-0496

Occupation N/A Employer N/A

Employer Address Street N/A City N/A

State N/A Zip N/A Work Phone (____) N/A

Are you currently a student? (Yes) No Name of School Padre Elementary

Spouse's Name _____ Marital Status M S D W SEP

Spouse's SS# ___-___-___ Spouse's Employer _____

In case of emergency, notify Tonya Larson Relationship Mother

Home Phone (209) 555-0496 Work Phone (209) 555-1918

If you are a minor: Parent's Name Tonya Larson SS# 508-48-1962

Street Same City _____ State ___ Zip ___

Home Phone (209) 555-0496 Work Phone (209) 555-1918

Reason for Visit Hearing

Work related injury? Yes (No) Date of injury_____

Automobile accident? Yes (No) Date of injury_____

Other injury? Yes (No) Date of injury_____

Insurance (Primary) Company Name: Blue Cross/Blue Shield of Texas

Street 1514 Nest Road City Houston State TX Zip 99881

Subscriber's Name Tonya

Relationship to Subscriber: Daughter

Policy # XCV5589 Group # 2X4418

Insurance (Secondary) Company Name: None

Street _____ City _____ State ___ Zip ___

Subscriber's Name _____

Relationship to Subscriber: _____

Policy #_____ Group #_____

Assignment of Benefits:

I directly assign all medical/surgical benefits, including major medical benefits and Medicare, to South Padre Medical Center. I understand that this authorization for assignment remains in effect until I revoke it in writing. A photocopy of this assignment will be considered as valid as this original assignment. I further understand that I am responsible for my indebtedness no matter what charges the insurance pays for.

Insured or Guardian's Signature Tonya J. Larson Date 12/01/2007

SUPPLIES

TASK **1.5** 259

South Padre Medical Center

Patient's Name ___Bridget G. Larson___ Age _3_ Sex _F_ Marital Status ⓈM W D
Address ___9820 Bold View___ Insurance ___BC/BS of TX___
Telephone ___209-555-0496___ Referred ___Self___ (Mother: Tonya)

Date	Subsequent Findings
12/01/07	SUBJECTIVE: Bridget is a 3-year-old female who comes in today for evaluation. She has had a cough over the last couple of weeks but has had no congestion, sneezing, fever, or vomiting. No diarrhea. Last month, she was screened at Headstart and found to have flat tympanograms bilaterally, eye and hearing loss. She has had no ear pain. Mother brings her in today for evaluation. She is on no specific therapy. She has no known medicinal allergies. Immunizations are up to date according to her vaccination administration record.
	OBJECTIVE: On exam, she is afebrile. HEENT exam reveals wax in both external auditory canals. I was able to remove the wax particularly on the left side. The right side required irrigation. There is evidence of bilaterally serous otitis media on examination afterwards.
	IMPRESSION: Bilateral serous otitis media with associated hearing loss.
	RECOMMENDATIONS:
	1. I did give mother a prescription for amoxicillin 250 mg. p.o. t.i.d. for a 10-day-course should she develop persistent ear pain.
	2. Should she have recurrent otitis media in spite of antibiotic therapy or a persistent serous otitis media over the next several months with hearing loss, we can fix a surgical intervention at that time. Mother did have questions regarding indications for pressure equalization tubes, etc.
	3. Mother's questions were answered and she was in agreement with the outlined management plan.
	Ray Adams, MD
04/02/08	Patient has had several episodes of recurrent tonsillitis and adenoiditis over last several months. Referred to Dr. Bond for T&A.
	Ray Adams, MD

SUPPLIES

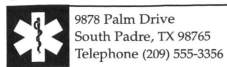

South Padre Medical Center

Gerald Bond, MD
Ray Adams, MD
Joyce Harkness, MD
Anthony Clark, MD

9878 Palm Drive
South Padre, TX 98765
Telephone (209) 555-3356

PATIENT INFORMATION
Please Print

Today's Date **March 3, 2008**

Last Name **Hoverson** First Name **Adam** Initial **G.**

Date of Birth **September 2, 1993** Age **14** Sex **M** SS# **220-11-3841**

Home Address Street **72 Georgian Square** City **South Padre**

State **TX** Zip **98765** Home Phone **(209) 555-1522**

Occupation **Student** Employer _____

Employer Address Street _____ City _____

State _____ Zip _____ Work Phone ( ) _____

Are you currently a student? (**Yes**) No Name of School **South Padre High**

Spouse's Name _____ Marital Status M S D W SEP

Spouse's SS# ___-___-_____ Spouse's Employer _____

In case of emergency, notify _____ Relationship _____

Home Phone ( ) _____ Work Phone ( ) _____

If you are a minor: Parent's Name **Martha** SS# **502-88-6768**

Street **Same** City _____ State _____ Zip_____

Home Phone (**209**) **555-1522** Work Phone ( ) _____

Reason for Visit **Plugged ears**

Work related injury? Yes No Date of injury _____

Automobile accident? Yes No Date of injury _____

Other injury? Yes No Date of injury _____

Insurance (Primary) Company Name: **BC/BS of TX**

Street **1514 West Rd.** City **Houston** State **TX** Zip **99881**

Subscriber's Name **Ralph**

Relationship to Subscriber: **Son**

Policy # **ZAW2347** Group # **ZX4500**

Insurance (Secondary) Company Name: _____

Street _____ City _____ State _____ Zip_____

Subscriber's Name _____

Relationship to Subscriber: _____

Policy # _____ Group # _____

Assignment of Benefits:

I directly assign all medical/surgical benefits, including major medical benefits and Medicare, to South Padre Medical Center. I understand that this authorization for assignment remains in effect until I revoke it in writing. A photocopy of this assignment will be considered as valid as this original assignment. I further understand that I am responsible for my indebtedness no matter what charges the insurance pays for.

Insured or Guardian's Signature **Martha Hoverson** Date **March 3, 2008**

SUPPLIES

TASK **1.5** 263

South Padre Medical Center

Patient's Name __Adam G. Hoverson__ Age __14__ Sex __M__ Marital Status ⓢ M W D

Address __72 Georgian Square__ Insurance __BC/BS of TX__

Telephone __209-555-1522__ Referred __Self__

Date	Subsequent Findings
03/03/08	PROBLEM: Clogged ears.
	SUBJECTIVE: Adam has had some clogged ears for the last couple of weeks. He denies any specific pain. He tried to clean his ears out and did not really get anything. He did have PE tubes in about a year ago and he had apparently flat tympanograms at that time. He denies any runny nose, fever, or chills.
	PAST MEDICAL HISTORY: He is on no meds. He has no allergies.
	PHYSICAL EXAM: Reveals a well developed, well nourished young male in obvious distress. Temperature is 96.6. Pulse is 72 and regular. Respirations 14 and unlabored. TMs are both slightly dull and red. They have tympanosclerosis. I cannot detect an obvious effusion but the TMs appear retracted.
	ASSESSMENT:
	1. Otitis media.
	2. Tympanosclerosis.
	PLAN: I have given him Bactrim DS b.i.d. for two weeks and Claritin-D one p.o. b.i.d. for two weeks. If he is not symptom free in two weeks he will let us know and we will have to do another tympanogram.
	Ray Adams, MD

SUPPLIES

FILING

Colors for Alphabetic Filing Method

1. Carrie Anderson   _____ , _____

2. Karra Burthold   _____ , _____

3. Aggy Carlisle   _____ , _____

4. Kathy Forest   _____ , _____

5. Adam Hoverson   _____ , _____

Patient names from the Accession Ledger for a six-place filing system

Name	Number	Order	First Two Colors
1. Tony Mayer	345692	___	_____ , _____
2. Mathew Owens	560122	___	_____ , _____
3. Dalmer Garcia	789211	___	_____ , _____
4. Missy Butler	34099	___	_____ , _____
5. Kathy Sue Thompson	5678	___	_____ , _____
6. Louise Carabin	58900	___	_____ , _____
7. Hilton Smart	009091	___	_____ , _____
8. Ellisa Talbot	762900	___	_____ , _____
9. Joan Woods	980001	___	_____ , _____
10. Maureen Loopstoe	509821	___	_____ , _____

SUPPLIES

South Padre Medical Center

Gerald Bond, MD
Ray Adams, MD
Joyce Harkness, MD
Anthony Clark, MD

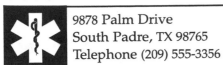

9878 Palm Drive
South Padre, TX 98765
Telephone (209) 555-3356

PATIENT INFORMATION

Please Print

Today's Date __04/08/2008__

Last Name __Rock__   First Name __Lewis__   Initial __L__

Date of Birth __03/06/1931__   Age __77__   Sex __M__   SS# __201 - 48 - 9201__

Home Address   Street __1000 Bass Ave__   City __S. Padre__

State __TX__   Zip __98765__   Home Phone __(209) 555-2292__

Occupation __Retired__   Employer _____

Employer Address   Street _____   City _____

State _____   Zip _____   Work Phone (____)_____

Are you currently a student?   Yes   (No)   Name of School _____

Spouse's Name __Rachelle__   Marital Status (M)   S   D   W   SEP

Spouse's SS# __101 - 88 - 6310__ Spouse's Employer __Retired__

In case of emergency, notify __Rachelle__   Relationship __Wife__

Home Phone (____)_____   Work Phone (____)_____

If you are a minor: Parent's Name _____   SS# ____-____-____

Street _____   City _____   State _____ Zip_____

Home Phone (____)_____   Work Phone (____)_____

Reason for Visit __Cancer of lymph nodes, Refered by Dr. Thomas Thompson__

Work related injury?   Yes   (No)   Date of injury_____

Automobile accident?   Yes   (No)   Date of injury_____

Other injury?   Yes   (No)   Date of injury_____

Insurance (Primary)   Company Name: __Medicare__

Street __402 Main Street__   City __South Padre__ State __TX__ Zip __98765__

Subscriber's Name _____

Relationship to Subscriber: __Self__

Policy # __201489201A__   Group # _____

Insurance (Secondary)   Company Name: __None__

Street _____   City _____   State _____ Zip_____

Subscriber's Name _____

Relationship to Subscriber: _____

Policy #_____   Group # _____

Assignment of Benefits:

I directly assign all medical/surgical benefits, including major medical benefits and Medicare, to South Padre Medical Center. I understand that this authorization for assignment remains in effect until I revoke it in writing. A photocopy of this assignment will be considered as valid as this original assignment. I further understand that I am responsible for my indebtedness no matter what charges the insurance pays for.

Insured or Guardian's Signature __Lewis L Rock__   Date __04/08/2008__

SUPPLIES

TASK **2.2**   269

South Padre Medical Center

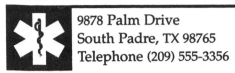

Gerald Bond, MD
Ray Adams, MD
Joyce Harkness, MD
Anthony Clark, MD

9878 Palm Drive
South Padre, TX 98765
Telephone (209) 555-3356

PATIENT INFORMATION
Please Print

Today's Date __April 8, 2008__

Last Name __Goldman__ First Name __Edward__ Initial __A.__

Date of Birth __June 2, 2007__ Age __10 mo.__ Sex __m__ SS# __780-11-8811__

Home Address Street __206 Cora Lee__ City __South Padre__

State __TX__ Zip __98765__ Home Phone __(209) 555-2234__

Occupation __None__ Employer _____

Employer Address Street _____ City _____

State _____ Zip _____ Work Phone (_____)_____

Are you currently a student? Yes (No) Name of School _____

Spouse's Name _____ Marital Status M (S) D W SEP

Spouse's SS# _____-_____-_____ Spouse's Employer _____

In case of emergency, notify __Gloria__ Relationship __mother__

Home Phone __(209) 555-2234__ Work Phone (___)_____

If you are a minor: Parent's __Gloria Goldman__ SS# __503-81-9991__

Street __Same__ City _____ State _____ Zip_____

Home Phone (___)_____ Work Phone (___)_____

Reason for Visit __Dr. Bethos referred__

Work related injury? Yes (No) Date of injury_____

Automobile accident? Yes (No) Date of injury_____

Other injury? Yes (No) Date of injury_____

Insurance (Primary) Company Name: __Medicaid__

Street __402 Main Street__ City __South Padre__ State __TX__ Zip __98765__

Subscriber's Name _____

Relationship to Subscriber: __Self__

Policy # __QYK956199__ Group # _____

Insurance (Secondary) Company Name: _____

Street _____ City _____ State _____ Zip_____

Subscriber's Name _____

Relationship to Subscriber: _____

Policy # _____ Group # _____

Assignment of Benefits:

I directly assign all medical/surgical benefits, including major medical benefits and Medicare, to South Padre Medical Center. I understand that this authorization for assignment remains in effect until I revoke it in writing. A photocopy of this assignment will be considered as valid as this original assignment. I further understand that I am responsible for my indebtedness no matter what charges the insurance pays for.

Insured or Guardian's Signature __Gloria Goldman__ Date __April 8, 2008__

SUPPLIES

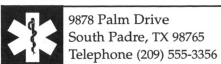

South Padre Medical Center

Gerald Bond, MD
Ray Adams, MD
Joyce Harkness, MD
Anthony Clark, MD

9878 Palm Drive
South Padre, TX 98765
Telephone (209) 555-3356

PATIENT INFORMATION
Please Print

Today's Date __4/8/08__

Last Name __Blair__   First Name __Thomas__   Initial __R__

Date of Birth __11/2/1943__   Age __64__   Sex __M__   SS# __162-48-7610__

Home Address   Street __437 West Monroe Rd__   City __South Padre__
               State __TX__   Zip __98765__   Home Phone (__209__) __555-5091__

Occupation __Welder__   Employer __Blair Steel, Inc.__

Employer Address   Street __120 E. Verna Dr__   City __South Padre__
                   State __TX__   Zip __98765__   Work Phone (__209__) __555-5251__

Are you currently a student?   Yes   (No)   Name of School _____

Spouse's Name __Maria__   Marital Status   (M)   S   D   W   SEP

Spouse's SS# __401-86-8610__   Spouse's Employer __None__

In case of emergency, notify __Maria__   Relationship __Wife__

            Home Phone (__) __SAME__   Work Phone (__) _____

If you are a minor: Parent's Name _____   SS# ___-__-___

            Street _____   City _____   State ____   Zip ____

            Home Phone (__) _____   Work Phone (__) _____

Reason for Visit __Swelling in groin area__

            Work related injury?   Yes   (No)   Date of injury_____
            Automobile accident?   Yes   (No)   Date of injury_____
            Other injury?   Yes   (No)   Date of injury_____

Insurance (Primary)   Company Name: __Texas Health Corporation__
            Street __1256 56th Ave__   City __Houston__   State __TX__ Zip __99881__
            Subscriber's Name __THOMAS__
            Relationship to Subscriber: __SELF__
            Policy # __UBt9742__   Group # __P868__

Insurance (Secondary)   Company Name: _____
            Street _____   City _____   State ____   Zip_____
            Subscriber's Name _____
            Relationship to Subscriber: _____
            Policy #_____   Group #_____

Assignment of Benefits:

I directly assign all medical/surgical benefits, including major medical benefits and Medicare, to South Padre Medical Center. I understand that this authorization for assignment remains in effect until I revoke it in writing. A photocopy of this assignment will be considered as valid as this original assignment. I further understand that I am responsible for my indebtedness no matter what charges the insurance pays for.

Insured or Guardian's Signature __Thomas R. Blair__   Date __4/8/08__

SUPPLIES

TASK **2.2**   273

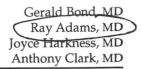

South Padre Medical Center

Gerald Bond, MD
Ray Adams, MD
Joyce Harkness, MD
Anthony Clark, MD

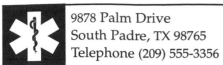

9878 Palm Drive
South Padre, TX 98765
Telephone (209) 555-3356

PATIENT INFORMATION
Please Print

Today's Date **April 8, 2008**

Last Name **King**   First Name **Jackie**   Initial **L**

Date of Birth **10/24/1980**   Age **27**   Sex **F**   SS# **448-61-8102**

Home Address   Street **669 Cherry Falls Avenue** City **S. Padre**

State **TX**   Zip **98765** Home Phone **(209) 555-8136**

Occupation **Teacher**   Employer **S. Padre High School**

Employer Address   Street _____   City **S. Padre**

State **TX**   Zip **98765** Work Phone **(209) 555-3932**

Are you currently a student?   Yes   (No)   Name of School _____

Spouse's Name **James**   Marital Status (M) S   D   W   SEP

Spouse's SS# **101-33.0009** Spouse's Employer **Self-rancher**

In case of emergency, notify **James**   Relationship **Husband**

Home Phone **(209) 555-8136**   Work Phone **(209) 555-0206**

If you are a minor: Parent's Name _____   SS# ___-___-___

Street _____ City _____ State ____ Zip _____

Home Phone (___) _____ Work Phone (___) _____

Reason for Visit **OB** _____

Work related injury?   Yes   (No)   Date of injury _____

Automobile accident?   Yes   (No)   Date of injury _____

Other injury?   Yes   (No)   Date of injury _____

Insurance (Primary)   Company Name: **Texas Health Corporation**

Street **1256 56th ave.** City **Houston** State **TX** Zip **99881**

Subscriber's Name **Self**

Relationship to Subscriber: _____

Policy # **HIKL5697**   Group # **P121**

Insurance (Secondary)   Company Name: _____

Street _____ City _____ State ____ Zip _____

Subscriber's Name _____

Relationship to Subscriber: _____

Policy # _____   Group # _____

Assignment of Benefits:

I directly assign all medical/surgical benefits, including major medical benefits and Medicare, to South Padre Medical Center. I understand that this authorization for assignment remains in effect until I revoke it in writing. A photocopy of this assignment will be considered as valid as this original assignment. I further understand that I am responsible for my indebtedness no matter what charges the insurance pays for.

Insured or Guardian's Signature **Jackie L. King**   Date **04/08/08**

SUPPLIES

South Padre Medical Center

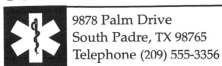

9878 Palm Drive
South Padre, TX 98765
Telephone (209) 555-3356

PATIENT INFORMATION

Please Print

Today's Date __April 8, 2008__

Last Name __Knight__   First Name __Joe__   Initial __J__

Date of Birth __09/28/86__   Age __21__   Sex __M__   SS# __409-19-1979__

Home Address   Street __1817 36 Avenue West__   City __S. Padre__

State __TX__   Zip __98765__   Home Phone (__209__) __555-8196__

Occupation __Labor__   Employer __S. Padre Construction__

Employer Address   Street __Business Hwy Z__   City __S. Padre__

State __TX__   Zip __98765__   Work Phone (__209__) __555-6591__

Are you currently a student?   Yes   (No)   Name of School _____

Spouse's Name _____   Marital Status   M   (S)   D   W   SEP

Spouse's SS# __-__-__   Spouse's Employer _____

In case of emergency, notify __Alice Knight__   Relationship __Mother__

Home Phone (__209__) __555-0712__   Work Phone (__) __None__

If you are a minor: Parent's Name _____   SS# __-__-__

Street _____   City _____   State _____   Zip _____

Home Phone (__) _____   Work Phone (__) _____

Reason for Visit __Hearing check__

Work related injury?   Yes   (No)   Date of injury _____

Automobile accident?   Yes   (No)   Date of injury _____

Other injury?   Yes   (No)   Date of injury _____

Insurance (Primary)   Company Name: __BC/BS of TX__

Street __1514 West Road__   City __Houston__   State __TX__   Zip __99881__

Subscriber's Name _____

Relationship to Subscriber: __Self__

Policy # __YTR5512__   Group # _____

Insurance (Secondary)   Company Name: __none__

Street _____   City _____   State _____   Zip _____

Subscriber's Name _____

Relationship to Subscriber: _____

Policy # _____   Group # _____

Assignment of Benefits:

I directly assign all medical/surgical benefits, including major medical benefits and Medicare, to South Padre Medical Center. I understand that this authorization for assignment remains in effect until I revoke it in writing. A photocopy of this assignment will be considered as valid as this original assignment. I further understand that I am responsible for my indebtedness no matter what charges the insurance pays for.

Insured or Guardian's Signature __Joe Knight__   Date __04/08/08__

SUPPLIES

South Padre Medical Center

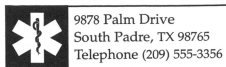

Gerald Bond, MD
Ray Adams, MD
Joyce Harkness, MD
Anthony Clark, MD

9878 Palm Drive
South Padre, TX 98765
Telephone (209) 555-3356

PATIENT INFORMATION
Please Print

Today's Date **April 8, 2008**

Last Name **Silverman**   First Name **Peter**   Initial **F**

Date of Birth **03/21/38**   Age **70**   Sex **M**   SS# **817-10-1124**

Home Address   Street **1608 Todd Ave.**   City **S. Padre**

State **TX**   Zip **98765**   Home Phone (**209**) **555-7675**

Occupation **Retired**   Employer _____

Employer Address   Street _____ City _____

State _____ Zip _____ Work Phone (_____)

Are you currently a student?   Yes   (No)   Name of School _____

Spouse's Name **Emma**   Marital Status (M) S   D   W   SEP

Spouse's SS# **102-45-6982** Spouse's Employer **Retired**

In case of emergency, notify **Emma**   Relationship **Wife**

Home Phone (_____) _____ Work Phone (_____) _____

If you are a minor: Parent's Name _____ SS# _____-____-_____

Street _____ City _____ State _____ Zip _____

Home Phone (_____) _____ Work Phone (_____) _____

Reason for Visit **Headache**

     Work related injury?   Yes (No)   Date of injury _____

     Automobile accident?   Yes (No)   Date of injury _____

     Other injury?   Yes (No)   Date of injury _____

Insurance (Primary)   Company Name: **Medicare**

Street **402 Main St.**   City **South Padre** State **TX** Zip **98765**

Subscriber's Name _____

Relationship to Subscriber: **Self**

Policy # **817101248**   Group # _____

Insurance (Secondary)   Company Name: **None**

Street _____ City _____ State _____ Zip _____

Subscriber's Name _____

Relationship to Subscriber: _____

Policy # _____ Group # _____

Assignment of Benefits:

I directly assign all medical/surgical benefits, including major medical benefits and Medicare, to South Padre Medical Center. I understand that this authorization for assignment remains in effect until I revoke it in writing. A photocopy of this assignment will be considered as valid as this original assignment. I further understand that I am responsible for my indebtedness no matter what charges the insurance pays for.

Insured or Guardian's Signature **Peter F. Silverman**   Date **04/08/08**

SUPPLIES

South Padre Medical Center

Patient Face Sheet

4/7/2008

Patient Chart #: ROCLE000   D.O.B: 03/06/1931   Age: 77
Patient Name: Lewis L. Rock   Sex: Male
Street 1: 100 Bass Ave   SSN: 201489201
Street 2:   Mar Status: Married
City: South Padre, TX 98765   S.O.F: 4/8/2008
Phone: (209)555-6825   Assigned Provider: Gerald Bond

Employer Name:
Street 1:
City:
Phone:

Case Information

Case Desc: New Patient   Diagnosis 1:
Last Visit: Diagnosis 2:
Referral: Thomas Thompson MD   Diagnosis 3:
Guarantor Name: Lewis L. Rock   Diagnosis 4:
Street 1: 100 Bass Ave
City: South Padre, TX 98765
Phone: (209)555-6825
SSN: 201489201

Ins Co #: MCR   Insured 1 Name: Lewis L. Rock
Insurance 1: Medicare   Street 1:   100 Bass Ave
Street 1: 402 Main Street   Street 2:
Street 2:   Phone: (209)555-6825
City: South Padre, TX 98765   D.O.B.:   03/06/1931   Sex: Male
Phone: Policy Number: 201489201A
Ins-Start: Group Number:
End:

Ins Co #:   Insured 2 Name:
Insurance 2:   Street 1:
Street 1:   Street 2:
Street 2:   City:
City: Phone:
Phone: D.O.B.:
Ins-Start: Policy Number: Sex:
End: Group Number:

Ins Co #:   Insured 3 Name:
Insurance 3:   Street 1:
Street 1:   Street 2:
Street 2:   City:
City: Phone:
Phone: D.O.B.:   Sex:
Ins-Start: Policy Number:
End: Group Number:

SUPPLIES

South Padre Medical Center

Patient Face Sheet

4/8/2008

Patient Chart #: GOLED000
Patient Name: Edward A. Goldman
Street 1: 206 Cora Lee
Street 2:
City: South Padre, TX 98765
Phone: (209)555-2234

D.O.B: 06/02/2007   Age: 0
Sex: Female
SSN: 780118811
Mar Status:
S.O.F: 4/8/2008
Assigned Provider:

Employer Name:
Street 1:
City:
Phone:

Case Information

Case Desc: New Patient
Last Visit:
Referral:
Guarantor Name: Gloria Goldman
Street 1: 206 Cora Lee
City: South Padre, TX 98765
Phone: (209)555-2234
SSN: 503819991

Diagnosis 1:
Diagnosis 2:
Diagnosis 3:
Diagnosis 4:

Ins Co #: MCD
Insurance 1: Medicaid
Street 1: 402 Main Street
Street 2:
City: South Padre, TX 98765
Phone:
Ins-Start:
End:

Insured 1 Name: Gloria Goldman
Street 1: 206 Cora Lee
Street 2:
Phone: (209)555-2234
D.O.B.:   Sex: Female
Policy Number: QYK956199
Group Number:

Ins Co #:
Insurance 2:
Street 1:
Street 2:
City:
Phone:
Ins-Start:
End:

Insured 2 Name:
Street 1:
Street 2:
City:
Phone:
D.O.B.:
Policy Number: Sex:
Group Number:

Ins Co #:
Insurance 3:
Street 1:
Street 2:
City:
Phone:
Ins-Start:
End:

Insured 3 Name:
Street 1:
Street 2:
City:
Phone:
D.O.B.:   Sex:
Policy Number:
Group Number:

SUPPLIES

South Padre Medical Center

Patient Face Sheet
4/7/2008

Patient Chart #: BLATH000   D.O.B: 11/02/1943   Age: 64
Patient Name: Thomas R. Blair   Sex: Male
    Street 1: 437 West Monroe St   SSN: 161487610
    Street 2:   Mar Status: Married
       City: South Padre, TX 98765   S.O.F: 4/8/2008
     Phone: (209)555-5091   Assigned Provider:

Employer Name: Blair Steel Inc
    Street 1: 120 E Verna
       City: South Padre, TX 98765
     Phone: (209)555-5251

Case Information

Case Desc: New Patient
Last Visit: Diagnosis 1:
Referral: Bert Bethos, MD   Diagnosis 2:
Guarantor Name: Thomas R. Blair   Diagnosis 3:
    Street 1: 437 West Monroe St   Diagnosis 4:
       City: South Padre, TX 98765
     Phone: (209)555-5091
       SSN: 161487610

Ins Co #: THC   Insured 1 Name: Thomas R. Blair
Insurance 1: Texas Health Corporation   Street 1: 437 West Monroe St
    Street 1: 1256 56th Ave   Street 2:
    Street 2:   Phone: (209)555-5091
       City: Houston, TX 99881   D.O.B.: 11/02/1943   Sex: Male
     Phone: Policy Number: UBT9742
   Ins-Start: Group Number: P868
       End:

Ins Co #:   Insured 2 Name:
Insurance 2:   Street 1:
    Street 1:   Street 2:
    Street 2:   City:
       City: Phone:
     Phone: D.O.B.:
   Ins-Start: Policy Number: Sex:
       End: Group Number:

Ins Co #:   Insured 3 Name:
Insurance 3:   Street 1:
    Street 1:   Street 2:
    Street 2:   City:
       City: Phone:
     Phone: D.O.B.:   Sex:
   Ins-Start: Policy Number:
       End: Group Number:

SUPPLIES

South Padre Medical Center

Patient Face Sheet

4/7/2008

Patient Chart #: KINJA000
Patient Name: Jackie L. King
Street 1: 669 Cherry Falls Road
Street 2:
City: South Padre, TX 98765
Phone: (209)555-8136

D.O.B: 10/24/1980   Age: 27
Sex: Female
SSN: 448618102
Mar Status: Married
S.O.F: 4/8/2008
Assigned Provider: Ray Adams

Employer Name: South Padre High School
Street 1:
City: South Padre, TX 98765
Phone: (209)555-3932

Case Information

Case Desc: New Patient
Last Visit: Diagnosis 1:
Referral: Diagnosis 2:
Guarantor Name: Jackie L. King   Diagnosis 3:
Street 1: 669 Cherry Falls Road   Diagnosis 4:
City: South Padre, TX 98765
Phone: (209)555-8136
SSN: 448618102

Ins Co #: THC   Insured 1 Name: Jackie L. King
Insurance 1: Texas Health Corporation   Street 1: 669 Cherry Falls Road
Street 1: 1256 56th Ave   Street 2:
Street 2:   Phone: (209)555-8136
City: Houston, TX 99881   D.O.B.: 10/24/1980   Sex: Female
Phone: Policy Number: HIKL5697
Ins-Start: Group Number: P121
End:

Ins Co #:   Insured 2 Name:
Insurance 2:   Street 1:
Street 1:   Street 2:
Street 2:   City:
City: Phone:
Phone: D.O.B.:
Ins-Start: Policy Number: Sex:
End: Group Number:

Ins Co #:   Insured 3 Name:
Insurance 3:   Street 1:
Street 1:   Street 2:
Street 2:   City:
City: Phone:
Phone: D.O.B.:   Sex:
Ins-Start: Policy Number:
End: Group Number:

SUPPLIES

South Padre Medical Center

Patient Face Sheet

4/7/2008

Patient Chart #: KNIJO000
Patient Name: Joe J. Knight
Street 1: 1817 36 Ave
Street 2:
City: South Padre, TX 98765
Phone: (209)555-8196

D.O.B: 09/28/1986   Age: 21
Sex: Male
SSN: 409191979
Mar Status: Single
S.O.F: 4/8/2008
Assigned Provider:

Employer Name: South Padre Construction
Street 1: Business HWY Z
City: South Padre, TX 98765
Phone: (209)555-6591

Case Information

Case Desc: New Patient
Last Visit:
Referral:
Guarantor Name: Joe J. Knight
Street 1: 1817 36 Ave
City: South Padre, TX 98765
Phone: (209)555-8196
SSN: 409191979

Diagnosis 1:
Diagnosis 2:
Diagnosis 3:
Diagnosis 4:

Ins Co #: BCBS
Insurance 1: Blue Cross/Blue Shield of TX
Street 1: 1514 West Road
Street 2:
City: Houston, TX 99881
Phone:
Ins-Start:
End:

Insured 1 Name: Joe J. Knight
Street 1: 1817 36 Ave
Street 2:
Phone: (209)555-8196
D.O.B.: 09/28/1986   Sex: Male
Policy Number: YRT5512
Group Number:

Ins Co #:
Insurance 2:
Street 1:
Street 2:
City:
Phone:
Ins-Start:
End:

Insured 2 Name:
Street 1:
Street 2:
City:
Phone:
D.O.B.:
Policy Number: Sex:
Group Number:

Ins Co #:
Insurance 3:
Street 1:
Street 2:
City:
Phone:
Ins-Start:
End:

Insured 3 Name:
Street 1:
Street 2:
City:
Phone:
D.O.B.:   Sex:
Policy Number:
Group Number:

SUPPLIES

South Padre Medical Center

Patient Face Sheet

4/7/2008

Patient Chart #: SILPE000   D.O.B: 03/21/1938   Age: 70

Patient Name: Peter F. Silverman   Sex: Male

Street 1: 1608 Todd Ave   SSN: 817101124

Street 2:   Mar Status: Married

City: South Padre, TX 98765   S.O.F: 4/8/2008

Phone: (209)555-7675   Assigned Provider:

Employer Name:

Street 1:

City:

Phone:

Case Information

Case Desc: New Patient   Diagnosis 1:

Last Visit: Diagnosis 2:

Referral: Diagnosis 3:

Guarantor Name: Peter F. Silverman   Diagnosis 4:

Street 1: 1608 Todd Ave

City: South Padre, TX 98765

Phone: (209)555-7675

SSN: 817101124

Ins Co #: MCR   Insured 1 Name: Peter F. Silverman

Insurance 1: Medicare   Street 1: 1608 Todd Ave

Street 1: 402 Main Street   Street 2:

Street 2:   Phone: (209)555-7675

City: South Padre, TX 98765   D.O.B.: 03/21/1938   Sex: Male

Phone: Policy Number: 817101124A

Ins-Start: Group Number:

End:

Ins Co #:   Insured 2 Name:

Insurance 2:   Street 1:

Street 1:   Street 2:

Street 2:   City:

City: Phone:

Phone: D.O.B.:

Ins-Start: Policy Number: Sex:

End: Group Number:

Ins Co #:   Insured 3 Name:

Insurance 3:   Street 1:

Street 1:   Street 2:

Street 2:   City:

City: Phone:

Phone: D.O.B.:   Sex:

Ins-Start: Policy Number:

End: Group Number:

SUPPLIES

South Padre Medical Center

Patient's Name _____ Age _____ Sex _____ Marital Status S M W D

Address _____ Insurance _____

Telephone _____ Referred _____

Date	Subsequent Findings

SUPPLIES

South Padre Medical Center

Patient's Name _____ Age _____ Sex _____ Marital Status S M W D

Address _____ Insurance _____

Telephone _____ Referred _____

Date	Subsequent Findings

SUPPLIES

South Padre Medical Center

Patient's Name _____ Age _____ Sex _____ Marital Status S M W D

Address _____ Insurance _____

Telephone _____ Referred _____

Date	Subsequent Findings

SUPPLIES

South Padre Medical Center

Patient's Name _____ Age _____ Sex _____ Marital Status S M W D

Address _____ Insurance _____

Telephone _____ Referred _____

Date	Subsequent Findings

SUPPLIES

South Padre Medical Center

Patient's Name _____ Age _____ Sex _____ Marital Status S M W D

Address _____ Insurance _____

Telephone _____ Referred _____

Date	Subsequent Findings

SUPPLIES

South Padre Medical Center

Patient's Name _____ Age _____ Sex _____ Marital Status S M W D

Address _____ Insurance _____

Telephone _____ Referred _____

Date	Subsequent Findings

SUPPLIES

South Padre Medical Center

Patient's Name _____ Age _____ Sex _____ Marital Status S M W D

Address _____ Insurance _____

Telephone _____ Referred _____

Date	Subsequent Findings

SUPPLIES

South Padre Medical Center

Patient's Name _____ Age _____ Sex _____ Marital Status S M W D

Address _____ Insurance _____

Telephone _____ Referred _____

Date	Subsequent Findings

SUPPLIES

South Padre Medical Center

Patient's Name _____ Age _____ Sex _____ Marital Status S M W D

Address _____ Insurance _____

Telephone _____ Referred _____

Date	Subsequent Findings

SUPPLIES

South Padre Medical Center

Patient's Name _____ Age _____ Sex _____ Marital Status S M W D

Address _____ Insurance _____

Telephone _____ Referred _____

Date	Subsequent Findings

SUPPLIES

South Padre Medical Center

Patient's Name _____ Age _____ Sex _____ Marital Status   S   M   W   D

Address _____ Insurance _____

Telephone _____ Referred _____

Date	Subsequent Findings

SUPPLIES

South Padre Medical Center

Patient's Name _____ Age _____ Sex _____ Marital Status S M W D

Address _____ Insurance _____

Telephone _____ Referred _____

Date	Subsequent Findings

SUPPLIES

South Padre Medical Center

Patient Face Sheet

4/7/2008

Patient Chart #: ESKJA000
Patient Name: Jason W. Eskew
Street 1: 233 2nd Ave NW
Street 2:
City: South Padre, TX 98765
Phone: (209)555-5551

D.O.B: 02/20/1941   Age: 67
Sex: Male
SSN: 111320051
Mar Status: Married
S.O.F:
Assigned Provider:

Employer Name:
Street 1:
City:
Phone:

Case Information

Case Desc: New Patient
Last Visit:
Referral: Thomas Thompson MD
Guarantor Name: Jason W. Eskew
Street 1: 233 2nd Ave NW
City: South Padre, TX 98765
Phone: (209)555-5551
SSN: 111320051

Diagnosis 1:
Diagnosis 2:
Diagnosis 3:
Diagnosis 4:

Ins Co #: MCR
Insurance 1: Medicare
Street 1: 402 Main Street
Street 2:
City: South Padre, TX 98765
Phone:
Ins-Start:
End:

Insured 1 Name: Jason W. Eskew
Street 1: 233 2nd Ave NW
Street 2:
Phone: (209)555-5551
D.O.B.: 02/20/1941   Sex: Male
Policy Number: 111320051A
Group Number:

Ins Co #:
Insurance 2:
Street 1:
Street 2:
City:
Phone:
Ins-Start:
End:

Insured 2 Name:
Street 1:
Street 2:
City:
Phone:
D.O.B.:
Policy Number: Sex:
Group Number:

Ins Co #:
Insurance 3:
Street 1:
Street 2:
City:
Phone:
Ins-Start:
End:

Insured 3 Name:
Street 1:
Street 2:
City:
Phone:
D.O.B.:   Sex:
Policy Number:
Group Number:

SUPPLIES

South Padre Medical Center

Patient Face Sheet

4/7/2008

Patient Chart #: KOLHE000　　　　　　　　　D.O.B: 09/22/1930　　　Age: 77
Patient Name: Henry E. Kolper　　　　　　　　Sex: Male
Street 1: 1405 Elm St　　　　　　　　　　　　SSN: 501886391
Street 2:　　　　　　　　　　　　　　　　　Mar Status: Widowed
City: South Padre, TX 98765　　　　　　　　　S.O.F:
Phone: (209)555-6407　　　　　　　　　　　Assigned Provider: Joyce Harkness

Employer Name:
Street 1:
City:
Phone:

Case Information

Case Desc: Open　　　　　　　　　　　　　　Diagnosis 1:
Last Visit:　　　　　　　　　　　　　　　　Diagnosis 2:
Referral:　　　　　　　　　　　　　　　　　Diagnosis 3:
Guarantor Name: Henry E. Kolper　　　　　　　Diagnosis 4:
Street 1: 1405 Elm St
City: South Padre, TX 98765
Phone: (209)555-6407
SSN: 501886391

Ins Co #: MCR　　　　　　　　　　　　　Insured 1 Name:　Henry E. Kolper
Insurance 1: Medicare　　　　　　　　　　　　Street 1:　1405 Elm St
Street 1: 402 Main Street　　　　　　　　　　Street 2:
Street 2:　　　　　　　　　　　　　　　　Phone:　(209)555-6407
City: South Padre, TX 98765　　　　　　　　　D.O.B.:　09/22/1930　　　Sex: Male
Phone:　　　　　　　　　　　　　　Policy Number:　501886391A
Ins-Start:　　　　　　　　　　　　　Group Number:
End:

Ins Co #:　　　　　　　　　　　　　Insured 2 Name:
Insurance 2:　　　　　　　　　　　　　Street 1:
Street 1:　　　　　　　　　　　　　　Street 2:
Street 2:　　　　　　　　　　　　　　City:
City:　　　　　　　　　　　　　　　Phone:
Phone:　　　　　　　　　　　　　　D.O.B.:
Ins-Start:　　　　　　　　　　　　　Policy Number:　　　　　Sex:
End:　　　　　　　　　　　　　　Group Number:

Ins Co #:　　　　　　　　　　　　　Insured 3 Name:
Insurance 3:　　　　　　　　　　　　　Street 1:
Street 1:　　　　　　　　　　　　　　Street 2:
Street 2:　　　　　　　　　　　　　　City:
City:　　　　　　　　　　　　　　　Phone:
Phone:　　　　　　　　　　　　　　D.O.B.:　　　　　　　Sex:
Ins-Start:　　　　　　　　　　　　　Policy Number:
End:　　　　　　　　　　　　　　Group Number:

SUPPLIES

South Padre Medical Center

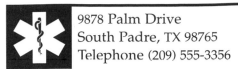

Gerald Bond, MD
Ray Adams, MD
Joyce Harkness, MD
Anthony Clark, MD

9878 Palm Drive
South Padre, TX 98765
Telephone (209) 555-3356

PATIENT INFORMATION

Please Print

Today's Date _____

Last Name _____ First Name _____ Initial _____

Date of Birth _____ Age _____ Sex _____ SS# _____-_____-_____

Home Address   Street _____ City _____

                 State _____ Zip_____ Home Phone (_____)_____

Occupation _____ Employer _____

Employer Address   Street _____ City_____

                 State _____ Zip _____ Work Phone (_____)_____

Are you currently a student?   Yes   No   Name of School _____

Spouse's Name _____ Marital Status   M   S   D   W   SEP

Spouse's SS# _____-_____-_____ Spouse's Employer _____

In case of emergency, notify _____ Relationship_____

                 Home Phone (____) _____ Work Phone (____) _____

If you are a minor: Parent's _____SS# _____-_____-_____

                 Street _____ City _____ State _____ Zip_____

                 Home Phone (____) _____ Work Phone (____) _____

Reason for Visit _____

                 Work related injury?   Yes   No   Date of injury_____

                 Automobile accident?   Yes   No   Date of injury_____

                 Other injury?   Yes   No   Date of injury_____

Insurance (Primary)   Company Name: _____

                 Street _____ City _____ State _____ Zip_____

                 Subscriber's Name _____

                 Relationship to Subscriber: _____

                 Policy #_____ Group #_____

Insurance (Secondary) Company Name: _____

                 Street _____ City _____ State _____ Zip_____

                 Subscriber's Name _____

                 Relationship to Subscriber: _____

                 Policy #_____ Group #_____

Assignment of Benefits:

I directly assign all medical/surgical benefits, including major medical benefits and Medicare, to South Padre Medical Center. I understand that this
authorization for assignment remains in effect until I revoke it in writing. A photocopy of this assignment will be considered as valid as this original assignment.
I further understand that I am responsible for my indebtedness no matter what charges the insurance pays for.

Insured or Guardian's Signature _____ Date _____

SUPPLIES

South Padre Medical Center

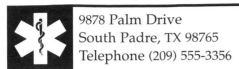

Gerald Bond, MD
Ray Adams, MD
Joyce Harkness, MD
Anthony Clark, MD

9878 Palm Drive
South Padre, TX 98765
Telephone (209) 555-3356

PATIENT INFORMATION

Please Print

Today's Date _____

Last Name _____ First Name _____ Initial _____

Date of Birth _____ Age _____ Sex _____ SS# _____-____-_____

Home Address   Street _____ City _____

State _____ Zip_____ Home Phone (_____)_____

Occupation _____ Employer _____

Employer Address   Street _____ City_____

State _____ Zip _____ Work Phone (_____)_____

Are you currently a student?   Yes   No   Name of School _____

Spouse's Name _____ Marital Status   M   S   D   W   SEP

Spouse's SS# _____-____-_____ Spouse's Employer _____

In case of emergency, notify _____ Relationship_____

    Home Phone (____) _____ Work Phone (____) _____

If you are a minor: Parent's _____ SS# _____-____-_____

    Street _____ City _____ State _____ Zip_____

    Home Phone (____) _____ Work Phone (____) _____

Reason for Visit _____

Work related injury?	Yes	No	Date of injury_____
Automobile accident?	Yes	No	Date of injury_____
Other injury?	Yes	No	Date of injury_____

Insurance (Primary)   Company Name: _____

    Street _____ City _____ State _____ Zip_____

    Subscriber's Name _____

    Relationship to Subscriber: _____

    Policy #_____ Group #_____

Insurance (Secondary)   Company Name: _____

    Street _____ City _____ State _____ Zip_____

    Subscriber's Name _____

    Relationship to Subscriber: _____

    Policy #_____ Group #_____

Assignment of Benefits:

I directly assign all medical/surgical benefits, including major medical benefits and Medicare, to South Padre Medical Center. I understand that this authorization for assignment remains in effect until I revoke it in writing. A photocopy of this assignment will be considered as valid as this original assignment. I further understand that I am responsible for my indebtedness no matter what charges the insurance pays for.

Insured or Guardian's Signature _____ Date _____

SUPPLIES

TASK **3.1**   323

South Padre Medical Center

Patient's Name _____ Age _____ Sex _____ Marital Status   S   M   W   D

Address _____ Insurance _____

Telephone _____ Referred _____

Date	Subsequent Findings

SUPPLIES

TASK **3.1**   325

South Padre Medical Center

Patient's Name _____ Age _____ Sex _____ Marital Status S M W D

Address _____ Insurance _____

Telephone _____ Referred _____

Date	Subsequent Findings

SUPPLIES

TASK **3.1**   327

REFERRAL

FROM: Gerald Bond, MD _____ TO: _____

    Ray Adams, MD _____

    Joyce Harkness, MD _____ TELEPHONE: _____

    Anthony Clark, MD _____ ADDRESS: _____

                   Requested Date and Time: _____

PATIENT: _____ PATIENT'S PHONE NUMBER: _____

ADDRESS: _____

REASON FOR REFERRAL: _____

_____

_____

APPOINTMENT DATE AND TIME: _____

REFERRAL COMPLETED BY: _____ ARRANGEMENTS MADE BY: _____
       (INITIAL AND DATE)   (INITIAL AND DATE)

SUPPLIES

South Padre Medical Center

Patient's Name _____ Age _____ Sex _____ Marital Status S M W D

Address _____ Insurance _____

Telephone _____ Referred _____

Date	Subsequent Findings

SUPPLIES

TASK **3.2**   331

South Padre Medical Center

Patient's Name _____ Age _____ Sex _____ Marital Status   S   M   W   D

Address _____ Insurance _____

Telephone _____ Referred _____

Date	Subsequent Findings

SUPPLIES

1500

HEALTH INSURANCE CLAIM FORM

APPROVED BY NATIONAL UNIFORM CLAIM COMMITTEE 08/05

PICA | | |

| 1. MEDICARE | MEDICAID | TRICARE CHAMPUS | CHAMPVA | GROUP HEALTH PLAN | FECA BLK LUNG | OTHER | 1a. INSURED'S I.D. NUMBER | (For Program in Item 1) |

☐ (Medicare #) ☐ (Medicaid #) ☐ (Sponsor's SSN) ☐ (Member ID#) ☐ (SSN or ID) ☐ (SSN) ☐ (ID)

| 2. PATIENT'S NAME (Last Name, First Name, Middle Initial) | 3. PATIENT'S BIRTH DATE MM DD YY / SEX M☐ F☐ | 4. INSURED'S NAME (Last Name, First Name, Middle Initial) |

| 5. PATIENT'S ADDRESS (No., Street) | 6. PATIENT RELATIONSHIP TO INSURED Self☐ Spouse☐ Child☐ Other☐ | 7. INSURED'S ADDRESS (No., Street) |

| CITY | STATE | 8. PATIENT STATUS Single☐ Married☐ Other☐ | CITY | STATE |

| ZIP CODE | TELEPHONE (Include Area Code) ( ) | Employed☐ Full-Time Student☐ Part-Time Student☐ | ZIP CODE | TELEPHONE (Include Area Code) ( ) |

| 9. OTHER INSURED'S NAME (Last Name, First Name, Middle Initial) | 10. IS PATIENT'S CONDITION RELATED TO: | 11. INSURED'S POLICY GROUP OR FECA NUMBER |

| a. OTHER INSURED'S POLICY OR GROUP NUMBER | a. EMPLOYMENT? (Current or Previous) YES☐ NO☐ | a. INSURED'S DATE OF BIRTH MM DD YY / SEX M☐ F☐ |

| b. OTHER INSURED'S DATE OF BIRTH MM DD YY / SEX M☐ F☐ | b. AUTO ACCIDENT? PLACE (State) YES☐ NO☐ | b. EMPLOYER'S NAME OR SCHOOL NAME |

| c. EMPLOYER'S NAME OR SCHOOL NAME | c. OTHER ACCIDENT? YES☐ NO☐ | c. INSURANCE PLAN NAME OR PROGRAM NAME |

| d. INSURANCE PLAN NAME OR PROGRAM NAME | 10d. RESERVED FOR LOCAL USE | d. IS THERE ANOTHER HEALTH BENEFIT PLAN? YES☐ NO☐ If yes, return to and complete item 9 a-d. |

READ BACK OF FORM BEFORE COMPLETING & SIGNING THIS FORM.

12. PATIENT'S OR AUTHORIZED PERSON'S SIGNATURE I authorize the release of any medical or other information necessary to process this claim. I also request payment of government benefits either to myself or to the party who accepts assignment below.

SIGNED _____ DATE _____

13. INSURED'S OR AUTHORIZED PERSON'S SIGNATURE I authorize payment of medical benefits to the undersigned physician or supplier for services described below.

SIGNED _____

| 14. DATE OF CURRENT: MM DD YY ◄ ILLNESS (First symptom) OR INJURY (Accident) OR PREGNANCY(LMP) | 15. IF PATIENT HAS HAD SAME OR SIMILAR ILLNESS. GIVE FIRST DATE MM DD YY | 16. DATES PATIENT UNABLE TO WORK IN CURRENT OCCUPATION MM DD YY MM DD YY FROM TO |

| 17. NAME OF REFERRING PROVIDER OR OTHER SOURCE | 17a. | 18. HOSPITALIZATION DATES RELATED TO CURRENT SERVICES MM DD YY MM DD YY FROM TO |
| | 17b. NPI | |

| 19. RESERVED FOR LOCAL USE | | 20. OUTSIDE LAB? $ CHARGES YES☐ NO☐ |

21. DIAGNOSIS OR NATURE OF ILLNESS OR INJURY (Relate Items 1, 2, 3 or 4 to Item 24E by Line) ↓	22. MEDICAID RESUBMISSION CODE ORIGINAL REF. NO.
1. └___.___ 3. └___.___	
2. └___.___ 4. └___.___	23. PRIOR AUTHORIZATION NUMBER

24. A. DATE(S) OF SERVICE						B. PLACE OF SERVICE	C. EMG	D. PROCEDURES, SERVICES, OR SUPPLIES (Explain Unusual Circumstances)		E. DIAGNOSIS POINTER	F. $ CHARGES	G. DAYS OR UNITS	H. EPSDT Family Plan	I. ID. QUAL.	J. RENDERING PROVIDER ID. #
From			To					CPT/HCPCS	MODIFIER						
MM	DD	YY	MM	DD	YY										
1														NPI	
2														NPI	
3														NPI	
4														NPI	
5														NPI	
6														NPI	

| 25. FEDERAL TAX I.D. NUMBER SSN☐ EIN☐ | 26. PATIENT'S ACCOUNT NO. | 27. ACCEPT ASSIGNMENT? (For govt. claims, see back) YES☐ NO☐ | 28. TOTAL CHARGE $ | 29. AMOUNT PAID $ | 30. BALANCE DUE $ |

| 31. SIGNATURE OF PHYSICIAN OR SUPPLIER INCLUDING DEGREES OR CREDENTIALS (I certify that the statements on the reverse apply to this bill and are made a part thereof.) SIGNED ____ DATE ____ | 32. SERVICE FACILITY LOCATION INFORMATION a. | b. | 33. BILLING PROVIDER INFO & PH # ( ) a. | b. |

NUCC Instruction Manual available at: www.nucc.org

OMB APPROVAL PENDING

CARRIER

PATIENT AND INSURED INFORMATION

PHYSICIAN OR SUPPLIER INFORMATION

SUPPLIES

HEALTH INSURANCE CLAIM FORM

APPROVED BY NATIONAL UNIFORM CLAIM COMMITTEE 08/05

PICA ☐☐☐ ... PICA ☐☐☐

1. ☐ MEDICARE *(Medicare #)* ☐ MEDICAID *(Medicaid #)* ☐ TRICARE CHAMPUS *(Sponsor's SSN)* ☐ CHAMPVA *(Member ID#)* ☐ GROUP HEALTH PLAN *(SSN or ID)* ☐ FECA BLK LUNG *(SSN)* ☐ OTHER *(ID)* | 1a. INSURED'S I.D. NUMBER   *(For Program in Item 1)*

2. PATIENT'S NAME (Last Name, First Name, Middle Initial)

3. PATIENT'S BIRTH DATE MM ｜ DD ｜ YY   SEX M ☐ F ☐

4. INSURED'S NAME (Last Name, First Name, Middle Initial)

5. PATIENT'S ADDRESS (No., Street)

6. PATIENT RELATIONSHIP TO INSURED Self ☐ Spouse ☐ Child ☐ Other ☐

7. INSURED'S ADDRESS (No., Street)

CITY   STATE

8. PATIENT STATUS Single ☐ Married ☐ Other ☐

CITY   STATE

ZIP CODE   TELEPHONE (Include Area Code) ( )

Employed ☐ Full-Time Student ☐ Part-Time Student ☐

ZIP CODE   TELEPHONE (Include Area Code) ( )

9. OTHER INSURED'S NAME (Last Name, First Name, Middle Initial)

10. IS PATIENT'S CONDITION RELATED TO:

11. INSURED'S POLICY GROUP OR FECA NUMBER

a. OTHER INSURED'S POLICY OR GROUP NUMBER

a. EMPLOYMENT? (Current or Previous) ☐ YES ☐ NO

a. INSURED'S DATE OF BIRTH MM ｜ DD ｜ YY   SEX M ☐ F ☐

b. OTHER INSURED'S DATE OF BIRTH MM ｜ DD ｜ YY   SEX M ☐ F ☐

b. AUTO ACCIDENT?   PLACE (State) ☐ YES ☐ NO

b. EMPLOYER'S NAME OR SCHOOL NAME

c. EMPLOYER'S NAME OR SCHOOL NAME

c. OTHER ACCIDENT? ☐ YES ☐ NO

c. INSURANCE PLAN NAME OR PROGRAM NAME

d. INSURANCE PLAN NAME OR PROGRAM NAME

10d. RESERVED FOR LOCAL USE

d. IS THERE ANOTHER HEALTH BENEFIT PLAN? ☐ YES ☐ NO *If yes*, return to and complete item 9 a-d.

READ BACK OF FORM BEFORE COMPLETING & SIGNING THIS FORM.

12. PATIENT'S OR AUTHORIZED PERSON'S SIGNATURE I authorize the release of any medical or other information necessary to process this claim. I also request payment of government benefits either to myself or to the party who accepts assignment below.

SIGNED _____ DATE _____

13. INSURED'S OR AUTHORIZED PERSON'S SIGNATURE I authorize payment of medical benefits to the undersigned physician or supplier for services described below.

SIGNED _____

14. DATE OF CURRENT: MM ｜ DD ｜ YY ◄ ILLNESS (First symptom) OR INJURY (Accident) OR PREGNANCY(LMP)

15. IF PATIENT HAS HAD SAME OR SIMILAR ILLNESS. GIVE FIRST DATE MM ｜ DD ｜ YY

16. DATES PATIENT UNABLE TO WORK IN CURRENT OCCUPATION FROM MM ｜ DD ｜ YY TO MM ｜ DD ｜ YY

17. NAME OF REFERRING PROVIDER OR OTHER SOURCE

17a.
17b. NPI

18. HOSPITALIZATION DATES RELATED TO CURRENT SERVICES FROM MM ｜ DD ｜ YY TO MM ｜ DD ｜ YY

19. RESERVED FOR LOCAL USE

20. OUTSIDE LAB? ☐ YES ☐ NO $ CHARGES

21. DIAGNOSIS OR NATURE OF ILLNESS OR INJURY (Relate Items 1, 2, 3 or 4 to Item 24E by Line)

1. L___ . ___   3. L___ . ___

2. L___ . ___   4. L___ . ___

22. MEDICAID RESUBMISSION CODE   ORIGINAL REF. NO.

23. PRIOR AUTHORIZATION NUMBER

24. A. DATE(S) OF SERVICE						B. PLACE OF SERVICE	C. EMG	D. PROCEDURES, SERVICES, OR SUPPLIES (Explain Unusual Circumstances)		E. DIAGNOSIS POINTER	F. $ CHARGES	G. DAYS OR UNITS	H. EPSDT Family Plan	I. ID. QUAL.	J. RENDERING PROVIDER ID. #
From			To					CPT/HCPCS	MODIFIER						
MM	DD	YY	MM	DD	YY										
1														NPI	
2														NPI	
3														NPI	
4														NPI	
5														NPI	
6														NPI	

25. FEDERAL TAX I.D. NUMBER ☐ SSN ☐ EIN

26. PATIENT'S ACCOUNT NO.

27. ACCEPT ASSIGNMENT? (For govt. claims, see back) ☐ YES ☐ NO

28. TOTAL CHARGE $

29. AMOUNT PAID $

30. BALANCE DUE $

31. SIGNATURE OF PHYSICIAN OR SUPPLIER INCLUDING DEGREES OR CREDENTIALS (I certify that the statements on the reverse apply to this bill and are made a part thereof.)

SIGNED _____ DATE _____

32. SERVICE FACILITY LOCATION INFORMATION

a.   b.

33. BILLING PROVIDER INFO & PH # ( )

a.   b.

NUCC Instruction Manual available at: www.nucc.org

OMB APPROVAL PENDING

SUPPLIES

HEALTH INSURANCE CLAIM FORM

APPROVED BY NATIONAL UNIFORM CLAIM COMMITTEE 08/05

| | PICA | | | | | | | PICA | |

1. MEDICARE ☐ (Medicare #)   MEDICAID ☐ (Medicaid #)   TRICARE CHAMPUS ☐ (Sponsor's SSN)   CHAMPVA ☐ (Member ID#)   GROUP HEALTH PLAN ☐ (SSN or ID)   FECA BLK LUNG ☐ (SSN)   OTHER ☐ (ID)   **1a. INSURED'S I.D. NUMBER** (For Program in Item 1)

2. PATIENT'S NAME (Last Name, First Name, Middle Initial)

3. PATIENT'S BIRTH DATE MM   DD   YY   **SEX** M ☐ F ☐

4. INSURED'S NAME (Last Name, First Name, Middle Initial)

5. PATIENT'S ADDRESS (No., Street)

6. PATIENT RELATIONSHIP TO INSURED   Self ☐   Spouse ☐   Child ☐   Other ☐

7. INSURED'S ADDRESS (No., Street)

CITY   STATE

8. PATIENT STATUS   Single ☐   Married ☐   Other ☐

CITY   STATE

ZIP CODE   TELEPHONE (Include Area Code) ( )

Employed ☐   Full-Time Student ☐   Part-Time Student ☐

ZIP CODE   TELEPHONE (Include Area Code) ( )

9. OTHER INSURED'S NAME (Last Name, First Name, Middle Initial)

10. IS PATIENT'S CONDITION RELATED TO:

11. INSURED'S POLICY GROUP OR FECA NUMBER

a. OTHER INSURED'S POLICY OR GROUP NUMBER

a. EMPLOYMENT? (Current or Previous)   YES ☐   NO ☐

a. INSURED'S DATE OF BIRTH MM   DD   YY   **SEX** M ☐ F ☐

b. OTHER INSURED'S DATE OF BIRTH MM   DD   YY   **SEX** M ☐ F ☐

b. AUTO ACCIDENT?   PLACE (State)   YES ☐   NO ☐

b. EMPLOYER'S NAME OR SCHOOL NAME

c. EMPLOYER'S NAME OR SCHOOL NAME

c. OTHER ACCIDENT?   YES ☐   NO ☐

c. INSURANCE PLAN NAME OR PROGRAM NAME

d. INSURANCE PLAN NAME OR PROGRAM NAME

10d. RESERVED FOR LOCAL USE

d. IS THERE ANOTHER HEALTH BENEFIT PLAN?   YES ☐   NO ☐   **If yes,** return to and complete item 9 a-d.

READ BACK OF FORM BEFORE COMPLETING & SIGNING THIS FORM.
12. PATIENT'S OR AUTHORIZED PERSON'S SIGNATURE I authorize the release of any medical or other information necessary to process this claim. I also request payment of government benefits either to myself or to the party who accepts assignment below.

SIGNED _____ DATE _____

13. INSURED'S OR AUTHORIZED PERSON'S SIGNATURE I authorize payment of medical benefits to the undersigned physician or supplier for services described below.

SIGNED _____

14. DATE OF CURRENT: MM DD YY ILLNESS (First symptom) OR INJURY (Accident) OR PREGNANCY(LMP)

15. IF PATIENT HAS HAD SAME OR SIMILAR ILLNESS. GIVE FIRST DATE MM DD YY

16. DATES PATIENT UNABLE TO WORK IN CURRENT OCCUPATION MM DD YY FROM   TO MM DD YY

17. NAME OF REFERRING PROVIDER OR OTHER SOURCE

17a.
17b. NPI

18. HOSPITALIZATION DATES RELATED TO CURRENT SERVICES MM DD YY FROM   TO MM DD YY

19. RESERVED FOR LOCAL USE

20. OUTSIDE LAB?   YES ☐   NO ☐ $ CHARGES

21. DIAGNOSIS OR NATURE OF ILLNESS OR INJURY (Relate Items 1, 2, 3 or 4 to Item 24E by Line)

1. |___.___
2. |___.___
3. |___.___
4. |___.___

22. MEDICAID RESUBMISSION CODE   ORIGINAL REF. NO.

23. PRIOR AUTHORIZATION NUMBER

24. A. DATE(S) OF SERVICE						B. PLACE OF SERVICE	C. EMG	D. PROCEDURES, SERVICES, OR SUPPLIES (Explain Unusual Circumstances)		E. DIAGNOSIS POINTER	F. $ CHARGES	G. DAYS OR UNITS	H. EPSDT Family Plan	I. ID. QUAL.	J. RENDERING PROVIDER ID. #
From			To					CPT/HCPCS	MODIFIER						
MM	DD	YY	MM	DD	YY										
1														NPI	
2														NPI	
3														NPI	
4														NPI	
5														NPI	
6														NPI	

25. FEDERAL TAX I.D. NUMBER   SSN ☐ EIN ☐

26. PATIENT'S ACCOUNT NO.

27. ACCEPT ASSIGNMENT? (For govt. claims, see back)   YES ☐   NO ☐

28. TOTAL CHARGE $

29. AMOUNT PAID $

30. BALANCE DUE $

31. SIGNATURE OF PHYSICIAN OR SUPPLIER INCLUDING DEGREES OR CREDENTIALS (I certify that the statements on the reverse apply to this bill and are made a part thereof.)

SIGNED _____ DATE _____

32. SERVICE FACILITY LOCATION INFORMATION

a.   b.

33. BILLING PROVIDER INFO & PH # ( )

a.   b.

NUCC Instruction Manual available at: www.nucc.org   OMB APPROVAL PENDING

HEALTH INSURANCE CLAIM FORM

APPROVED BY NATIONAL UNIFORM CLAIM COMMITTEE 08/05

| | PICA | | | | | | | | PICA | | |

1. MEDICARE ☐ (Medicare #) MEDICAID ☐ (Medicaid #) TRICARE CHAMPUS ☐ (Sponsor's SSN) CHAMPVA ☐ (Member ID#) GROUP HEALTH PLAN ☐ (SSN or ID) FECA BLK LUNG ☐ (SSN) OTHER ☐ (ID)   1a. INSURED'S I.D. NUMBER   (For Program in Item 1)

2. PATIENT'S NAME (Last Name, First Name, Middle Initial)

3. PATIENT'S BIRTH DATE MM | DD | YY   SEX M ☐ F ☐

4. INSURED'S NAME (Last Name, First Name, Middle Initial)

5. PATIENT'S ADDRESS (No., Street)

6. PATIENT RELATIONSHIP TO INSURED   Self ☐ Spouse ☐ Child ☐ Other ☐

7. INSURED'S ADDRESS (No., Street)

CITY   STATE

8. PATIENT STATUS   Single ☐ Married ☐ Other ☐

CITY   STATE

ZIP CODE   TELEPHONE (Include Area Code) (   )

Employed ☐ Full-Time Student ☐ Part-Time Student ☐

ZIP CODE   TELEPHONE (Include Area Code) (   )

9. OTHER INSURED'S NAME (Last Name, First Name, Middle Initial)

10. IS PATIENT'S CONDITION RELATED TO:

11. INSURED'S POLICY GROUP OR FECA NUMBER

a. OTHER INSURED'S POLICY OR GROUP NUMBER

a. EMPLOYMENT? (Current or Previous)   ☐ YES ☐ NO

a. INSURED'S DATE OF BIRTH MM | DD | YY   SEX M ☐ F ☐

b. OTHER INSURED'S DATE OF BIRTH MM | DD | YY   SEX M ☐ F ☐

b. AUTO ACCIDENT?   PLACE (State)   ☐ YES ☐ NO

b. EMPLOYER'S NAME OR SCHOOL NAME

c. EMPLOYER'S NAME OR SCHOOL NAME

c. OTHER ACCIDENT?   ☐ YES ☐ NO

c. INSURANCE PLAN NAME OR PROGRAM NAME

d. INSURANCE PLAN NAME OR PROGRAM NAME

10d. RESERVED FOR LOCAL USE

d. IS THERE ANOTHER HEALTH BENEFIT PLAN?   ☐ YES ☐ NO   If yes, return to and complete item 9 a-d.

READ BACK OF FORM BEFORE COMPLETING & SIGNING THIS FORM.

12. PATIENT'S OR AUTHORIZED PERSON'S SIGNATURE I authorize the release of any medical or other information necessary to process this claim. I also request payment of government benefits either to myself or to the party who accepts assignment below.

SIGNED _____ DATE _____

13. INSURED'S OR AUTHORIZED PERSON'S SIGNATURE I authorize payment of medical benefits to the undersigned physician or supplier for services described below.

SIGNED _____

14. DATE OF CURRENT: MM | DD | YY   ILLNESS (First symptom) OR INJURY (Accident) OR PREGNANCY(LMP)

15. IF PATIENT HAS HAD SAME OR SIMILAR ILLNESS. GIVE FIRST DATE MM | DD | YY

16. DATES PATIENT UNABLE TO WORK IN CURRENT OCCUPATION FROM MM | DD | YY TO MM | DD | YY

17. NAME OF REFERRING PROVIDER OR OTHER SOURCE

17a.
17b. NPI

18. HOSPITALIZATION DATES RELATED TO CURRENT SERVICES FROM MM | DD | YY TO MM | DD | YY

19. RESERVED FOR LOCAL USE

20. OUTSIDE LAB?   ☐ YES ☐ NO $ CHARGES

21. DIAGNOSIS OR NATURE OF ILLNESS OR INJURY (Relate Items 1, 2, 3 or 4 to Item 24E by Line)

1. ⌊___ . ___⌋   3. ⌊___ . ___⌋

2. ⌊___ . ___⌋   4. ⌊___ . ___⌋

22. MEDICAID RESUBMISSION CODE   ORIGINAL REF. NO.

23. PRIOR AUTHORIZATION NUMBER

24. A. DATE(S) OF SERVICE						B. PLACE OF SERVICE	C. EMG	D. PROCEDURES, SERVICES, OR SUPPLIES (Explain Unusual Circumstances)		E. DIAGNOSIS POINTER	F. $ CHARGES	G. DAYS OR UNITS	H. EPSDT Family Plan	I. ID. QUAL.	J. RENDERING PROVIDER ID. #
From MM	DD	YY	To MM	DD	YY			CPT/HCPCS	MODIFIER						
1														NPI	
2														NPI	
3														NPI	
4														NPI	
5														NPI	
6														NPI	

25. FEDERAL TAX I.D. NUMBER   SSN ☐ EIN ☐

26. PATIENT'S ACCOUNT NO.

27. ACCEPT ASSIGNMENT? (For govt. claims, see back) ☐ YES ☐ NO

28. TOTAL CHARGE $

29. AMOUNT PAID $

30. BALANCE DUE $

31. SIGNATURE OF PHYSICIAN OR SUPPLIER INCLUDING DEGREES OR CREDENTIALS (I certify that the statements on the reverse apply to this bill and are made a part thereof.)

SIGNED _____ DATE _____

32. SERVICE FACILITY LOCATION INFORMATION

a.   b.

33. BILLING PROVIDER INFO & PH # (   )

a.   b.

OMB APPROVAL PENDING

1500

HEALTH INSURANCE CLAIM FORM

APPROVED BY NATIONAL UNIFORM CLAIM COMMITTEE 08/05

□□ PICA   PICA □□

1. MEDICARE	MEDICAID	TRICARE CHAMPUS	CHAMPVA	GROUP HEALTH PLAN	FECA BLK LUNG	OTHER	1a. INSURED'S I.D. NUMBER	(For Program in Item 1)
(Medicare #)	(Medicaid #)	(Sponsor's SSN)	(Member ID#)	(SSN or ID)	(SSN)	(ID)		

2. PATIENT'S NAME (Last Name, First Name, Middle Initial)

3. PATIENT'S BIRTH DATE MM | DD | YY   SEX M □ F □

4. INSURED'S NAME (Last Name, First Name, Middle Initial)

5. PATIENT'S ADDRESS (No., Street)

6. PATIENT RELATIONSHIP TO INSURED Self □ Spouse □ Child □ Other □

7. INSURED'S ADDRESS (No., Street)

CITY   STATE

8. PATIENT STATUS Single □ Married □ Other □

Employed □ Full-Time Student □ Part-Time Student □

CITY   STATE

ZIP CODE   TELEPHONE (Include Area Code) (   )

ZIP CODE   TELEPHONE (Include Area Code) (   )

9. OTHER INSURED'S NAME (Last Name, First Name, Middle Initial)

10. IS PATIENT'S CONDITION RELATED TO:

11. INSURED'S POLICY GROUP OR FECA NUMBER

a. OTHER INSURED'S POLICY OR GROUP NUMBER

a. EMPLOYMENT? (Current or Previous) YES □ NO □

a. INSURED'S DATE OF BIRTH MM | DD | YY   SEX M □ F □

b. OTHER INSURED'S DATE OF BIRTH MM | DD | YY   SEX M □ F □

b. AUTO ACCIDENT?   PLACE (State) YES □ NO □

b. EMPLOYER'S NAME OR SCHOOL NAME

c. EMPLOYER'S NAME OR SCHOOL NAME

c. OTHER ACCIDENT? YES □ NO □

c. INSURANCE PLAN NAME OR PROGRAM NAME

d. INSURANCE PLAN NAME OR PROGRAM NAME

10d. RESERVED FOR LOCAL USE

d. IS THERE ANOTHER HEALTH BENEFIT PLAN? YES □ NO □ If yes, return to and complete item 9 a-d.

READ BACK OF FORM BEFORE COMPLETING & SIGNING THIS FORM.
12. PATIENT'S OR AUTHORIZED PERSON'S SIGNATURE I authorize the release of any medical or other information necessary to process this claim. I also request payment of government benefits either to myself or to the party who accepts assignment below.

SIGNED _____ DATE _____

13. INSURED'S OR AUTHORIZED PERSON'S SIGNATURE I authorize payment of medical benefits to the undersigned physician or supplier for services described below.

SIGNED _____

14. DATE OF CURRENT: MM | DD | YY ◄ ILLNESS (First symptom) OR INJURY (Accident) OR PREGNANCY(LMP)

15. IF PATIENT HAS HAD SAME OR SIMILAR ILLNESS. GIVE FIRST DATE MM | DD | YY

16. DATES PATIENT UNABLE TO WORK IN CURRENT OCCUPATION MM | DD | YY FROM   TO MM | DD | YY

17. NAME OF REFERRING PROVIDER OR OTHER SOURCE

17a. |
17b. | NPI

18. HOSPITALIZATION DATES RELATED TO CURRENT SERVICES MM | DD | YY FROM   TO MM | DD | YY

19. RESERVED FOR LOCAL USE

20. OUTSIDE LAB? YES □ NO □ $ CHARGES

21. DIAGNOSIS OR NATURE OF ILLNESS OR INJURY (Relate Items 1, 2, 3 or 4 to Item 24E by Line)

1. |___.___| 3. |___.___|

2. |___.___| 4. |___.___|

22. MEDICAID RESUBMISSION CODE   ORIGINAL REF. NO.

23. PRIOR AUTHORIZATION NUMBER

24. A. DATE(S) OF SERVICE						B. PLACE OF SERVICE	C. EMG	D. PROCEDURES, SERVICES, OR SUPPLIES (Explain Unusual Circumstances)		E. DIAGNOSIS POINTER	F. $ CHARGES	G. DAYS OR UNITS	H. EPSDT Family Plan	I. ID. QUAL.	J. RENDERING PROVIDER ID. #
From MM	DD	YY	To MM	DD	YY			CPT/HCPCS	MODIFIER						
1														NPI	
2														NPI	
3														NPI	
4														NPI	
5														NPI	
6														NPI	

25. FEDERAL TAX I.D. NUMBER   SSN □ EIN □

26. PATIENT'S ACCOUNT NO.

27. ACCEPT ASSIGNMENT? (For govt. claims, see back) YES □ NO □

28. TOTAL CHARGE $

29. AMOUNT PAID $

30. BALANCE DUE $

31. SIGNATURE OF PHYSICIAN OR SUPPLIER INCLUDING DEGREES OR CREDENTIALS (I certify that the statements on the reverse apply to this bill and are made a part thereof.)

SIGNED _____ DATE _____

32. SERVICE FACILITY LOCATION INFORMATION

a.   b.

33. BILLING PROVIDER INFO & PH # (   )

a.   b.

SUPPLIES

HEALTH INSURANCE CLAIM FORM

APPROVED BY NATIONAL UNIFORM CLAIM COMMITTEE 08/05

| | PICA | | | | | | | | PICA | | |

1. MEDICARE	MEDICAID	TRICARE CHAMPUS	CHAMPVA	GROUP HEALTH PLAN	FECA BLK LUNG	OTHER	1a. INSURED'S I.D. NUMBER	(For Program in Item 1)
(Medicare #)	(Medicaid #)	(Sponsor's SSN)	(Member ID#)	(SSN or ID)	(SSN)	(ID)		

2. PATIENT'S NAME (Last Name, First Name, Middle Initial)

3. PATIENT'S BIRTH DATE MM DD YY   SEX   M ☐   F ☐

4. INSURED'S NAME (Last Name, First Name, Middle Initial)

5. PATIENT'S ADDRESS (No., Street)

6. PATIENT RELATIONSHIP TO INSURED
Self ☐   Spouse ☐   Child ☐   Other ☐

7. INSURED'S ADDRESS (No., Street)

CITY   STATE

8. PATIENT STATUS
Single ☐   Married ☐   Other ☐
Employed ☐   Full-Time Student ☐   Part-Time Student ☐

CITY   STATE

ZIP CODE   TELEPHONE (Include Area Code) (   )

ZIP CODE   TELEPHONE (Include Area Code) (   )

9. OTHER INSURED'S NAME (Last Name, First Name, Middle Initial)

10. IS PATIENT'S CONDITION RELATED TO:

11. INSURED'S POLICY GROUP OR FECA NUMBER

a. OTHER INSURED'S POLICY OR GROUP NUMBER

a. EMPLOYMENT? (Current or Previous)
☐ YES   ☐ NO

a. INSURED'S DATE OF BIRTH MM DD YY   SEX   M ☐   F ☐

b. OTHER INSURED'S DATE OF BIRTH MM DD YY   SEX   M ☐   F ☐

b. AUTO ACCIDENT?   PLACE (State)
☐ YES   ☐ NO

b. EMPLOYER'S NAME OR SCHOOL NAME

c. EMPLOYER'S NAME OR SCHOOL NAME

c. OTHER ACCIDENT?
☐ YES   ☐ NO

c. INSURANCE PLAN NAME OR PROGRAM NAME

d. INSURANCE PLAN NAME OR PROGRAM NAME

10d. RESERVED FOR LOCAL USE

d. IS THERE ANOTHER HEALTH BENEFIT PLAN?
☐ YES   ☐ NO   If yes, return to and complete item 9 a-d.

READ BACK OF FORM BEFORE COMPLETING & SIGNING THIS FORM.
12. PATIENT'S OR AUTHORIZED PERSON'S SIGNATURE I authorize the release of any medical or other information necessary to process this claim. I also request payment of government benefits either to myself or to the party who accepts assignment below.

SIGNED _____   DATE _____

13. INSURED'S OR AUTHORIZED PERSON'S SIGNATURE I authorize payment of medical benefits to the undersigned physician or supplier for services described below.

SIGNED _____

14. DATE OF CURRENT: MM DD YY   ILLNESS (First symptom) OR INJURY (Accident) OR PREGNANCY(LMP)

15. IF PATIENT HAS HAD SAME OR SIMILAR ILLNESS. GIVE FIRST DATE MM DD YY

16. DATES PATIENT UNABLE TO WORK IN CURRENT OCCUPATION
FROM MM DD YY   TO MM DD YY

17. NAME OF REFERRING PROVIDER OR OTHER SOURCE

17a.
17b. NPI

18. HOSPITALIZATION DATES RELATED TO CURRENT SERVICES
FROM MM DD YY   TO MM DD YY

19. RESERVED FOR LOCAL USE

20. OUTSIDE LAB? $ CHARGES
☐ YES   ☐ NO

21. DIAGNOSIS OR NATURE OF ILLNESS OR INJURY (Relate Items 1, 2, 3 or 4 to Item 24E by Line)

1. L___ . ___   3. L___ . ___

2. L___ . ___   4. L___ . ___

22. MEDICAID RESUBMISSION CODE   ORIGINAL REF. NO.

23. PRIOR AUTHORIZATION NUMBER

24. A. DATE(S) OF SERVICE						B. PLACE OF SERVICE	C. EMG	D. PROCEDURES, SERVICES, OR SUPPLIES (Explain Unusual Circumstances) CPT/HCPCS	MODIFIER	E. DIAGNOSIS POINTER	F. $ CHARGES	G. DAYS OR UNITS	H. EPSDT Family Plan	I. ID. QUAL.	J. RENDERING PROVIDER ID. #
From MM DD YY			To MM DD YY												
1														NPI	
2														NPI	
3														NPI	
4														NPI	
5														NPI	
6														NPI	

25. FEDERAL TAX I.D. NUMBER   SSN ☐ EIN ☐

26. PATIENT'S ACCOUNT NO.

27. ACCEPT ASSIGNMENT? (For govt. claims, see back)
☐ YES   ☐ NO

28. TOTAL CHARGE $

29. AMOUNT PAID $

30. BALANCE DUE $

31. SIGNATURE OF PHYSICIAN OR SUPPLIER INCLUDING DEGREES OR CREDENTIALS (I certify that the statements on the reverse apply to this bill and are made a part thereof.)

SIGNED _____   DATE _____

32. SERVICE FACILITY LOCATION INFORMATION

a.   b.

33. BILLING PROVIDER INFO & PH # (   )

a.   b.

NUCC Instruction Manual available at: www.nucc.org

OMB APPROVAL PENDING

South Padre Medical Center

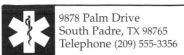

9878 Palm Drive
South Padre, TX 98765
Telephone (209) 555-3356

Gerald Bond, MD
Ray Adams, MD
Joyce Harkness, MD
Anthony Clark, MD

PATIENT'S LAST NAME	FIRST	ACCOUNT #	BIRTHDATE	SEX	TODAY'S DATE
Rock	Lewis L		03/06/1931	☒ MALE ☐ FEMALE	04/08/2008

INSURANCE COMPANY	SUBSCRIBER	GROUP/PLAN #	SUB. #	TIME
Medicare	Same		201489201A	10:15AM

ASSIGNMENT: I hereby assign my insurance benefits to be paid directly to the undersigned physician. I am financially responsible for non-covered services.
SIGNED: (Patient, Or parent, if Minor) Lewis Rock   DATE: 04/08/2008

RELEASE: I hereby authorize the physician to release to my insurance carriers any information required to process this claim.
SIGNED: (Patient, Or Parent, if Minor) Lewis Rock   DATE: 04/08/2008

✓	DESCRIPTION	CPT	Diag.	FEE	✓	DESCRIPTION	CPT	Diag.	FEE	✓	DESCRIPTION	CPT	Diag.	FEE
	OFFICE VISIT					**IMMUNIZATIONS/INJECTIONS**					**PROCEDURES**			
	NEW PATIENT					Admin of Vaccine 1	90471				Inhalation treatment	94640		
	Problem Focused					Admin of Vac 2+	90472				Demo/eval treatment	94664		
	Exp Problem Focused	99202				TB Tine, skin	86486				Vital Capacity	94150		
	Detailed	99203				Pneumococcal	90732				Spirometry	94010		
✓	Comp/ Mod MDM	99204	1	105.00		Medicare code	G0009				EKG w/Interpretation	93000		
	Comp/ High MDM	99205				Influenza <3	90657				I&D abscess	10060		
	ESTABLISHED PATEINT					Influenza 3 and >	90658				Remove skin tag <15	11200		
	Minimal/Nurse Visit	99211				Medicare code	G0008				**EXCISION BENIGN LESIONS (inc. margins)**			
	Problem Focused	99212				Varicella	90716				Trunk, arms, legs			
	Exp Problem Forcused	99213				DPT	90701				0.5 cm or less	11400		
	Detailed	99214				DT children	90702				0.6 to 1.0 cm	11401		
	Comprehensive	99215				Td adult	90718				1.1 to 2.0 cm	11402		
	CONSULTATION					DtaP	90700				2.1 to 3.0 cm	11403		
	Problem Focused	99241				IPV	90713				Scalp, neck, hand, ft			
	Exp Problem Focused	99242				Rubella	90706				0.5 cm or less	11420		
	Detailed	99243				MMR	90707				0.6 to 1.0 cm	11421		
	Comp/ Mod MDM	99244				Hep B Child	90744				1.1 to 2.0 cm	11422		
	Comp/High MDM	99245				Hep B Adult	90746				2.1 to 3.0 cm	11423		
	Requesting Provider _____					IM Administration	96372				Face, ears, eyelids, lip			
						Compazine	J0780				0.5 cm or less	11440		
	Post-op Exam	99024		0.00		Demerol	J2175				0.6 to 1.0 cm	11441		
	PREVENTIVE MEDICINE					Depo-Provera	J1055				1.1 to 2.0 cm	11442		
	NEW PATIENT					Dexamethasone	J1100				2.1 to 3.0 cm	11443		
	Infant – 1 yr	99381				Solumedrol	J1720				**EXCISION MALIGNANT LESIONS (inc. margins)**			
	1 yr – 4 yr	99382				Antigen admin 1	95115				Trunk, arms, legs			
	5 yr – 11 yr	99383				Antigen admin 2+	95117				0.5 cm or less	11600		
	12 yr – 17 yr	99384				**LABORATORY**					0.6 to 1.0 cm	11601		
	18 yr – 39 yr	99385				Blood collect Vein	36415				1.1 to 2.0 cm	11602		
	40 yr – 64 yr	99386				Capillary	36416				2.1 to 3.0 cm	11603		
	65 yr and over	99387				Hemoglobin	85018				Scalp, neck, hand, ft			
	ESTABLISHED PATIENT					Glucose, reagent	82948				0.5 cm or less	11620		
	Infant – 1 yr	99391				Pregnancy, Serum	84702				0.6 to 1.0 cm	11621		
	1 yr – 4 yr	99392				Pregnancy, Urine	81025				1.1 to 2.0 cm	11622		
	5 yr – 11 yr	99393				Health panel	80050				2.1 to 3.0 cm	11623		
	12 yr – 17 yr	99394				B Met Pan Cal ion	80047				Face, ears, eyelids, lip			
	18 yr – 39 yr	99395				B Met Pan Cal tot	80048				0.5 cm or less	11640		
	40 yr – 64 yr	99396				C Metabolic panel	80053				0.6 to 1.0 cm	11641		
	65 yr and over	99397				Ob panel	80055				1.1 to 2.0 cm	11642		
	SUPPLIES					Lipid panel	80061				2.1 to 3.0 cm	11643		
	Take home burn kit	99070				UA Auto w/o micro	81003				*Awaiting path report*	☐ *Yes*		☐ *No*
	Take home wound kit	99070				UA dip stck	81000				Wart destruction < 14	17110		
	Miscellaneous					Strep test	87880				Cerumen removal	69210		
						Hemoccult	82270				Endometrial biopsy	58100		
	MODIFIERS					Lab Handling	99000							
	Significant/Sep EM provided with other service	-25				30 DAYS					60 DAYS		90 DAYS	
	Unrelated EM in post op period	-24												
	Repeat procedure, same physician, same day	-76												

DIAGNOSIS:	RETURN APPOINTMENT: (days) (wks) (mos) (PRN)	TODAY'S TOTAL	105.00
1) 171.9	NEXT APPOINTMENT: M - T - W - TH - F - S	PREVIOUS BALANCE	
2) _____	DATE / / TIME	AMOUNT REC'D TODAY REC'D BY _____	
3) _____	Provider's Signature:		
4) _____		BALANCE DUE	

SUPPLIES

South Padre Medical Center

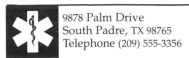

9878 Palm Drive
South Padre, TX 98765
Telephone (209) 555-3356

Gerald Bond, MD
Ray Adams, MD
Joyce Harkness, MD
Anthony Clark, MD

PATIENT'S LAST NAME	FIRST	ACCOUNT #	BIRTHDATE	SEX	TODAY'S DATE
Goldman	Edward	A	06/02/2007	☒ MALE ☐ FEMALE	04/08/08

INSURANCE COMPANY	SUBSCRIBER	GROUP/PLAN #	SUB. #	TIME
Medicaid	Same		QJK956199	2:00PM

ASSIGNMENT: I hereby assign my insurance benefits to be paid directly to the undersigned physician. I am financially responsible for non-covered services.
SIGNED: (Patient, Or parent, if Minor) **Gloria Goldman**   DATE: 04/08/08

RELEASE: I hereby authorize the physician to release to my insurance carriers any information required to process this claim.
SIGNED: (Patient, Or Parent, if Minor) **Gloria Goldman**   DATE: 04/08/08

✓	DESCRIPTION	CPT	Diag.	FEE	✓	DESCRIPTION	CPT	Diag.	FEE	✓	DESCRIPTION	CPT	Diag.	FEE
	OFFICE VISIT					**IMMUNIZATIONS/INJECTIONS**					**PROCEDURES**			
	NEW PATIENT					Admin of Vaccine 1	90471				Inhalation treatment	94640		
	Problem Focused					Admin of Vac 2+	90472				Demo/eval treatment	94664		
	Exp Problem Focused	99202				TB Tine, skin	86486				Vital Capacity	94150		
	Detailed	99203				Pneumococcal	90732				Spirometry	94010		
✓	Comp/ Mod MDM	99204	1	105.00		Medicare code	G0009				EKG w/interpretation	93000		
	Comp/ High MDM	99205				Influenza <3	90657				I&D abscess	10060		
	ESTABLISHED PATEINT					Influenza 3 and >	90658				Remove skin tag <15	11200		
	Minimal/Nurse Visit	99211				Medicare code	G0008				**EXCISION BENIGN LESIONS (inc. margins)**			
	Problem Focused	99212				Varicella	90716				Trunk, arms, legs			
	Exp Problem Forcused	99213				DPT	90701				0.5 cm or less	11400		
	Detailed	99214				DT children	90702				0.6 to 1.0 cm	11401		
	Comprehensive	99215				Td adult	90718				1.1 to 2.0 cm	11402		
	CONSULTATION					DtaP	90700				2.1 to 3.0 cm	11403		
	Problem Focused	99241				IPV	90713				Scalp, neck, hand, ft			
	Exp Problem Focused	99242				Rubella	90706				0.5 cm or less	11420		
	Detailed	99243				MMR	90707				0.6 to 1.0 cm	11421		
	Comp/ Mod MDM	99244				Hep B Child	90744				1.1 to 2.0 cm	11422		
	Comp/High MDM	99245				Hep B Adult	90746				2.1 to 3.0 cm	11423		
						IM Administration	96372				Face, ears, eyelids, lip			
	Requesting Provider _____					Compazine	J0780				0.5 cm or less	11440		
	Post-op Exam	99024		0.00		Demerol	J2175				0.6 to 1.0 cm	11441		
	PREVENTIVE MEDICINE					Depo-Provera	J1055				1.1 to 2.0 cm	11442		
	NEW PATIENT					Dexamethasone	J1100				2.1 to 3.0 cm	11443		
	Infant – 1 yr	99381				Solumedrol	J1720				**EXCISION MALIGNANT LESIONS (inc. margins)**			
	1 yr – 4 yr	99382				Antigen admin 1	95115				Trunk, arms, legs			
	5 yr – 11 yr	99383				Antigen admin 2+	95117				0.5 cm or less	11600		
	12 yr – 17 yr	99384				**LABORATORY**					0.6 to 1.0 cm	11601		
	18 yr – 39 yr	99385				Blood collect Vein	36415				1.1 to 2.0 cm	11602		
	40 yr – 64 yr	99386				Capillary	36416				2.1 to 3.0 cm	11603		
	65 yr and over	99387				Hemoglobin	85018				Scalp, neck, hand, ft			
	ESTABLISHED PATIENT					Glucose, reagent	82948				0.5 cm or less	11620		
	Infant – 1 yr	99391				Pregnancy, Serum	84702				0.6 to 1.0 cm	11621		
	1 yr – 4 yr	99392				Pregnancy, Urine	81025				1.1 to 2.0 cm	11622		
	5 yr – 11 yr	99393				Health panel	80050				2.1 to 3.0 cm	11623		
	12 yr – 17 yr	99394				B Met Pan Cal ion	80047				Face, ears, eyelids, lip			
	18 yr – 39 yr	99395				B Met Pan Cal tot	80048				0.5 cm or less	11640		
	40 yr – 64 yr	99396				C Metabolic panel	80053				0.6 to 1.0 cm	11641		
	65 yr and over	99397				Ob panel	80055				1.1 to 2.0 cm	11642		
	SUPPLIES					Lipid panel	80061				2.1 to 3.0 cm	11643		
	Take home burn kit	99070				UA Auto w/o micro	81003				*Awaiting path report*	☐ *Yes*		☐ *No*
	Take home wound kit	99070				UA dip stck	81000				Wart destruction < 14	17110		
	Miscellaneous					Strep test	87880				Cerumen removal	69210		
						Hemoccult	82270				Endometrial biopsy	58100		
	MODIFIERS					Lab Handling	99000							

			30 DAYS	60 DAYS	90 DAYS
Significant/Sep EM provided with other service	-25				
Unrelated EM in post op period	-24				
Repeat procedure, same physician, same day	-76				

DIAGNOSIS:

1) __752.51__

2) _____

3) _____

4) _____

RETURN APPOINTMENT: (days) (wks) (mos) ((PRN))	TODAY'S TOTAL	105.00
NEXT APPOINTMENT: M - T - W - TH - F - S	PREVIOUS BALANCE	
DATE / / TIME	AMOUNT REC'D TODAY REC'D BY _____	
Provider's Signature:	BALANCE DUE	

SUPPLIES

South Padre Medical Center

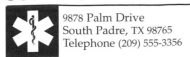

9878 Palm Drive
South Padre, TX 98765
Telephone (209) 555-3356

Gerald Bond, MD
Ray Adams, MD
Joyce Harkness, MD
Anthony Clark, MD

PATIENT'S LAST NAME	FIRST	ACCOUNT #	BIRTHDATE	SEX	TODAY'S DATE
Blair	Thomas	R	11/02/1943	☒ MALE ☐ FEMALE	04/08/08

INSURANCE COMPANY	SUBSCRIBER	GROUP/PLAN #	SUB. #	TIME
Texas Health Corporation	Same	P868	UBT9742	3:00 PM

ASSIGNMENT: I hereby assign my insurance benefits to be paid directly to the undersigned physician. I am financially responsible for non-covered services.
SIGNED: (Patient, Or parent, if Minor) **Thomas R. Blair** DATE: 04/08/08

RELEASE: I hereby authorize the physician to release to my insurance carriers any information required to process this claim.
SIGNED: (Patient, Or Parent, if Minor) **Thomas R. Blair** DATE: 04/08/08

✓	DESCRIPTION	CPT	Diag.	FEE	✓	DESCRIPTION	CPT	Diag.	FEE	✓	DESCRIPTION	CPT	Diag.	FEE
	OFFICE VISIT					**IMMUNIZATIONS/INJECTIONS**					**PROCEDURES**			
	NEW PATIENT					Admin of Vaccine 1	90471				Inhalation treatment	94640		
	Problem Focused					Admin of Vac 2+	90472				Demo/eval treatment	94664		
	Exp Problem Focused	99202				TB Tine, skin	86486				Vital Capacity	94150		
	Detailed	99203				Pneumococcal	90732				Spirometry	94010		
	Comp/ Mod MDM	99204				Medicare code	G0009				EKG w/interpretation	93000		
✓	Comp/ High MDM	99205	1	120.00		Influenza <3	90657				I&D abscess	10060		
	ESTABLISHED PATEINT					Influenza 3 and >	90658				Remove skin tag <15	11200		
	Minimal/Nurse Visit	99211				Medicare code	G0008				**EXCISION BENIGN LESIONS (inc. margins)**			
	Problem Focused	99212				Varicella	90716				Trunk, arms, legs			
	Exp Problem Forcused	99213				DPT	90701				0.5 cm or less	11400		
	Detailed	99214				DT children	90702				0.6 to 1.0 cm	11401		
	Comprehensive	99215				Td adult	90718				1.1 to 2.0 cm	11402		
	CONSULTATION					DtaP	90700				2.1 to 3.0 cm	11403		
	Problem Focused	99241				IPV	90713				Scalp, neck, hand, ft			
	Exp Problem Focused	99242				Rubella	90706				0.5 cm or less	11420		
	Detailed	99243				MMR	90707				0.6 to 1.0 cm	11421		
	Comp/ Mod MDM	99244				Hep B Child	90744				1.1 to 2.0 cm	11422		
	Comp/High MDM	99245				Hep B Adult	90746				2.1 to 3.0 cm	11423		
						IM Administration	96372				Face, ears, eyelids, lip			
	Requesting Provider _____					Compazine	J0780				0.5 cm or less	11440		
	Post-op Exam	99024	0.00			Demerol	J2175				0.6 to 1.0 cm	11441		
	PREVENTIVE MEDICINE					Depo-Provera	J1055				1.1 to 2.0 cm	11442		
	NEW PATIENT					Dexamethasone	J1100				2.1 to 3.0 cm	11443		
	Infant – 1 yr	99381				Solumedrol	J1720				**EXCISION MALIGNANT LESIONS (inc. margins)**			
	1 yr – 4 yr	99382				Antigen admin 1	95115				Trunk, arms, legs			
	5 yr – 11 yr	99383				Antigen admin 2+	95117				0.5 cm or less	11600		
	12 yr – 17 yr	99384				**LABORATORY**					0.6 to 1.0 cm	11601		
	18 yr – 39 yr	99385				Blood collect Vein	36415				1.1 to 2.0 cm	11602		
	40 yr – 64 yr	99386				Capillary	36416				2.1 to 3.0 cm	11603		
	65 yr and over	99387				Hemoglobin	85018				Scalp, neck, hand, ft			
	ESTABLISHED PATIENT					Glucose, reagent	82948				0.5 cm or less	11620		
	Infant – 1 yr	99391				Pregnancy, Serum	84702				0.6 to 1.0 cm	11621		
	1 yr – 4 yr	99392				Pregnancy, Urine	81025				1.1 to 2.0 cm	11622		
	5 yr – 11 yr	99393				Health panel	80050				2.1 to 3.0 cm	11623		
	12 yr – 17 yr	99394				B Met Pan Cal ion	80047				Face, ears, eyelids, lip			
	18 yr – 39 yr	99395				B Met Pan Cal tot	80048				0.5 cm or less	11640		
	40 yr – 64 yr	99396				C Metabolic panel	80053				0.6 to 1.0 cm	11641		
	65 yr and over	99397				Ob panel	80055				1.1 to 2.0 cm	11642		
	SUPPLIES					Lipid panel	80061				2.1 to 3.0 cm	11643		
	Take home burn kit	99070				UA Auto w/o micro	81003				*Awaiting path report*	☐ Yes		☐ No
	Take home wound kit	99070				UA dip stck	81000				Wart destruction < 14	17110		
	Miscellaneous					Strep test	87880				Cerumen removal	69210		
						Hemoccult	82270				Endometrial biopsy	58100		
	MODIFIERS					Lab Handling	99000							

MODIFIERS		
Significant/Sep EM provided with other service	-25	
Unrelated EM in post op period	-24	
Repeat procedure, same physician, same day	-76	

30 DAYS	60 DAYS	90 DAYS

DIAGNOSIS:

1) ____608.4____

2) _____

3) _____

4) _____

RETURN APPOINTMENT: (days) (wks) (mos) (PRN)	TODAY'S TOTAL	120.00
NEXT APPOINTMENT: M - T - W - TH - F - S	PREVIOUS BALANCE	
DATE / / TIME	AMOUNT REC'D TODAY REC'D BY _____	
Provider's Signature:	BALANCE DUE	

SUPPLIES

South Padre Medical Center

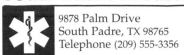

9878 Palm Drive
South Padre, TX 98765
Telephone (209) 555-3356

Gerald Bond, MD
Ray Adams, MD
Joyce Harkness, MD
Anthony Clark, MD

PATIENT'S LAST NAME	FIRST		ACCOUNT #	BIRTHDATE	SEX	TODAY'S DATE
King	Jackie	L.		10/24/1980	☐ MALE ☒ FEMALE	04/08/08

INSURANCE COMPANY	SUBSCRIBER	GROUP/PLAN #	SUB. #	TIME
Texas Health Corporation	Same	P121	HIKL 5697	10:15 AM

ASSIGNMENT: I hereby assign my insurance benefits to be paid directly to the undersigned physician. I am financially responsible for non-covered services.
SIGNED: (Patient, Or parent, if Minor) Jackie L. King   DATE: 04/08/08

RELEASE: I hereby authorize the physician to release to my insurance carriers any information required to process this claim.
SIGNED: (Patient, Or Parent, if Minor) Jackie L. King   DATE: 04/08/08

✓	DESCRIPTION	CPT	Diag.	FEE	✓	DESCRIPTION	CPT	Diag.	FEE	✓	DESCRIPTION	CPT	Diag.	FEE
	OFFICE VISIT					**IMMUNIZATIONS/INJECTIONS**					**PROCEDURES**			
	NEW PATIENT					Admin of Vaccine 1	90471				Inhalation treatment	94640		
	Problem Focused					Admin of Vac 2+	90472				Demo/eval treatment	94664		
	Exp Problem Focused	99202				TB Tine, skin	86486				Vital Capacity	94150		
	Detailed	99203				Pneumococcal	90732				Spirometry	94010		
✓	Comp/ Mod MDM	99204	1	105.00		Medicare code	G0009				EKG w/interpretation	93000		
	Comp/ High MDM	99205				Influenza <3	90657				I&D abscess	10060		
	ESTABLISHED PATIENT					Influenza 3 and >	90658				Remove skin tag <15	11200		
	Minimal/Nurse Visit	99211				Medicare code	G0008				**EXCISION BENIGN LESIONS (inc. margins)**			
	Problem Focused	99212				Varicella	90716				Trunk, arms, legs			
	Exp Problem Forcused	99213				DPT	90701				0.5 cm or less	11400		
	Detailed	99214				DT children	90702				0.6 to 1.0 cm	11401		
	Comprehensive	99215				Td adult	90718				1.1 to 2.0 cm	11402		
	CONSULTATION					DtaP	90700				2.1 to 3.0 cm	11403		
	Problem Focused	99241				IPV	90713				Scalp, neck, hand, ft			
	Exp Problem Focused	99242				Rubella	90706				0.5 cm or less	11420		
	Detailed	99243				MMR	90707				0.6 to 1.0 cm	11421		
	Comp/ Mod MDM	99244				Hep B Child	90744				1.1 to 2.0 cm	11422		
	Comp/High MDM	99245				Hep B Adult	90746				2.1 to 3.0 cm	11423		
						IM Administration	96372				Face, ears, eyelids, lip			
	Requesting Provider _____					Compazine	J0780				0.5 cm or less	11440		
	Post-op Exam	99024		0.00		Demerol	J2175				0.6 to 1.0 cm	11441		
	PREVENTIVE MEDICINE					Depo-Provera	J1055				1.1 to 2.0 cm	11442		
	NEW PATIENT					Dexamethasone	J1100				2.1 to 3.0 cm	11443		
	Infant – 1 yr	99381				Solumedrol	J1720				**EXCISION MALIGNANT LESIONS (inc. margins)**			
	1 yr – 4 yr	99382				Antigen admin 1	95115				Trunk, arms, legs			
	5 yr – 11 yr	99383				Antigen admin 2+	95117				0.5 cm or less	11600		
	12 yr – 17 yr	99384				**LABORATORY**					0.6 to 1.0 cm	11601		
	18 yr – 39 yr	99385				Blood collect Vein	36415				1.1 to 2.0 cm	11602		
	40 yr – 64 yr	99386				Capillary	36416				2.1 to 3.0 cm	11603		
	65 yr and over	99387				Hemoglobin	85018				Scalp, neck, hand, ft			
	ESTABLISHED PATIENT					Glucose, reagent	82948				0.5 cm or less	11620		
	Infant – 1 yr	99391				Pregnancy, Serum	84702				0.6 to 1.0 cm	11621		
	1 yr – 4 yr	99392				Pregnancy, Urine	81025				1.1 to 2.0 cm	11622		
	5 yr – 11 yr	99393				Health panel	80050				2.1 to 3.0 cm	11623		
	12 yr – 17 yr	99394				B Met Pan Cal ion	80047				Face, ears, eyelids, lip			
	18 yr – 39 yr	99395				B Met Pan Cal tot	80048				0.5 cm or less	11640		
	40 yr – 64 yr	99396				C Metabolic panel	80053				0.6 to 1.0 cm	11641		
	65 yr and over	99397				Ob panel	80055				1.1 to 2.0 cm	11642		
	SUPPLIES					Lipid panel	80061				2.1 to 3.0 cm	11643		
	Take home burn kit	99070				UA Auto w/o micro	81003				*Awaiting path report*		☐ Yes	☐ No
	Take home wound kit	99070				UA dip stck	81000				Wart destruction < 14	17110		
	Miscellaneous					Strep test	87880				Cerumen removal	69210		
						Hemoccult	82270				Endometrial biopsy	58100		
	MODIFIERS					Lab Handling	99000							
	Significant/Sep EM provided with other service	-25				30 DAYS					60 DAYS		90 DAYS	
	Unrelated EM in post op period	-24												
	Repeat procedure, same physician, same day	-76												

DIAGNOSIS:	RETURN APPOINTMENT: (days) (wks) (mos) (PRN)	TODAY'S TOTAL	105.00
1) V 22.0	NEXT APPOINTMENT: M – T – W – TH – F – S	PREVIOUS BALANCE	
2) _____			
3) _____	DATE / / TIME	AMOUNT REC'D TODAY REC'D BY _____	
4) _____	Provider's Signature:	BALANCE DUE	

SUPPLIES

South Padre Medical Center

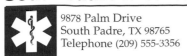

9878 Palm Drive
South Padre, TX 98765
Telephone (209) 555-3356

Gerald Bond, MD
Ray Adams, MD
Joyce Harkness, MD
Anthony Clark, MD

PATIENT'S LAST NAME	FIRST	ACCOUNT #	BIRTHDATE	SEX	TODAY'S DATE
Knight Joe	J		09/28/1986	☒ MALE ☐ FEMALE	04/08/08

INSURANCE COMPANY	SUBSCRIBER	GROUP/PLAN #	SUB. #	TIME
BC/BS of Texas	Same		JTR5512	10:15 AM

ASSIGNMENT: I hereby assign my insurance benefits to be paid directly to the undersigned physician. I am financially responsible for non-covered services.
SIGNED: (Patient, Or parent, if Minor) Joe Knight   DATE: 04/08/08

RELEASE: I hereby authorize the physician to release to my insurance carriers any information required to process this claim.
SIGNED: (Patient, Or Parent, if Minor) Joe Knight   DATE: 04/08/08

√	DESCRIPTION	CPT	Diag.	FEE	√	DESCRIPTION	CPT	Diag.	FEE	√	DESCRIPTION	CPT	Diag.	FEE
	OFFICE VISIT					IMMUNIZATIONS/INJECTIONS					PROCEDURES			
	NEW PATIENT					Admin of Vaccine 1	90471				Inhalation treatment	94640		
	Problem Focused					Admin of Vac 2+	90472				Demo/eval treatment	94664		
	Exp Problem Focused	99202				TB Tine, skin	86486				Vital Capacity	94150		
√	Detailed	99203	1	95.00		Pneumococcal	90732				Spirometry	94010		
	Comp/ Mod MDM	99204				Medicare code	G0009				EKG w/interpretation	93000		
	Comp/ High MDM	99205				Influenza <3	90657				I&D abscess	10060		
	ESTABLISHED PATEINT					Influenza 3 and >	90658				Remove skin tag <15	11200		
	Minimal/Nurse Visit	99211				Medicare code	G0008				EXCISION BENIGN LESIONS (inc. margins)			
	Problem Focused	99212				Varicella	90716				Trunk, arms, legs			
	Exp Problem Forcused	99213				DPT	90701				0.5 cm or less	11400		
	Detailed	99214				DT children	90702				0.6 to 1.0 cm	11401		
	Comprehensive	99215				Td adult	90718				1.1 to 2.0 cm	11402		
	CONSULTATION					DtaP	90700				2.1 to 3.0 cm	11403		
	Problem Focused	99241				IPV	90713				Scalp, neck, hand, ft			
	Exp Problem Focused	99242				Rubella	90706				0.5 cm or less	11420		
	Detailed	99243				MMR	90707				0.6 to 1.0 cm	11421		
	Comp/ Mod MDM	99244				Hep B Child	90744				1.1 to 2.0 cm	11422		
	Comp/High MDM	99245				Hep B Adult	90746				2.1 to 3.0 cm	11423		
	Requesting Provider ___					IM Administration	96372				Face, ears, eyelids, lip			
						Compazine	J0780				0.5 cm or less	11440		
	Post-op Exam	99024		0.00		Demerol	J2175				0.6 to 1.0 cm	11441		
	PREVENTIVE MEDICINE					Depo-Provera	J1055				1.1 to 2.0 cm	11442		
	NEW PATIENT					Dexamethasone	J1100				2.1 to 3.0 cm	11443		
	Infant – 1 yr	99381				Solumedrol	J1720				EXCISION MALIGNANT LESIONS (inc. margins)			
	1 yr – 4 yr	99382				Antigen admin 1	95115				Trunk, arms, legs			
	5 yr – 11 yr	99383				Antigen admin 2+	95117				0.5 cm or less	11600		
	12 yr – 17 yr	99384				LABORATORY					0.6 to 1.0 cm	11601		
	18 yr – 39 yr	99385				Blood collect Vein	36415				1.1 to 2.0 cm	11602		
	40 yr – 64 yr	99386				Capillary	36416				2.1 to 3.0 cm	11603		
	65 yr and over	99387				Hemoglobin	85018				Scalp, neck, hand, ft			
	ESTABLISHED PATIENT					Glucose, reagent	82948				0.5 cm or less	11620		
	Infant – 1 yr	99391				Pregnancy, Serum	84702				0.6 to 1.0 cm	11621		
	1 yr – 4 yr	99392				Pregnancy, Urine	81025				1.1 to 2.0 cm	11622		
	5 yr – 11 yr	99393				Health panel	80050				2.1 to 3.0 cm	11623		
	12 yr – 17 yr	99394				B Met Pan Cal ion	80047				Face, ears, eyelids, lip			
	18 yr – 39 yr	99395				B Met Pan Cal tot	80048				0.5 cm or less	11640		
	40 yr – 64 yr	99396				C Metabolic panel	80053				0.6 to 1.0 cm	11641		
	65 yr and over	99397				Ob panel	80055				1.1 to 2.0 cm	11642		
	SUPPLIES					Lipid panel	80061				2.1 to 3.0 cm	11643		
	Take home burn kit	99070				UA Auto w/o micro	81003				Awaiting path report	☐ Yes	☐ No	
	Take home wound kit	99070				UA dip stck	81000				Wart destruction < 14	17110		
	Miscellaneous					Strep test	87880				Cerumen removal	69210		
						Hemoccult	82270				Endometrial biopsy	58100		
	MODIFIERS					Lab Handling	99000							

MODIFIERS		
Significant/Sep EM provided with other service	-25
Unrelated EM in post op period	-24
Repeat procedure, same physician, same day	-76

	30 DAYS	60 DAYS	90 DAYS

DIAGNOSIS:

1) V 72.1

2) _____

3) _____

4) _____

RETURN APPOINTMENT: (30 days) (wks) (mos) (PRN)	TODAY'S TOTAL	95.00
NEXT APPOINTMENT: M - T - W - TH - F - S	PREVIOUS BALANCE	
DATE / / TIME	AMOUNT REC'D TODAY REC'D BY ___	
Provider's Signature:	BALANCE DUE	

SUPPLIES

South Padre Medical Center

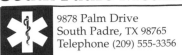

9878 Palm Drive
South Padre, TX 98765
Telephone (209) 555-3356

Gerald Bond, MD
Ray Adams, MD
Joyce Harkness, MD
Anthony Clark, MD

PATIENT'S LAST NAME	FIRST	ACCOUNT #	BIRTHDATE	SEX	TODAY'S DATE
Silverman	Peter F		03/21/1938	☒ MALE ☐ FEMALE	04/08/08

INSURANCE COMPANY	SUBSCRIBER	GROUP/PLAN #	SUB. #	TIME
Medicare	Same		817101124A	9:45 AM

ASSIGNMENT: I hereby assign my insurance benefits to be paid directly to the undersigned physician. I am financially responsible for non-covered services.
SIGNED: (Patient, Or parent, if Minor) _Peter Silverman_ DATE: 04/08/08

RELEASE: I hereby authorize the physician to release to my insurance carriers any information required to process this claim.
SIGNED: (Patient, Or Parent, if Minor) _Peter Silverman_ DATE: 04/08/08

√	DESCRIPTION	CPT	Diag.	FEE	√	DESCRIPTION	CPT	Diag.	FEE	√	DESCRIPTION	CPT	Diag.	FEE
	OFFICE VISIT					**IMMUNIZATIONS/INJECTIONS**					**PROCEDURES**			
	NEW PATIENT					Admin of Vaccine 1	90471				Inhalation treatment	94640		
	Problem Focused					Admin of Vac 2+	90472				Demo/eval treatment	94664		
	Exp Problem Focused	99202				TB Tine, skin	86486				Vital Capacity	94150		
	Detailed	99203				Pneumococcal	90732				Spirometry	94010		
	Comp/ Mod MDM	99204				Medicare code	G0009				EKG w/interpretation	93000		
√	Comp/ High MDM	99205	\	120.00		Influenza <3	90657				I&D abscess	10060		
	ESTABLISHED PATEINT					Influenza 3 and >	90658				Remove skin tag <15	11200		
	Minimal/Nurse Visit	99211				Medicare code	G0008				**EXCISION BENIGN LESIONS (inc. margins)**			
	Problem Focused	99212				Varicella	90716				Trunk, arms, legs			
	Exp Problem Forcused	99213				DPT	90701				0.5 cm or less	11400		
	Detailed	99214				DT children	90702				0.6 to 1.0 cm	11401		
	Comprehensive	99215				Td adult	90718				1.1 to 2.0 cm	11402		
	CONSULTATION					DtaP	90700				2.1 to 3.0 cm	11403		
	Problem Focused	99241				IPV	90713				Scalp, neck, hand, ft			
	Exp Problem Focused	99242				Rubella	90706				0.5 cm or less	11420		
	Detailed	99243				MMR	90707				0.6 to 1.0 cm	11421		
	Comp/ Mod MDM	99244				Hep B Child	90744				1.1 to 2.0 cm	11422		
	Comp/High MDM	99245				Hep B Adult	90746				2.1 to 3.0 cm	11423		
						IM Administration	96372				Face, ears, eyelids, lip			
	Requesting Provider _____					Compazine	J0780				0.5 cm or less	11440		
	Post-op Exam	99024		0.00		Demerol	J2175				0.6 to 1.0 cm	11441		
	PREVENTIVE MEDICINE					Depo-Provera	J1055				1.1 to 2.0 cm	11442		
	NEW PATIENT					Dexamethasone	J1100				2.1 to 3.0 cm	11443		
	Infant – 1 yr	99381				Solumedrol	J1720				**EXCISION MALIGNANT LESIONS (inc. margins)**			
	1 yr – 4 yr	99382				Antigen admin 1	95115				Trunk, arms, legs			
	5 yr – 11 yr	99383				Antigen admin 2+	95117				0.5 cm or less	11600		
	12 yr – 17 yr	99384				**LABORATORY**					0.6 to 1.0 cm	11601		
	18 yr – 39 yr	99385				Blood collect Vein	36415				1.1 to 2.0 cm	11602		
	40 yr – 64 yr	99386				Capillary	36416				2.1 to 3.0 cm	11603		
	65 yr and over	99387				Hemoglobin	85018				Scalp, neck, hand, ft			
	ESTABLISHED PATIENT					Glucose, reagent	82948				0.5 cm or less	11620		
	Infant – 1 yr	99391				Pregnancy, Serum	84702				0.6 to 1.0 cm	11621		
	1 yr – 4 yr	99392				Pregnancy, Urine	81025				1.1 to 2.0 cm	11622		
	5 yr – 11 yr	99393				Health panel	80050				2.1 to 3.0 cm	11623		
	12 yr – 17 yr	99394				B Met Pan Cal ion	80047				Face, ears, eyelids, lip			
	18 yr – 39 yr	99395				B Met Pan Cal tot	80048				0.5 cm or less	11640		
	40 yr – 64 yr	99396				C Metabolic panel	80053				0.6 to 1.0 cm	11641		
	65 yr and over	99397				Ob panel	80055				1.1 to 2.0 cm	11642		
	SUPPLIES					Lipid panel	80061				2.1 to 3.0 cm	11643		
	Take home burn kit	99070				UA Auto w/o micro	81003				**Awaiting path report**	☐ Yes	☐ No	
	Take home wound kit	99070				UA dip stck	81000				Wart destruction < 14	17110		
	Miscellaneous					Strep test	87880				Cerumen removal	69210		
						Hemoccult	82270				Endometrial biopsy	58100		
	MODIFIERS					Lab Handling	99000							

MODIFIERS		
Significant/Sep EM provided with other service	-25
Unrelated EM in post op period	-24
Repeat procedure, same physician, same day	-76

30 DAYS	60 DAYS	90 DAYS

DIAGNOSIS:		
1) _784.0_	RETURN APPOINTMENT: (days) (wks) (mos) (PRN)	TODAY'S TOTAL — 120.00
2) _____	NEXT APPOINTMENT: M - T - W - TH - F - S	PREVIOUS BALANCE
3) _____	DATE / / TIME	AMOUNT REC'D TODAY REC'D BY _____
4) _____	Provider's Signature:	BALANCE DUE

SUPPLIES

South Padre Medical Center

Patient's Name _____ Age _____ Sex _____ Marital Status S M W D

Address _____ Insurance _____

Telephone _____ Referred _____

Date	Subsequent Findings

SUPPLIES

Raymond Edwards

Problem: Recheck Ears

Subjective: The patient returns to the clinic 04/04/08. He still has the sensation of stuffiness and plugged feeling in his ears. He has had two courses of antibiotics now without any real relief. He had previous PE tubes a number of years ago for recurrent ear problems. He does not appear to have any obvious hearing deficit, although he sometimes has an echo in his ears. He has been trying Tylenol and Sudafed. The antibiotic did not seem to help at all. He has no allergies to medicines.

Physical Exam: His TMs do not appear red or dull. They do have the tympanosclerosis. I do not detect an obvious effusion, but the area of tympanosclerosis is prominent enough that I do not think I could see an effusion if it was present.

Assessment: Tympanosclerosis.

Plan: We are going to check a typanogram and audiogram and have him be rechecked by Ear, Nose and Throat to see if there is anything else that he needs.

Gerald Bond, MD

SUPPLIES

South Padre Medical Center

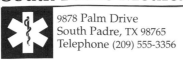

9878 Palm Drive
South Padre, TX 98765
Telephone (209) 555-3356

Gerald Bond, MD
Ray Adams, MD
Joyce Harkness, MD
Anthony Clark, MD

PATIENT'S LAST NAME			FIRST		ACCOUNT #	BIRTHDATE / /	SEX ☐ MALE ☐ FEMALE		TODAY'S DATE / /

INSURANCE COMPANY	SUBSCRIBER	GROUP/PLAN #	SUB. #	TIME

ASSIGNMENT: I hereby assign my insurance benefits to be paid directly to the undersigned physician. I am financially responsible for non-covered services.
SIGNED: (Patient,
Or parent, if Minor) _____ DATE: / /

RELEASE: I hereby authorize the physician to release to my insurance carriers any information required to process this claim.
SIGNED: (Patient,
Or Parent, if Minor) _____ DATE: / /

√	DESCRIPTION	CPT	Diag.	FEE	√	DESCRIPTION	CPT	Diag.	FEE	√	DESCRIPTION	CPT	Diag.	FEE
	OFFICE VISIT					**IMMUNIZATIONS/INJECTIONS**					**PROCEDURES**			
	NEW PATIENT					Admin of Vaccine 1	90471				Inhalation treatment	94640		
	Problem Focused					Admin of Vac 2+	90472				Demo/eval treatment	94664		
	Exp Problem Focused	99202				TB Tine, skin	86486				Vital Capacity	94150		
	Detailed	99203				Pneumococcal	90732				Spirometry	94010		
	Comp/ Mod MDM	99204				Medicare code	G0009				EKG w/interpretation	93000		
	Comp/ High MDM	99205				Influenza <3	90657				I&D abscess	10060		
	ESTABLISHED PATEINT					Influenza 3 and >	90658				Remove skin tag <15	11200		
	Minimal/Nurse Visit	99211				Medicare code	G0008				**EXCISION BENIGN LESIONS (inc. margins)**			
	Problem Focused	99212				Varicella	90716				Trunk, arms, legs			
	Exp Problem Forcused	99213				DPT	90701				0.5 cm or less	11400		
	Detailed	99214				DT children	90702				0.6 to 1.0 cm	11401		
	Comprehensive	99215				Td adult	90718				1.1 to 2.0 cm	11402		
	CONSULTATION					DtaP	90700				2.1 to 3.0 cm	11403		
	Problem Focused	99241				IPV	90713				Scalp, neck, hand, ft			
	Exp Problem Focused	99242				Rubella	90706				0.5 cm or less	11420		
	Detailed	99243				MMR	90707				0.6 to 1.0 cm	11421		
	Comp/ Mod MDM	99244				Hep B Child	90744				1.1 to 2.0 cm	11422		
	Comp/High MDM	99245				Hep B Adult	90746				2.1 to 3.0 cm	11423		
						IM Administration	96372				Face, ears, eyelids, lip			
	Requesting Provider _____					Compazine	J0780				0.5 cm or less	11440		
	Post-op Exam	99024		0.00		Demerol	J2175				0.6 to 1.0 cm	11441		
	PREVENTIVE MEDICINE					Depo-Provera	J1055				1.1 to 2.0 cm	11442		
	NEW PATIENT					Dexamethasone	J1100				2.1 to 3.0 cm	11443		
	Infant – 1 yr	99381				Solumedrol	J1720				**EXCISION MALIGNANT LESIONS (inc. margins)**			
	1 yr – 4 yr	99382				Antigen admin 1	95115				Trunk, arms, legs			
	5 yr – 11 yr	99383				Antigen admin 2+	95117				0.5 cm or less	11600		
	12 yr – 17 yr	99384				**LABORATORY**					0.6 to 1.0 cm	11601		
	18 yr – 39 yr	99385				Blood collect Vein	36415				1.1 to 2.0 cm	11602		
	40 yr – 64 yr	99386				Capillary	36416				2.1 to 3.0 cm	11603		
	65 yr and over	99387				Hemoglobin	85018				Scalp, neck, hand, ft			
	ESTABLISHED PATIENT					Glucose, reagent	82948				0.5 cm or less	11620		
	Infant – 1 yr	99391				Pregnancy, Serum	84702				0.6 to 1.0 cm	11621		
	1 yr – 4 yr	99392				Pregnancy, Urine	81025				1.1 to 2.0 cm	11622		
	5 yr – 11 yr	99393				Health panel	80050				2.1 to 3.0 cm	11623		
	12 yr – 17 yr	99394				B Met Pan Cal ion	80047				Face, ears, eyelids, lip			
	18 yr – 39 yr	99395				B Met Pan Cal tot	80048				0.5 cm or less	11640		
	40 yr – 64 yr	99396				C Metabolic panel	80053				0.6 to 1.0 cm	11641		
	65 yr and over	99397				Ob panel	80055				1.1 to 2.0 cm	11642		
	SUPPLIES					Lipid panel	80061				2.1 to 3.0 cm	11643		
	Take home burn kit	99070				UA Auto w/o micro	81003				*Awaiting path report*	☐ Yes	☐ No	
	Take home wound kit	99070				UA dip stck	81000				Wart destruction < 14	17110		
	Miscellaneous					Strep test	87880				Cerumen removal	69210		
						Hemoccult	82270				Endometrial biopsy	58100		
	MODIFIERS					Lab Handling	99000							

MODIFIERS				
Significant/Sep EM provided with other service	-25	30 DAYS	60 DAYS	90 DAYS
Unrelated EM in post op period	-24			
Repeat procedure, same physician, same day	-76			

DIAGNOSIS:	RETURN APPOINTMENT: (days) (wks) (mos) (PRN)	TODAY'S TOTAL	
1) _____	NEXT APPOINTMENT: M - T - W - TH - F - S	PREVIOUS BALANCE	
2) _____			
3) _____	DATE / / TIME	AMOUNT REC'D TODAY REC'D BY _____	
4) _____	Provider's Signature:	BALANCE DUE	

SUPPLIES

South Padre Medical Center

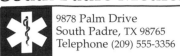

9878 Palm Drive
South Padre, TX 98765
Telephone (209) 555-3356

Gerald Bond, MD
Ray Adams, MD
Joyce Harkness, MD
Anthony Clark, MD

PATIENT'S LAST NAME	FIRST	ACCOUNT #	BIRTHDATE	SEX □ MALE □ FEMALE	TODAY'S DATE
			/ /		/ /

INSURANCE COMPANY	SUBSCRIBER	GROUP/PLAN #	SUB. #	TIME

ASSIGNMENT: I hereby assign my insurance benefits to be paid directly to the undersigned physician. I am financially responsible for non-covered services.
SIGNED: (Patient, Or parent, if Minor)_____ DATE: / /

RELEASE: I hereby authorize the physician to release to my insurance carriers any information required to process this claim.
SIGNED: (Patient, Or Parent, if Minor) _____ DATE: / /

✓	DESCRIPTION	CPT	Diag.	FEE	✓	DESCRIPTION	CPT	Diag.	FEE	✓	DESCRIPTION	CPT	Diag.	FEE
	OFFICE VISIT					**IMMUNIZATIONS/INJECTIONS**					**PROCEDURES**			
	NEW PATIENT					Admin of Vaccine 1	90471				Inhalation treatment	94640		
	Problem Focused					Admin of Vac 2+	90472				Demo/eval treatment	94664		
	Exp Problem Focused	99202				TB Tine, skin	86486				Vital Capacity	94150		
	Detailed	99203				Pneumococcal	90732				Spirometry	94010		
	Comp/ Mod MDM	99204				Medicare code	G0009				EKG w/interpretation	93000		
	Comp/ High MDM	99205				Influenza <3	90657				I&D abscess	10060		
	ESTABLISHED PATEINT					Influenza 3 and >	90658				Remove skin tag <15	11200		
	Minimal/Nurse Visit	99211				Medicare code	G0008				**EXCISION BENIGN LESIONS (inc. margins)**			
	Problem Focused	99212				Varicella	90716				Trunk, arms, legs			
	Exp Problem Forcused	99213				DPT	90701				0.5 cm or less	11400		
	Detailed	99214				DT children	90702				0.6 to 1.0 cm	11401		
	Comprehensive	99215				Td adult	90718				1.1 to 2.0 cm	11402		
	CONSULTATION					DtaP	90700				2.1 to 3.0 cm	11403		
	Problem Focused	99241				IPV	90713				Scalp, neck, hand, ft			
	Exp Problem Focused	99242				Rubella	90706				0.5 cm or less	11420		
	Detailed	99243				MMR	90707				0.6 to 1.0 cm	11421		
	Comp/ Mod MDM	99244				Hep B Child	90744				1.1 to 2.0 cm	11422		
	Comp/High MDM	99245				Hep B Adult	90746				2.1 to 3.0 cm	11423		
						IM Administration	96372				Face, ears, eyelids, lip			
	Requesting Provider _____					Compazine	J0780				0.5 cm or less	11440		
	Post-op Exam	99024		0.00		Demerol	J2175				0.6 to 1.0 cm	11441		
	PREVENTIVE MEDICINE					Depo-Provera	J1055				1.1 to 2.0 cm	11442		
	NEW PATIENT					Dexamethasone	J1100				2.1 to 3.0 cm	11443		
	Infant – 1 yr	99381				Solumedrol	J1720				**EXCISION MALIGNANT LESIONS (inc. margins)**			
	1 yr – 4 yr	99382				Antigen admin 1	95115				Trunk, arms, legs			
	5 yr – 11 yr	99383				Antigen admin 2+	95117				0.5 cm or less	11600		
	12 yr – 17 yr	99384				**LABORATORY**					0.6 to 1.0 cm	11601		
	18 yr – 39 yr	99385				Blood collect Vein	36415				1.1 to 2.0 cm	11602		
	40 yr – 64 yr	99386				Capillary	36416				2.1 to 3.0 cm	11603		
	65 yr and over	99387				Hemoglobin	85018				Scalp, neck, hand, ft			
	ESTABLISHED PATIENT					Glucose, reagent	82948				0.5 cm or less	11620		
	Infant – 1 yr	99391				Pregnancy, Serum	84702				0.6 to 1.0 cm	11621		
	1 yr – 4 yr	99392				Pregnancy, Urine	81025				1.1 to 2.0 cm	11622		
	5 yr – 11 yr	99393				Health panel	80050				2.1 to 3.0 cm	11623		
	12 yr – 17 yr	99394				B Met Pan Cal ion	80047				Face, ears, eyelids, lip			
	18 yr – 39 yr	99395				B Met Pan Cal tot	80048				0.5 cm or less	11640		
	40 yr – 64 yr	99396				C Metabolic panel	80053				0.6 to 1.0 cm	11641		
	65 yr and over	99397				Ob panel	80055				1.1 to 2.0 cm	11642		
	SUPPLIES					Lipid panel	80061				2.1 to 3.0 cm	11643		
	Take home burn kit	99070				UA Auto w/o micro	81003				***Awaiting path report***		□ **Yes**	□ **No**
	Take home wound kit	99070				UA dip stck	81000				Wart destruction < 14	17110		
	Miscellaneous					Strep test	87880				Cerumen removal	69210		
						Hemoccult	82270				Endometrial biopsy	58100		
	MODIFIERS					Lab Handling	99000							
	Significant/Sep EM provided with other service	-25				30 DAYS					60 DAYS		90 DAYS	
	Unrelated EM in post op period	-24												
	Repeat procedure, same physician, same day	-76												

DIAGNOSIS:

1) _____
2) _____
3) _____
4) _____

RETURN APPOINTMENT: (days) (wks) (mos) (PRN)	TODAY'S TOTAL	
NEXT APPOINTMENT: M - T - W - TH - F - S DATE / / TIME	PREVIOUS BALANCE	
	AMOUNT REC'D TODAY REC'D BY _____	
Provider's Signature:	BALANCE DUE	

SUPPLIES

South Padre Medical Center

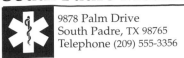

9878 Palm Drive
South Padre, TX 98765
Telephone (209) 555-3356

Gerald Bond, MD
Ray Adams, MD
Joyce Harkness, MD
Anthony Clark, MD

PATIENT'S LAST NAME	FIRST	ACCOUNT #	BIRTHDATE / /	SEX ☐ MALE ☐ FEMALE	TODAY'S DATE / /

INSURANCE COMPANY	SUBSCRIBER	GROUP/PLAN #	SUB. #	TIME

ASSIGNMENT: I hereby assign my insurance benefits to be paid directly to the undersigned physician. I am financially responsible for non-covered services.
SIGNED: (Patient, Or parent, if Minor)_____ DATE: / /

RELEASE: I hereby authorize the physician to release to my insurance carriers any information required to process this claim.
SIGNED: (Patient, Or Parent, if Minor) _____ DATE: / /

√	DESCRIPTION	CPT	Diag.	FEE	√	DESCRIPTION	CPT	Diag.	FEE	√	DESCRIPTION	CPT	Diag.	FEE
	OFFICE VISIT					**IMMUNIZATIONS/INJECTIONS**					**PROCEDURES**			
	NEW PATIENT					Admin of Vaccine 1	90471				Inhalation treatment	94640		
	Problem Focused					Admin of Vac 2+	90472				Demo/eval treatment	94664		
	Exp Problem Focused	99202				TB Tine, skin	86486				Vital Capacity	94150		
	Detailed	99203				Pneumococcal	90732				Spirometry	94010		
	Comp/ Mod MDM	99204				Medicare code	G0009				EKG w/interpretation	93000		
	Comp/ High MDM	99205				Influenza <3	90657				I&D abscess	10060		
	ESTABLISHED PATEINT					Influenza 3 and >	90658				Remove skin tag <15	11200		
	Minimal/Nurse Visit	99211				Medicare code	G0008				**EXCISION BENIGN LESIONS (inc. margins)**			
	Problem Focused	99212				Varicella	90716				Trunk, arms, legs			
	Exp Problem Forcused	99213				DPT	90701				0.5 cm or less	11400		
	Detailed	99214				DT children	90702				0.6 to 1.0 cm	11401		
	Comprehensive	99215				Td adult	90718				1.1 to 2.0 cm	11402		
	CONSULTATION					DtaP	90700				2.1 to 3.0 cm	11403		
	Problem Focused	99241				IPV	90713				Scalp, neck, hand, ft			
	Exp Problem Focused	99242				Rubella	90706				0.5 cm or less	11420		
	Detailed	99243				MMR	90707				0.6 to 1.0 cm	11421		
	Comp/ Mod MDM	99244				Hep B Child	90744				1.1 to 2.0 cm	11422		
	Comp/High MDM	99245				Hep B Adult	90746				2.1 to 3.0 cm	11423		
						IM Administration	96372				Face, ears, eyelids, lip			
	Requesting Provider _____					Compazine	J0780				0.5 cm or less	11440		
	Post-op Exam	99024		0.00		Demerol	J2175				0.6 to 1.0 cm	11441		
	PREVENTIVE MEDICINE					Depo-Provera	J1055				1.1 to 2.0 cm	11442		
	NEW PATIENT					Dexamethasone	J1100				2.1 to 3.0 cm	11443		
	Infant – 1 yr	99381				Solumedrol	J1720				**EXCISION MALIGNANT LESIONS (inc. margins)**			
	1 yr – 4 yr	99382				Antigen admin 1	95115				Trunk, arms, legs			
	5 yr – 11 yr	99383				Antigen admin 2+	95117				0.5 cm or less	11600		
	12 yr – 17 yr	99384				**LABORATORY**					0.6 to 1.0 cm	11601		
	18 yr – 39 yr	99385				Blood collect Vein	36415				1.1 to 2.0 cm	11602		
	40 yr – 64 yr	99386				Capillary	36416				2.1 to 3.0 cm	11603		
	65 yr and over	99387				Hemoglobin	85018				Scalp, neck, hand, ft			
	ESTABLISHED PATIENT					Glucose, reagent	82948				0.5 cm or less	11620		
	Infant – 1 yr	99391				Pregnancy, Serum	84702				0.6 to 1.0 cm	11621		
	1 yr – 4 yr	99392				Pregnancy, Urine	81025				1.1 to 2.0 cm	11622		
	5 yr – 11 yr	99393				Health panel	80050				2.1 to 3.0 cm	11623		
	12 yr – 17 yr	99394				B Met Pan Cal ion	80047				Face, ears, eyelids, lip			
	18 yr – 39 yr	99395				B Met Pan Cal tot	80048				0.5 cm or less	11640		
	40 yr – 64 yr	99396				C Metabolic panel	80053				0.6 to 1.0 cm	11641		
	65 yr and over	99397				Ob panel	80055				1.1 to 2.0 cm	11642		
	SUPPLIES					Lipid panel	80061				2.1 to 3.0 cm	11643		
	Take home burn kit	99070				UA Auto w/o micro	81003				*Awaiting path report*	☐ **Yes**		☐ **No**
	Take home wound kit	99070				UA dip stck	81000				Wart destruction < 14	17110		
	Miscellaneous					Strep test	87880				Cerumen removal	69210		
						Hemoccult	82270				Endometrial biopsy	58100		
	MODIFIERS					Lab Handling	99000							

MODIFIERS		
Significant/Sep EM provided with other service	-25
Unrelated EM in post op period	-24
Repeat procedure, same physician, same day	-76

30 DAYS	60 DAYS	90 DAYS

DIAGNOSIS:
1) _____
2) _____
3) _____
4) _____

RETURN APPOINTMENT:
(days) (wks) (mos) (PRN)

NEXT APPOINTMENT:
M - T - W - TH - F - S
DATE / / TIME

Provider's Signature:

TODAY'S TOTAL	
PREVIOUS BALANCE	
AMOUNT REC'D TODAY REC'D BY _____	
BALANCE DUE	

SUPPLIES

South Padre Medical Center

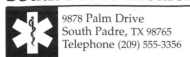

9878 Palm Drive
South Padre, TX 98765
Telephone (209) 555-3356

Gerald Bond, MD
Ray Adams, MD
Joyce Harkness, MD
Anthony Clark, MD

PATIENT'S LAST NAME	FIRST	ACCOUNT #	BIRTHDATE	SEX	TODAY'S DATE
			/ /	☐ MALE ☐ FEMALE	/ /

INSURANCE COMPANY	SUBSCRIBER	GROUP/PLAN #	SUB. #	TIME

ASSIGNMENT: I hereby assign my insurance benefits to be paid directly to the undersigned physician. I am financially responsible for non-covered services.
SIGNED: (Patient,
Or parent, if Minor)_____ DATE: / /

RELEASE: I hereby authorize the physician to release to my insurance carriers any information required to process this claim.
SIGNED: (Patient,
Or Parent, if Minor) _____ DATE: / /

√	DESCRIPTION	CPT	Diag.	FEE	√	DESCRIPTION	CPT	Diag.	FEE	√	DESCRIPTION	CPT	Diag.	FEE
	OFFICE VISIT					**IMMUNIZATIONS/INJECTIONS**					**PROCEDURES**			
	NEW PATIENT					Admin of Vaccine 1	90471				Inhalation treatment	94640		
	Problem Focused					Admin of Vac 2+	90472				Demo/eval treatment	94664		
	Exp Problem Focused	99202				TB Tine, skin	86486				Vital Capacity	94150		
	Detailed	99203				Pneumococcal	90732				Spirometry	94010		
	Comp/ Mod MDM	99204				Medicare code	G0009				EKG w/interpretation	93000		
	Comp/ High MDM	99205				Influenza <3	90657				I&D abscess	10060		
	ESTABLISHED PATEINT					Influenza 3 and >	90658				Remove skin tag <15	11200		
	Minimal/Nurse Visit	99211				Medicare code	G0008				**EXCISION BENIGN LESIONS (inc. margins)**			
	Problem Focused	99212				Varicella	90716				Trunk, arms, legs			
	Exp Problem Forcused	99213				DPT	90701				0.5 cm or less	11400		
	Detailed	99214				DT children	90702				0.6 to 1.0 cm	11401		
	Comprehensive	99215				Td adult	90718				1.1 to 2.0 cm	11402		
	CONSULTATION					DtaP	90700				2.1 to 3.0 cm	11403		
	Problem Focused	99241				IPV	90713				Scalp, neck, hand, ft			
	Exp Problem Focused	99242				Rubella	90706				0.5 cm or less	11420		
	Detailed	99243				MMR	90707				0.6 to 1.0 cm	11421		
	Comp/ Mod MDM	99244				Hep B Child	90744				1.1 to 2.0 cm	11422		
	Comp/High MDM	99245				Hep B Adult	90746				2.1 to 3.0 cm	11423		
						IM Administration	96372				Face, ears, eyelids, lip			
	Requesting Provider _____					Compazine	J0780				0.5 cm or less	11440		
	Post-op Exam	99024	0.00			Demerol	J2175				0.6 to 1.0 cm	11441		
	PREVENTIVE MEDICINE					Depo-Provera	J1055				1.1 to 2.0 cm	11442		
	NEW PATIENT					Dexamethasone	J1100				2.1 to 3.0 cm	11443		
	Infant – 1 yr	99381				Solumedrol	J1720				**EXCISION MALIGNANT LESIONS (inc. margins)**			
	1 yr – 4 yr	99382				Antigen admin 1	95115				Trunk, arms, legs			
	5 yr – 11 yr	99383				Antigen admin 2+	95117				0.5 cm or less	11600		
	12 yr – 17 yr	99384				**LABORATORY**					0.6 to 1.0 cm	11601		
	18 yr – 39 yr	99385				Blood collect Vein	36415				1.1 to 2.0 cm	11602		
	40 yr – 64 yr	99386				Capillary	36416				2.1 to 3.0 cm	11603		
	65 yr and over	99387				Hemoglobin	85018				Scalp, neck, hand, ft			
	ESTABLISHED PATIENT					Glucose, reagent	82948				0.5 cm or less	11620		
	Infant – 1 yr	99391				Pregnancy, Serum	84702				0.6 to 1.0 cm	11621		
	1 yr – 4 yr	99392				Pregnancy, Urine	81025				1.1 to 2.0 cm	11622		
	5 yr – 11 yr	99393				Health panel	80050				2.1 to 3.0 cm	11623		
	12 yr – 17 yr	99394				B Met Pan Cal ion	80047				Face, ears, eyelids, lip			
	18 yr – 39 yr	99395				B Met Pan Cal tot	80048				0.5 cm or less	11640		
	40 yr – 64 yr	99396				C Metabolic panel	80053				0.6 to 1.0 cm	11641		
	65 yr and over	99397				Ob panel	80055				1.1 to 2.0 cm	11642		
	SUPPLIES					Lipid panel	80061				2.1 to 3.0 cm	11643		
	Take home burn kit	99070				UA Auto w/o micro	81003				*Awaiting path report*	☐ Yes	☐ No	
	Take home wound kit	99070				UA dip stck	81000				Wart destruction < 14	17110		
	Miscellaneous					Strep test	87880				Cerumen removal	69210		
						Hemoccult	82270				Endometrial biopsy	58100		
	MODIFIERS					Lab Handling	99000							

Significant/Sep EM provided with other service	-25	**30 DAYS**	**60 DAYS**	**90 DAYS**
Unrelated EM in post op period	-24		
Repeat procedure, same physician, same day	-76		

DIAGNOSIS:	RETURN APPOINTMENT: (days) (wks) (mos) (PRN)	TODAY'S TOTAL	
1) _____	NEXT APPOINTMENT: M - T - W - TH - F - S	PREVIOUS BALANCE	
2) _____		AMOUNT REC'D TODAY REC'D BY _____	
3) _____	DATE / / TIME		
4) _____	Provider's Signature:	BALANCE DUE	

SUPPLIES

South Padre Medical Center

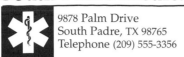

9878 Palm Drive
South Padre, TX 98765
Telephone (209) 555-3356

Gerald Bond, MD
Ray Adams, MD
Joyce Harkness, MD
Anthony Clark, MD

PATIENT'S LAST NAME	FIRST	ACCOUNT #	BIRTHDATE / /	SEX ☐ MALE ☐ FEMALE	TODAY'S DATE / /

INSURANCE COMPANY	SUBSCRIBER	GROUP/PLAN #	SUB. #	TIME

ASSIGNMENT: I hereby assign my insurance benefits to be paid directly to the undersigned physician. I am financially responsible for non-covered services.
SIGNED: (Patient, Or parent, if Minor)_____ DATE: / /

RELEASE: I hereby authorize the physician to release to my insurance carriers any information required to process this claim.
SIGNED: (Patient, Or Parent, if Minor) _____ DATE: / /

√	DESCRIPTION	CPT	Diag.	FEE	√	DESCRIPTION	CPT	Diag.	FEE	√	DESCRIPTION	CPT	Diag.	FEE
	OFFICE VISIT					**IMMUNIZATIONS/INJECTIONS**					**PROCEDURES**			
	NEW PATIENT					Admin of Vaccine 1	90471				Inhalation treatment	94640		
	Problem Focused					Admin of Vac 2+	90472				Demo/eval treatment	94664		
	Exp Problem Focused	99202				TB Tine, skin	86486				Vital Capacity	94150		
	Detailed	99203				Pneumococcal	90732				Spirometry	94010		
	Comp/ Mod MDM	99204				Medicare code	G0009				EKG w/interpretation	93000		
	Comp/ High MDM	99205				Influenza <3	90657				I&D abscess	10060		
	ESTABLISHED PATEINT					Influenza 3 and >	90658				Remove skin tag <15	11200		
	Minimal/Nurse Visit	99211				Medicare code	G0008				**EXCISION BENIGN LESIONS (inc. margins)**			
	Problem Focused	99212				Varicella	90716				Trunk, arms, legs			
	Exp Problem Forcused	99213				DPT	90701				0.5 cm or less	11400		
	Detailed	99214				DT children	90702				0.6 to 1.0 cm	11401		
	Comprehensive	99215				Td adult	90718				1.1 to 2.0 cm	11402		
	CONSULTATION					DtaP	90700				2.1 to 3.0 cm	11403		
	Problem Focused	99241				IPV	90713				Scalp, neck, hand, ft			
	Exp Problem Focused	99242				Rubella	90706				0.5 cm or less	11420		
	Detailed	99243				MMR	90707				0.6 to 1.0 cm	11421		
	Comp/ Mod MDM	99244				Hep B Child	90744				1.1 to 2.0 cm	11422		
	Comp/High MDM	99245				Hep B Adult	90746				2.1 to 3.0 cm	11423		
						IM Administration	96372				Face, ears, eyelids, lip			
	Requesting Provider _____					Compazine	J0780				0.5 cm or less	11440		
	Post-op Exam	99024		0.00		Demerol	J2175				0.6 to 1.0 cm	11441		
	PREVENTIVE MEDICINE					Depo-Provera	J1055				1.1 to 2.0 cm	11442		
	NEW PATIENT					Dexamethasone	J1100				2.1 to 3.0 cm	11443		
	Infant – 1 yr	99381				Solumedrol	J1720				**EXCISION MALIGNANT LESIONS (inc. margins)**			
	1 yr – 4 yr	99382				Antigen admin 1	95115				Trunk, arms, legs			
	5 yr – 11 yr	99383				Antigen admin 2+	95117				0.5 cm or less	11600		
	12 yr – 17 yr	99384				**LABORATORY**					0.6 to 1.0 cm	11601		
	18 yr – 39 yr	99385				Blood collect Vein	36415				1.1 to 2.0 cm	11602		
	40 yr – 64 yr	99386				Capillary	36416				2.1 to 3.0 cm	11603		
	65 yr and over	99387				Hemoglobin	85018				Scalp, neck, hand, ft			
	ESTABLISHED PATIENT					Glucose, reagent	82948				0.5 cm or less	11620		
	Infant – 1 yr	99391				Pregnancy, Serum	84702				0.6 to 1.0 cm	11621		
	1 yr – 4 yr	99392				Pregnancy, Urine	81025				1.1 to 2.0 cm	11622		
	5 yr – 11 yr	99393				Health panel	80050				2.1 to 3.0 cm	11623		
	12 yr – 17 yr	99394				B Met Pan Cal ion	8004/				Face, ears, eyelids, lip			
	18 yr – 39 yr	99395				B Met Pan Cal tot	80048				0.5 cm or less	11640		
	40 yr – 64 yr	99396				C Metabolic panel	80053				0.6 to 1.0 cm	11641		
	65 yr and over	99397				Ob panel	80055				1.1 to 2.0 cm	11642		
	SUPPLIES					Lipid panel	80061				2.1 to 3.0 cm	11643		
	Take home burn kit	99070				UA Auto w/o micro	81003				**Awaiting path report**	☐ Yes		☐ No
	Take home wound kit	99070				UA dip stck	81000				Wart destruction < 14	17110		
	Miscellaneous					Strep test	87880				Cerumen removal	69210		
						Hemoccult	82270				Endometrial biopsy	58100		
	MODIFIERS					Lab Handling	99000							
	Significant/Sep EM provided with other service	-25				30 DAYS					60 DAYS		90 DAYS	
	Unrelated EM in post op period	-24												
	Repeat procedure, same physician, same day	-76												

DIAGNOSIS:	RETURN APPOINTMENT: (days) (wks) (mos) (PRN)	TODAY'S TOTAL	
1) _____	**NEXT APPOINTMENT:** M - T - W - TH - F - S	PREVIOUS BALANCE	
2) _____		AMOUNT REC'D TODAY REC'D BY _____	
3) _____	DATE / / TIME		
4) _____	Provider's Signature:	BALANCE DUE	

SUPPLIES

South Padre Medical Center

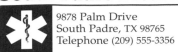

9878 Palm Drive
South Padre, TX 98765
Telephone (209) 555-3356

Gerald Bond, MD
Ray Adams, MD
Joyce Harkness, MD
Anthony Clark, MD

PATIENT'S LAST NAME		FIRST	ACCOUNT #	BIRTHDATE	SEX ☐ MALE ☐ FEMALE	TODAY'S DATE
				/ /		/ /

INSURANCE COMPANY	SUBSCRIBER	GROUP/PLAN #	SUB. #	TIME

ASSIGNMENT: I hereby assign my insurance benefits to be paid directly to the undersigned physician. I am financially responsible for non-covered services.
SIGNED: (Patient,
Or parent, if Minor)_____ DATE: / /

RELEASE: I hereby authorize the physician to release to my insurance carriers any information required to process this claim.
SIGNED: (Patient,
Or Parent, if Minor) _____ DATE: / /

✓	DESCRIPTION	CPT	Diag.	FEE	✓	DESCRIPTION	CPT	Diag.	FEE	✓	DESCRIPTION	CPT	Diag.	FEE
	OFFICE VISIT					**IMMUNIZATIONS/INJECTIONS**					**PROCEDURES**			
	NEW PATIENT					Admin of Vaccine 1	90471				Inhalation treatment	94640		
	Problem Focused					Admin of Vac 2+	90472				Demo/eval treatment	94664		
	Exp Problem Focused	99202				TB Tine, skin	86486				Vital Capacity	94150		
	Detailed	99203				Pneumococcal	90732				Spirometry	94010		
	Comp/ Mod MDM	99204				Medicare code	G0009				EKG w/interpretation	93000		
	Comp/ High MDM	99205				Influenza <3	90657				I&D abscess	10060		
	ESTABLISHED PATEINT					Influenza 3 and >	90658				Remove skin tag <15	11200		
	Minimal/Nurse Visit	99211				Medicare code	G0008				**EXCISION BENIGN LESIONS (inc. margins)**			
	Problem Focused	99212				Varicella	90716				Trunk, arms, legs			
	Exp Problem Forcused	99213				DPT	90701				0.5 cm or less	11400		
	Detailed	99214				DT children	90702				0.6 to 1.0 cm	11401		
	Comprehensive	99215				Td adult	90718				1.1 to 2.0 cm	11402		
	CONSULTATION					DtaP	90700				2.1 to 3.0 cm	11403		
	Problem Focused	99241				IPV	90713				Scalp, neck, hand, ft			
	Exp Problem Focused	99242				Rubella	90706				0.5 cm or less	11420		
	Detailed	99243				MMR	90707				0.6 to 1.0 cm	11421		
	Comp/ Mod MDM	99244				Hep B Child	90744				1.1 to 2.0 cm	11422		
	Comp/High MDM	99245				Hep B Adult	90746				2.1 to 3.0 cm	11423		
						IM Administration	96372				Face, ears, eyelids, lip			
	Requesting Provider _____					Compazine	J0780				0.5 cm or less	11440		
	Post-op Exam	99024		0.00		Demerol	J2175				0.6 to 1.0 cm	11441		
	PREVENTIVE MEDICINE					Depo-Provera	J1055				1.1 to 2.0 cm	11442		
	NEW PATIENT					Dexamethasone	J1100				2.1 to 3.0 cm	11443		
	Infant – 1 yr	99381				Solumedrol	J1720				**EXCISION MALIGNANT LESIONS (inc. margins)**			
	1 yr – 4 yr	99382				Antigen admin 1	95115				Trunk, arms, legs			
	5 yr – 11 yr	99383				Antigen admin 2+	95117				0.5 cm or less	11600		
	12 yr – 17 yr	99384				**LABORATORY**					0.6 to 1.0 cm	11601		
	18 yr – 39 yr	99385				Blood collect Vein	36415				1.1 to 2.0 cm	11602		
	40 yr – 64 yr	99386				Capillary	36416				2.1 to 3.0 cm	11603		
	65 yr and over	99387				Hemoglobin	85018				Scalp, neck, hand, ft			
	ESTABLISHED PATIENT					Glucose, reagent	82948				0.5 cm or less	11620		
	Infant – 1 yr	99391				Pregnancy, Serum	84702				0.6 to 1.0 cm	11621		
	1 yr – 4 yr	99392				Pregnancy, Urine	81025				1.1 to 2.0 cm	11622		
	5 yr – 11 yr	99393				Health panel	80050				2.1 to 3.0 cm	11623		
	12 yr – 17 yr	99394				B Met Pan Cal ion	80047				Face, ears, eyelids, lip			
	18 yr – 39 yr	99395				B Met Pan Cal tot	80048				0.5 cm or less	11640		
	40 yr – 64 yr	99396				C Metabolic panel	80053				0.6 to 1.0 cm	11641		
	65 yr and over	99397				Ob panel	80055				1.1 to 2.0 cm	11642		
	SUPPLIES					Lipid panel	80061				2.1 to 3.0 cm	11643		
	Take home burn kit	99070				UA Auto w/o micro	81003				***Awaiting path report***		☐ *Yes*	☐ *No*
	Take home wound kit	99070				UA dip stck	81000				Wart destruction < 14	17110		
	Miscellaneous					Strep test	87880				Cerumen removal	69210		
						Hemoccult	82270				Endometrial biopsy	58100		
	MODIFIERS					Lab Handling	99000							

MODIFIERS		
Significant/Sep EM provided with other service	-25
Unrelated EM in post op period	-24
Repeat procedure, same physician, same day	-76

30 DAYS	60 DAYS	90 DAYS

DIAGNOSIS:		
1) _____	RETURN APPOINTMENT: (days) (wks) (mos) (PRN)	TODAY'S TOTAL
2) _____	NEXT APPOINTMENT: M - T - W - TH - F - S	PREVIOUS BALANCE
3) _____	DATE / / TIME	AMOUNT REC'D TODAY REC'D BY _____
4) _____	Provider's Signature:	BALANCE DUE

SUPPLIES

South Padre Medical Center

Patient Face Sheet

4/4/2008

Patient Chart #: BOGMA000
Patient Name: Mary L. Bogert
Street 1: 2502 32nd Ave S
Street 2:
City: South Padre, TX 98765
Phone: (209)555-3690

D.O.B: 08/22/1955   Age: 52
Sex: Female
SSN: 502990207
Mar Status: Married
S.O.F:
Assigned Provider: Ray Adams

Employer Name:
Street 1:
City:
Phone:

Case Information

Case Desc: Patient Transfer
Last Visit:
Referral:
Guarantor Name: Mary L. Bogert
Street 1: 2502 32nd Ave S
City: South Padre, TX 98765
Phone: (209)555-3690
SSN: 502990207

Diagnosis 1:
Diagnosis 2:
Diagnosis 3:
Diagnosis 4:

Ins Co #: SPIC
Insurance 1: South Padre Insurance Company
Street 1: 2702 Oak Line Dr
Street 2:
City: South Padre, TX 98765
Phone:
Ins-Start:
End:

Insured 1 Name: Mark M. Bogert
Street 1: 2502 32nd Ave S
Street 2:
Phone: (209)555-3690
D.O.B.:   Sex: Male
Policy Number: MNY2691
Group Number:

Ins Co #:
Insurance 2:
Street 1:
Street 2:
City:
Phone:
Ins-Start:
End:

Insured 2 Name:
Street 1:
Street 2:
City:
Phone:
D.O.B.:
Policy Number: Sex:
Group Number:

Ins Co #:
Insurance 3:
Street 1:
Street 2:
City:
Phone:
Ins-Start:
End:

Insured 3 Name:
Street 1:
Street 2:
City:
Phone:
D.O.B.:   Sex:
Policy Number:
Group Number:

SUPPLIES

South Padre Medical Center

Patient Face Sheet

4/7/2008

Patient Chart #: FENEL000
Patient Name: Elizabeth M. Fenton
Street 1: 201 2nd Ave N
Street 2:
City: South Padre, TX 98765
Phone: (209)555-9199

D.O.B: 11/25/1941   Age: 66
Sex: Female
SSN: 222346688
Mar Status: Married
S.O.F:
Assigned Provider:

Employer Name:
Street 1:
City:
Phone:

Case Information

Case Desc: New Patient
Last Visit:
Referral:
Guarantor Name: Elizabeth M. Fenton
Street 1: 201 2nd Ave N
City: South Padre, TX 98765
Phone: (209)555-9199
SSN: 222346688

Diagnosis 1:
Diagnosis 2:
Diagnosis 3:
Diagnosis 4:

Ins Co #: MCR
Insurance 1: Medicare
Street 1: 402 Main Street
Street 2:
City: South Padre, TX 98765
Phone:
Ins-Start:
End:

Insured 1 Name: Elizabeth M. Fenton
Street 1: 201 2nd Ave N
Street 2:
Phone: (209)555-9199
D.O.B.: 11/25/1941   Sex: Female
Policy Number: 222346688A
Group Number:

Ins Co #:
Insurance 2:
Street 1:
Street 2:
City:
Phone:
Ins-Start:
End:

Insured 2 Name:
Street 1:
Street 2:
City:
Phone:
D.O.B.:
Policy Number: Sex:
Group Number:

Ins Co #:
Insurance 3:
Street 1:
Street 2:
City:
Phone:
Ins-Start:
End:

Insured 3 Name:
Street 1:
Street 2:
City:
Phone:
D.O.B.:   Sex:
Policy Number:
Group Number:

SUPPLIES

South Padre Medical Center

Patient Face Sheet

4/4/2008

Patient Chart #: FOSAM000   D.O.B: 06/18/1989   Age: 18

Patient Name: Amanda J. Foster   Sex Female

Street 1: 1603 Todd Ave   SSN: 502448754

Street 2:   Mar Status: Married

City: South Padre, TX 98765   S.O.F:

Phone: (209)555-7767   Assigned Provider:

Employer Name:

Street 1:

City:

Phone:

Case Information

Case Desc: Patient Transfer   Diagnosis 1:

Last Visit: Diagnosis 2:

Referral: Diagnosis 3:

Guarantor Name: Amanda J. Foster   Diagnosis 4:

Street 1: 1603 Todd Ave

City: South Padre, TX 98765

Phone: (209)555-7767

SSN: 502448754

Ins Co #: SPIC   Insured 1 Name: Todd Foster

Insurance 1: South Padre Insurance Company   Street 1: 1603 Todd Ave

Street 1: 2702 Oak Line Dr   Street 2:

Street 2:   Phone: (209)555-7767

City: South Padre, TX 98765   D.O.B.:   Sex Male

Phone: Policy Number: PJD9123

Ins-Start: Group Number:

End:

Ins Co #:   Insured 2 Name:

Insurance 2:   Street 1:

Street 1:   Street 2:

Street 2:   City:

City: Phone:

Phone: D.O.B.:

Ins-Start: Policy Number: Sex

End: Group Number:

Ins Co #:   Insured 3 Name:

Insurance 3:   Street 1:

Street 1:   Street 2:

Street 2:   City:

City: Phone:

Phone: D.O.B.:   Sex

Ins-Start: Policy Number:

End: Group Number:

SUPPLIES

South Padre Medical Center

Patient Face Sheet

4/4/2008

Patient Chart #: MASJA000
Patient Name: Jack W. Masci
Street 1: 809 Heights Dr
Street 2:
City: South Padre, TX 98765
Phone: (209)555-8191

D.O.B: 04/02/1950   Age: 58
Sex: Male
SSN: 501117845
Mar Status: Married
S.O.F:
Assigned Provider: Anthony Clark

Employer Name:
Street 1:
City:
Phone:

Case Information

Case Desc: Patient Transfer
Last Visit:
Referral:
Guarantor Name: Jack W. Masci
Street 1: 809 Heights Dr
City: South Padre, TX 98765
Phone: (209)555-8191
SSN: 501117845

Diagnosis 1:
Diagnosis 2:
Diagnosis 3:
Diagnosis 4:

Ins Co #: BCBS
Insurance 1: Blue Cross/Blue Shield of TX
Street 1: 1514 West Road
Street 2:
City: Houston, TX 99881
Phone:
Ins-Start:
End:

Insured 1 Name: Jack W. Masci
Street 1: 809 Heights Dr
Street 2:
Phone: (209)555-8191
D.O.B.: 04/02/1950   Sex: Male
Policy Number: XVC4582
Group Number:

Ins Co #:
Insurance 2:
Street 1:
Street 2:
City:
Phone:
Ins-Start:
End:

Insured 2 Name:
Street 1:
Street 2:
City:
Phone:
D.O.B.:
Policy Number: Sex
Group Number:

Ins Co #:
Insurance 3:
Street 1:
Street 2:
City:
Phone:
Ins-Start:
End:

Insured 3 Name:
Street 1:
Street 2:
City:
Phone:
D.O.B.:   Sex
Policy Number:
Group Number:

SUPPLIES

South Padre Medical Center

Patient Face Sheet
4/4/2008

Patient Chart #: OLSJE000
Patient Name: Jean S. Olson
Street 1: 2405 Elm Way Dr
Street 2:
City: South Padre, TX 98765
Phone: (209)555-5641

D.O.B: 01/06/1971   Age: 37
Sex: Female
SSN: 402096292
Mar Status: Single
S.O.F:
Assigned Provider: Anthony Clark

Employer Name: South Padre Mall
Street 1:
City: South Padre, TX 98765
Phone: (209)555-2400

Case Information

Case Desc: New Patient
Last Visit:
Referral: Thomas Thompson MD
Guarantor Name: Jean S. Olson
Street 1: 2405 Elm Way Dr
City: South Padre, TX 98765
Phone: (209)555-5641
SSN: 402096292

Diagnosis 1:
Diagnosis 2:
Diagnosis 3:
Diagnosis 4:

Ins Co #: BCBS
Insurance 1: Blue Cross/Blue Shield of TX
Street 1: 1514 West Road
Street 2:
City: Houston, TX 99881
Phone:
Ins-Start:
End:

Insured 1 Name: Jean S. Olson
Street 1: 2405 Elm Way Dr
Street 2:
Phone: (209)555-5641
D.O.B.: 01/06/1971   Sex: Female
Policy Number: CSJ4772
Group Number:

Ins Co #:
Insurance 2:
Street 1:
Street 2:
City:
Phone:
Ins-Start:
End:

Insured 2 Name:
Street 1:
Street 2:
City:
Phone:
D.O.B.:
Policy Number: Sex
Group Number:

Ins Co #:
Insurance 3:
Street 1:
Street 2:
City:
Phone:
Ins-Start:
End:

Insured 3 Name:
Street 1:
Street 2:
City:
Phone:
D.O.B.:   Sex
Policy Number:
Group Number:

SUPPLIES

South Padre Medical Center

Patient Face Sheet

4/7/2008

Patient Chart #: WHILO000

Patient Name: Lori H. Whittaker

Street 1: 3203 34 Ave S

Street 2:

City: South Padre, TX 98765

Phone: (209)555-1246

D.O.B: 11/02/1958   Age: 49

Sex: Female

SSN: 001996622

Mar Status: Unknown

S.O.F:

Assigned Provider: Gerald Bond

Employer Name:

Street 1:

City:

Phone:

Case Information

Case Desc: New Patient

Last Visit:

Referral:

Guarantor Name: Lori H. Whittaker

Street 1: 3203 34 Ave S

City: South Padre, TX 98765

Phone: (209)555-1246

SSN: 001996622

Diagnosis 1:

Diagnosis 2:

Diagnosis 3:

Diagnosis 4:

Ins Co #: MCR

Insurance 1: Medicare

Street 1: 402 Main Street

Street 2:

City: South Padre, TX 98765

Phone:

Ins-Start:

End:

Insured 1 Name: Lori H. Whittaker

Street 1: 3203 34 Ave S

Street 2:

Phone: (209)555-1246

D.O.B.: 11/02/1958   Sex: Female

Policy Number: 001996622A

Group Number:

Ins Co #:

Insurance 2:

Street 1:

Street 2:

City:

Phone:

Ins-Start:

End:

Insured 2 Name:

Street 1:

Street 2:

City:

Phone:

D.O.B.:

Policy Number: Sex:

Group Number:

Ins Co #:

Insurance 3:

Street 1:

Street 2:

City:

Phone:

Ins-Start:

End:

Insured 3 Name:

Street 1:

Street 2:

City:

Phone:

D.O.B.:   Sex:

Policy Number:

Group Number:

SUPPLIES

PRIORITY ☐

Telephone Record

Patient _____ Age _____

Caller _____

Telephone _____

Referred to _____

Chart # _____

Chart Attached ☐ YES ☐ NO

Date ___/___/___ Time _____ Rec'd By _____

Message _____

_____

Temp	Allergies

Response _____

PHY/RN Initials	Date ___/___/___	Time	Handled By

PRIORITY ☐

Telephone Record

Patient _____ Age _____

Caller _____

Telephone _____

Referred to _____

Chart # _____

Chart Attached ☐ YES ☐ NO

Date ___/___/___ Time _____ Rec'd By _____

Message _____

_____

Temp	Allergies

Response _____

PHY/RN Initials	Date ___/___/___	Time	Handled By

PRIORITY ☐

Telephone Record

Patient _____ Age _____

Caller _____

Telephone _____

Referred to _____

Chart # _____

Chart Attached ☐ YES ☐ NO

Date ___/___/___ Time _____ Rec'd By _____

Message _____

_____

Temp	Allergies

Response _____

PHY/RN Initials	Date ___/___/___	Time	Handled By

PRIORITY ☐

Telephone Record

Patient _____ Age _____

Caller _____

Telephone _____

Referred to _____

Chart # _____

Chart Attached ☐ YES ☐ NO

Date ___/___/___ Time _____ Rec'd By _____

Message _____

_____

Temp	Allergies

Response _____

PHY/RN Initials	Date ___/___/___	Time	Handled By

SUPPLIES

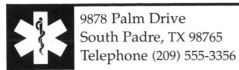

South Padre Medical Center

Gerald Bond, MD
Ray Adams, MD
Joyce Harkness, MD
Anthony Clark, MD

9878 Palm Drive
South Padre, TX 98765
Telephone (209) 555-3356

SUPPLIES

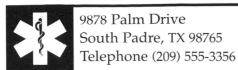

South Padre Medical Center

Gerald Bond, MD
Ray Adams, MD
Joyce Harkness, MD
Anthony Clark, MD

9878 Palm Drive
South Padre, TX 98765
Telephone (209) 555-3356

SUPPLIES

INCOMING MAIL FORM
THURSDAY, APRIL 10

1. Letter to Dr. Bond from Dr. Andrews
2. BC/BS of TX (payments)
3. Good Housekeeping magazine (Dr. Harkness's office)
4. Completed job applications from Job Service of TX
5. Letter from the Medicare Appeals Division
6. Pathology results State of Texas Pathology, Attn: Dr. Adams
7. Texas Health (payments)
8. People Magazine (Dr. Adams' office)
9. X-ray pouches for Dr. Clark
10. Blank IRS/W-4 forms
11. Envelope containing CMS-1500 forms, attn: Kerri Marshall
12. Personal marked letter to Dr. Harkness
13. 3 boxes of check blanks/South Padre Medical Center
14. South Padre Living (2 copies, magazine)
15. 1 box from South Padre Printing Company containing letterhead stationery
16. BC/BS of TX Appeals Division
17. Gold Prospector magazine (Dr. Gerald Bond)
18. 4 boxes of business cards, one for each Dr. in the clinic
19. Request for surgical consultation for Dr. Clark
20. Medicare (reimbursement)

SUPPLIES

MAIL SORTING

Dr. Bond

Dr. Harkness

Dr. Adams

Dr. Clark

Gladys

Accounts receivable

Insurance

Human Resources

Waiting Room

SUPPLIES

Telephone Record

PRIORITY ☐

Patient **Tom Seyfer**   Age

Caller **Est. pt.**

Telephone **555-6241**

Referred to **Dr. Bond**

Chart #

Chart Attached ☐ YES   ☒ NO

Date **04/10/08**   Time **12:00 NOON**   Rec'd By **GJ**

Message
Would like to see Dr. Bond for additional lesion removal, first available on 04/16.

Temp	Allergies

Response

PHY/RN Initials	Date / /	Time	Handled By

Telephone Record

PRIORITY ☐

Patient **Madison Owen**   Age **2 yr**

Caller **Polly (mother)**   **(est. pt.)**

Telephone **555-5255**

Referred to **Dr. Adams**

Chart #

Chart Attached ☐ YES   ☒ NO

Date **04/10/08**   Time **12:01 pm**   Rec'd By **G.J.**

Message
Needs 1st available appt. after 2 pm, either Friday 4/11 or Monday 4/14 for well child check

Temp	Allergies

Response

PHY/RN Initials	Date / /	Time	Handled By

Telephone Record

PRIORITY ☐

Patient **Kristie Olson**   Age **40**

Caller   **(NEW)**

Telephone **555-0603**

Referred to **Dr. Clark**

Chart #

Chart Attached ☐ YES   ☒ NO

Date **04/10/08**   Time **12:05 pm**   Rec'd By **GJ**

Message
Overweight – seeking gastric bypass – req appt for Thursday April 17, afternoon

Temp	Allergies

Response

PHY/RN Initials	Date / /	Time	Handled By

Telephone Record

PRIORITY ☐

Patient **Lilly Rice**   Age **33**

Caller **Dr. Andrews office**   **(NEW)**

Telephone **555-6563 (patient's telephone number)**

Referred to **Dr. Clark**

Chart #

Chart Attached ☐ YES   ☒ NO

Date **04/10/08**   Time **12:10 pm**   Rec'd By **G.J.**

Message
Consult Re: Pelvic pain Req appt for Wed. April 16 1st available time

Temp	Allergies

Response

PHY/RN Initials	Date / /	Time	Handled By

SUPPLIES

South Padre Medical Center

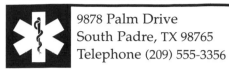

Gerald Bond, MD
Ray Adams, MD
Joyce Harkness, MD
Anthony Clark, MD

9878 Palm Drive
South Padre, TX 98765
Telephone (209) 555-3356

PATIENT INFORMATION
Please Print

Today's Date _____

Last Name _____ First Name _____ Initial _____

Date of Birth _____ Age _____ Sex _____ SS# _____-_____-_____

Home Address   Street _____ City _____

State _____ Zip_____ Home Phone (_____)_____

Occupation _____ Employer _____

Employer Address   Street _____ City_____

State _____ Zip _____ Work Phone (_____)_____

Are you currently a student?   Yes   No   Name of School _____

Spouse's Name _____ Marital Status   M   S   D   W   SEP

Spouse's SS# _____-_____-_____ Spouse's Employer _____

In case of emergency, notify _____ Relationship_____

Home Phone (____) _____ Work Phone (____) _____

If you are a minor: Parent's _____SS# _____-_____-_____

Street _____ City _____ State _____ Zip_____

Home Phone (____) _____ Work Phone (____) _____

Reason for Visit _____

            Work related injury?   Yes   No   Date of injury_____

            Automobile accident?   Yes   No   Date of injury_____

            Other injury?   Yes   No   Date of injury_____

Insurance (Primary)   Company Name: _____

Street _____ City _____ State _____ Zip_____

Subscriber's Name _____

Relationship to Subscriber: _____

Policy #_____ Group #_____

Insurance (Secondary)   Company Name: _____

Street _____ City _____ State _____ Zip_____

Subscriber's Name _____

Relationship to Subscriber: _____

Policy #_____ Group #_____

Assignment of Benefits:

I directly assign all medical/surgical benefits, including major medical benefits and Medicare, to South Padre Medical Center. I understand that this authorization for assignment remains in effect until I revoke it in writing. A photocopy of this assignment will be considered as valid as this original assignment. I further understand that I am responsible for my indebtedness no matter what charges the insurance pays for.

Insured or Guardian's Signature _____ Date _____

SUPPLIES

South Padre Medical Center

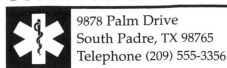

Gerald Bond, MD
Ray Adams, MD
Joyce Harkness, MD
Anthony Clark, MD

9878 Palm Drive
South Padre, TX 98765
Telephone (209) 555-3356

PATIENT INFORMATION
Please Print

Today's Date _____

Last Name _____ First Name _____ Initial _____

Date of Birth _____ Age _____ Sex _____ SS# _____-_____-_____

Home Address   Street _____ City _____

State _____ Zip _____ Home Phone (_____)_____

Occupation _____ Employer _____

Employer Address   Street _____ City_____

State _____ Zip _____ Work Phone (_____)_____

Are you currently a student?   Yes   No   Name of School _____

Spouse's Name _____ Marital Status   M   S   D   W   SEP

Spouse's SS# _____-_____-_____ Spouse's Employer _____

In case of emergency, notify _____ Relationship_____

Home Phone (____) _____ Work Phone (____) _____

If you are a minor: Parent's _____SS# _____-_____-_____

Street _____ City _____ State _____ Zip_____

Home Phone (____) _____ Work Phone (____) _____

Reason for Visit _____

    Work related injury?   Yes   No   Date of injury_____

    Automobile accident?   Yes   No   Date of injury_____

    Other injury?   Yes   No   Date of injury_____

Insurance (Primary)   Company Name: _____

Street _____ City _____ State _____ Zip_____

Subscriber's Name _____

Relationship to Subscriber: _____

Policy #_____ Group #_____

Insurance (Secondary) Company Name: _____

Street _____ City _____ State _____ Zip_____

Subscriber's Name _____

Relationship to Subscriber: _____

Policy #_____ Group #_____

Assignment of Benefits:

I directly assign all medical/surgical benefits, including major medical benefits and Medicare, to South Padre Medical Center. I understand that this authorization for assignment remains in effect until I revoke it in writing. A photocopy of this assignment will be considered as valid as this original assignment. I further understand that I am responsible for my indebtedness no matter what charges the insurance pays for.

Insured or Guardian's Signature _____ Date _____

SUPPLIES

TASK **4.4** 401

South Padre Medical Center

Patient's Name _____ Age _____ Sex _____ Marital Status S M W D

Address _____ Insurance _____

Telephone _____ Referred _____

Date	Subsequent Findings

SUPPLIES

South Padre Medical Center

Patient's Name _____ Age _____ Sex _____ Marital Status   S   M   W   D

Address _____ Insurance _____

Telephone _____ Referred _____

Date	Subsequent Findings

SUPPLIES

SOUTH PADRE HOSPITAL

980 Lagona Drive • South Padre, TX 98765 • Telephone (209) 555-4289

OPERATIVE REPORT

SUPPLIES

SOUTH PADRE HOSPITAL

980 Lagona Drive • South Padre, TX 98765 • Telephone (209) 555-4289

OPERATIVE REPORT

SUPPLIES

JOURNAL OF DAILY CHARGES & PAYMENTS

	DATE	PROFESSIONAL SERVICE	FEE	PAYMENT	ADJUST-MENT	NEW BALANCE	OLD BALANCE	PATIENT'S NAME		
1										1
2										2
3										3
4										4
5										5
6										6
7										7
8										8
9										9
10										10
11										11
12										12
13										13
14										14
15										15
16										16
17										17
18										18
19										19
20										20
21										21
22										22
23										23
24										24
25										25
26										26
27										27
28										28
29										29
30										30
31								TOTALS THIS PAGE		31
32								TOTAL PREVIOUS PAGE		32
33								TOTALS MONTH TO DATE		33

COLUMN A   COLUMN B   COLUMN C   COLUMN D   COLUMN E

MEMO _____

_____

_____

_____

DAILY - FROM LINE 31
ARITHMETIC POSTING PROOF

Column E	$
Plus Column A	
Sub-Total	
Minus Column B	
Sub-Total	
Minus Column C	
Equals Column D	

MONTH - FROM LINE 31
ACCOUNTS RECEIVABLE PROOF

Accts. Receivable Previous Day	$
Plus Column A	
Sub-Total	
Minus Column B	
Sub-Total	
Minus Column C	
Accts. receivable End of Day	

YEAR TO DATE - FROM LINE 33
ACCOUNTS RECEIVABLE PROOF

Accts. Receivable beginning of Month		$
Plus Column A	MONTH TO DATE	
Sub-Totaln C		
Minus Column B	MONTH TO DATE	
Sub-Total		
Minus Column C	MONTH TO DATE	
Accts. receivable End of Day	MONTH TO DATE	

SUPPLIES

TASK **5.3**   411

SOUTH PADRE MEDICAL CENTER
9878 Palm Drive
South Padre, TX 98765

Gerald Bond, MD
Ray Adams, MD
Joyce Harkness, MD
Anthony Clark, MD

Affiliated with:
Texas Health Corporation
1256 56th Avenue South
Houston, TX 99881

STATEMENT TO:

- -
TEAR OFF AND RETURN UPPER PORTION WITH PAYMENT

DATE	PROFESSIONAL SERVICE	FEE	PAYMENT	ADJUST-MENT	Balance Forward NEW BALANCE

SUPPLIES

SOUTH PADRE MEDICAL CENTER
9878 Palm Drive
South Padre, TX 98765

Gerald Bond, MD
Ray Adams, MD
Joyce Harkness, MD
Anthony Clark, MD

Affiliated with:
Texas Health Corporation
1256 56th Avenue South
Houston, TX 99881

STATEMENT TO:

- -

TEAR OFF AND RETURN UPPER PORTION WITH PAYMENT

Balance Forward

DATE	PROFESSIONAL SERVICE	FEE	PAYMENT	ADJUST-MENT	NEW BALANCE

SUPPLIES

SOUTH PADRE MEDICAL CENTER
9878 Palm Drive
South Padre, TX 98765

Gerald Bond, MD
Ray Adams, MD
Joyce Harkness, MD
Anthony Clark, MD

Affiliated with:
Texas Health Corporation
1256 56th Avenue South
Houston, TX 99881

STATEMENT TO:

- -

TEAR OFF AND RETURN UPPER PORTION WITH PAYMENT

Balance Forward

DATE	PROFESSIONAL SERVICE	FEE	PAYMENT	ADJUST-MENT	NEW BALANCE

SUPPLIES

SOUTH PADRE MEDICAL CENTER
9878 Palm Drive
South Padre, TX 98765

Gerald Bond, MD
Ray Adams, MD
Joyce Harkness, MD
Anthony Clark, MD

Affiliated with:
Texas Health Corporation
1256 56th Avenue South
Houston, TX 99881

STATEMENT TO:

TEAR OFF AND RETURN UPPER PORTION WITH PAYMENT

Balance Forward

DATE	PROFESSIONAL SERVICE	FEE	PAYMENT	ADJUST-MENT	NEW BALANCE

SUPPLIES

SOUTH PADRE MEDICAL CENTER
9878 Palm Drive
South Padre, TX 98765

Gerald Bond, MD
Ray Adams, MD
Joyce Harkness, MD
Anthony Clark, MD

Affiliated with:
Texas Health Corporation
1256 56th Avenue South
Houston, TX 99881

STATEMENT TO:

- -

TEAR OFF AND RETURN UPPER PORTION WITH PAYMENT

Balance Forward

DATE	PROFESSIONAL SERVICE	FEE	PAYMENT	ADJUST-MENT	NEW BALANCE

SUPPLIES

SOUTH PADRE MEDICAL CENTER
9878 Palm Drive
South Padre, TX 98765

Gerald Bond, MD
Ray Adams, MD
Joyce Harkness, MD
Anthony Clark, MD

Affiliated with:
Texas Health Corporation
1256 56th Avenue South
Houston, TX 99881

STATEMENT TO:

- -

TEAR OFF AND RETURN UPPER PORTION WITH PAYMENT

Balance
Forward

DATE	PROFESSIONAL SERVICE	FEE	PAYMENT	ADJUST-MENT	NEW BALANCE

SUPPLIES

SOUTH PADRE MEDICAL CENTER
9878 Palm Drive
South Padre, TX 98765

Gerald Bond, MD
Ray Adams, MD
Joyce Harkness, MD
Anthony Clark, MD

Affiliated with:
Texas Health Corporation
1256 56th Avenue South
Houston, TX 99881

STATEMENT TO:

THOMAS BLAIR
437 WEST MONROE
SOUTH PADRE TX 98764

- -

TEAR OFF AND RETURN UPPER PORTION WITH PAYMENT

Balance Forward   0

DATE	PROFESSIONAL SERVICE	FEE		PAYMENT		ADJUST-MENT		NEW BALANCE	
01/30/08	Consultation, New	200	00	50	00			150	00
02/15/08	BC/BS Payment			124	00			26	00

SUPPLIES

SOUTH PADRE MEDICAL CENTER
9878 Palm Drive
South Padre, TX 98765

Gerald Bond, MD
Ray Adams, MD
Joyce Harkness, MD
Anthony Clark, MD

Affiliated with:
Texas Health Corporation
1256 56th Avenue South
Houston, TX 99881

STATEMENT TO:

MAYNARD HOVLETT
2698 LANKY LANE
SOUTH PADRE TX 98765

- -
TEAR OFF AND RETURN UPPER PORTION WITH PAYMENT

Balance Forward *200.00*

DATE	PROFESSIONAL SERVICE	FEE	PAYMENT	ADJUST-MENT	NEW BALANCE

SUPPLIES

SOUTH PADRE MEDICAL CENTER
9878 Palm Drive
South Padre, TX 98765

Gerald Bond, MD
Ray Adams, MD
Joyce Harkness, MD
Anthony Clark, MD

Affiliated with:
Texas Health Corporation
1256 56th Avenue South
Houston, TX 99881

STATEMENT TO:

LARRY SMITH
90 LAZY DRIVE SOUTH
SOUTH PADRE TX 98765

TEAR OFF AND RETURN UPPER PORTION WITH PAYMENT

Balance Forward *0*

DATE	PROFESSIONAL SERVICE	FEE		PAYMENT		ADJUST-MENT		NEW BALANCE	
03/20/08	Office visit, New	45	00	10	00			35	00

SUPPLIES

SOUTH PADRE MEDICAL CENTER
9878 Palm Drive
South Padre, TX 98765

Gerald Bond, MD
Ray Adams, MD
Joyce Harkness, MD
Anthony Clark, MD

Affiliated with:
Texas Health Corporation
1256 56th Avenue South
Houston, TX 99881

STATEMENT TO:

> ANNE MEIRES
> 14 WESTERN WAY
> SOUTH PADRE TX 98765

TEAR OFF AND RETURN UPPER PORTION WITH PAYMENT

				Balance Forward	0	
DATE	PROFESSIONAL SERVICE	FEE	PAYMENT	ADJUST-MENT	NEW BALANCE	
02/15/08	Office visit Physical	200 00	200 00		0 00	
03/05/08	Office visit	65 00			65 00	

SUPPLIES

SOUTH PADRE MEDICAL CENTER
9878 Palm Drive
South Padre, TX 98765

Gerald Bond, MD
Ray Adams, MD
Joyce Harkness, MD
Anthony Clark, MD

Affiliated with:
Texas Health Corporation
1256 56th Avenue South
Houston, TX 99881

STATEMENT TO:

GLORIA GOLDMAN
PATIENT: EDWARD A GOLDMAN
206 CORA LEE
SOUTH PADRE TX 98765

TEAR OFF AND RETURN UPPER PORTION WITH PAYMENT

Balance Forward 225.00

DATE	PROFESSIONAL SERVICE	FEE	PAYMENT	ADJUST-MENT	NEW BALANCE
03/27/08	Office visit, New	25 00	50 00		200 00
04/01/08	Cash		25 00		175 00

SUPPLIES

SOUTH PADRE MEDICAL CENTER
9878 Palm Drive
South Padre, TX 98765

Gerald Bond, MD
Ray Adams, MD
Joyce Harkness, MD
Anthony Clark, MD

Affiliated with:
Texas Health Corporation
1256 56th Avenue South
Houston, TX 99881

STATEMENT TO:

JASPER HUNT
40 FELLOW DRIVE
SOUTH PADRE TX 98765

- -

TEAR OFF AND RETURN UPPER PORTION WITH PAYMENT

Balance Forward   0

DATE	PROFESSIONAL SERVICE	FEE		PAYMENT		ADJUST-MENT		NEW BALANCE	
01/02/08	Office visit, New	140	00	50	00			90	00
02/02/08	Office visit	65	00	10	00			145	00
03/03/08	Cash			45	00			100	00

SUPPLIES

SOUTH PADRE MEDICAL CENTER
9878 Palm Drive
South Padre, TX 98765

Gerald Bond, MD
Ray Adams, MD
Joyce Harkness, MD
Anthony Clark, MD

Affiliated with:
Texas Health Corporation
1256 56th Avenue South
Houston, TX 99881

STATEMENT TO:

LEWIS L ROCK
1000 BASS AVENUE
SOUTH PADRE TX 98765

TEAR OFF AND RETURN UPPER PORTION WITH PAYMENT

Balance Forward   0

DATE	PROFESSIONAL SERVICE	FEE		PAYMENT		ADJUST-MENT		NEW BALANCE	
03/10/08	Office visit, New	120	00	10	00			110	00
03/20/08	Office visit, Est	105	00					215	00

SUPPLIES

DEPOSIT TICKET

SOUTH PADRE MEDICAL CENTER
9878 PALM DRIVE
SOUTH PADRE, TX 98765

FIRST NATIONAL BANK
100 FIRST STREET
SOUTH PADRE, TX 98765

DATE _____

DEPOSITS MAY NOT BE AVAILABLE FOR IMMEDIATE WITHDRAWAL

		DOLLARS	CENTS
CURRENCY			
COIN			
CHECKS	LIST EACH SEPARATELY		
1			
2			
3			
4			
5			
6			
7			
8			
9			
10			
11			
12			
13			
14			
15			
16			
17			
18			
19			
20			
21			
22			
23			
24			
25			
26			
27			
28			
TOTAL FROM OTHER SIDE OR ATTACHED LIST			
PLEASE RE-ENTER TOTAL HERE	T O T A L		

$

0000100102005

Checks and other items are received for deposit subject to the provisions of the Uniform Commercial Code or any applicable colllection agreement.

SUPPLIES

Gerald Bond, MD
Ray Adams, MD
Joyce Harkness, MD
Anthony Clark, MD

South Padre Medical Center

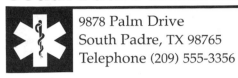

9878 Palm Drive
South Padre, TX 98765
Telephone (209) 555-3356

SUPPLIES

South Padre Medical Center
9878 Palm Drive
SOUTH PADRE, TX 98765

FIRST NATIONAL BANK
100 FIRST STREET
SOUTH PADRE, TX 98765

$\frac{98\text{-}95}{1251}$

N⁰   999

PAY _____ DOLLARS

	DATE	CHECK NO.	AMOUNT	

TO THE
ORDER OF _____

_____   _____

_____   _____

⑈0⑈0123⑈ ⑆4567⑈8901⑆ ⑈1234567890⑈

TASK **5.4**   443

SUPPLIES

South Padre Medical Center
9878 Palm Drive
SOUTH PADRE, TX 98765

FIRST NATIONAL BANK
100 FIRST STREET
SOUTH PADRE, TX 98765

98-95
‾‾‾‾
1251

Nº   1000

PAY _____ DOLLARS

DATE	CHECK NO.	AMOUNT	

TO THE
ORDER OF _____

⑈0⑈0123⑈ ⑊4567⑈8901⑊ ⑈1234567890⑈

TASK **5.4**   445

SUPPLIES

SOUTH PADRE MEDICAL CENTER
PETTY CASH JOURNAL

Beginning Balance:

DATE	STAFF	PURPOSE	AMOUNT	BALANCE

SUPPLIES

SOUTH PADRE MEDICAL CENTER
9878 Palm Drive
South Padre, TX 98765

Gerald Bond, MD
Ray Adams, MD
Joyce Harkness, MD
Anthony Clark, MD

Affiliated with:
Texas Health Corporation
1256 56th Avenue South
Houston, TX 99881

STATEMENT TO:

NORMA FIELD
227 MORNINGSIDE DRIVE
SOUTH PADRE TX 98765

TEAR OFF AND RETURN UPPER PORTION WITH PAYMENT

DATE	PROFESSIONAL SERVICE	FEE		PAYMENT		ADJUST-MENT		NEW BALANCE	
						Balance Forward			
03/02/08	Office visit	200	00	20	00			180	00
03/09/08	Medicare filed								

SUPPLIES

SOUTH PADRE MEDICAL CENTER
9878 Palm Drive
South Padre, TX 98765

Gerald Bond, MD
Ray Adams, MD
Joyce Harkness, MD
Anthony Clark, MD

Affiliated with:
Texas Health Corporation
1256 56th Avenue South
Houston, TX 99881

STATEMENT TO:

MAYNARD ZACHARIZISON
1399 PEARL WAY
SOUTH PADRE TX 98765

- -
TEAR OFF AND RETURN UPPER PORTION WITH PAYMENT

DATE	PROFESSIONAL SERVICE	FEE		PAYMENT		ADJUST-MENT		NEW BALANCE	
						Balance Forward			
09/01/07	Consultation	200	00					200	00
10/01/07	Notice 30 days								
11/01/07	Notice 60 days								
12/01/07	Notice 90 days								
01/01/08	Final notice								
02/01/08	Sent to Collection								
03/09/08	Island Collection			37	50			162	50

SUPPLIES

South Padre Medical Center

Interoffice Memo

SUPPLIES

South Padre Medical Center

Interoffice Memo

SUPPLIES

South Padre Medical Center

Interoffice Memo

SUPPLIES

South Padre Medical Center

Interoffice Memo

SUPPLIES

South Padre Medical Center

Interoffice Memo

SUPPLIES

PRIORITY ☐ | **Telephone Record**

Patient _____ Age _____

Caller _____

Telephone _____

Referred to _____

Chart # _____

Chart Attached ☐ YES ☐ NO

Date ___/___/___ Time ___ Rec'd By ___

Message _____
_____
_____

Temp	Allergies

Response _____
_____

PHY/RN Initials	Date	Time	Handled By
	___/___/___		

PRIORITY ☐ | **Telephone Record**

Patient _____ Age _____

Caller _____

Telephone _____

Referred to _____

Chart # _____

Chart Attached ☐ YES ☐ NO

Date ___/___/___ Time ___ Rec'd By ___

Message _____
_____
_____

Temp	Allergies

Response _____
_____

PHY/RN Initials	Date	Time	Handled By
	___/___/___		

PRIORITY ☐ | **Telephone Record**

Patient _____ Age _____

Caller _____

Telephone _____

Referred to _____

Chart # _____

Chart Attached ☐ YES ☐ NO

Date ___/___/___ Time ___ Rec'd By ___

Message _____
_____
_____

Temp	Allergies

Response _____
_____

PHY/RN Initials	Date	Time	Handled By
	___/___/___		

PRIORITY ☐ | **Telephone Record**

Patient _____ Age _____

Caller _____

Telephone _____

Referred to _____

Chart # _____

Chart Attached ☐ YES ☐ NO

Date ___/___/___ Time ___ Rec'd By ___

Message _____
_____
_____

Temp	Allergies

Response _____
_____

PHY/RN Initials	Date	Time	Handled By
	___/___/___		

SUPPLIES

PRIORITY ☐

Telephone Record

Patient _____ Age _____

Message _____

_____

_____

Caller _____

Telephone _____

Temp	Allergies

Referred to _____

Response _____

Chart # _____

_____

Chart Attached ☐ YES ☐ NO

PHY/RN Initials	Date / /	Time	Handled By

Date / / Time _____ Rec'd By _____

SUPPLIES

South Padre Medical Center

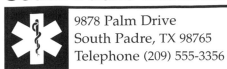

Gerald Bond, MD
Ray Adams, MD
Joyce Harkness, MD
Anthony Clark, MD

9878 Palm Drive
South Padre, TX 98765
Telephone (209) 555-3356

PATIENT INFORMATION

Please Print

Today's Date _____

Last Name _____ First Name _____ Initial _____

Date of Birth _____ Age _____ Sex _____ SS# _____-_____-_____

Home Address   Street _____ City _____

State _____ Zip_____ Home Phone (_____)_____

Occupation _____ Employer _____

Employer Address   Street _____ City_____

State _____ Zip _____ Work Phone (_____)_____

Are you currently a student?   Yes   No   Name of School _____

Spouse's Name _____ Marital Status   M   S   D   W   SEP

Spouse's SS# _____-_____-_____ Spouse's Employer _____

In case of emergency, notify _____ Relationship_____

Home Phone (_____) _____ Work Phone (_____) _____

If you are a minor: Parent's _____SS# _____-_____-_____

Street _____ City _____ State _____ Zip_____

Home Phone (_____) _____ Work Phone (_____) _____

Reason for Visit _____

Work related injury?   Yes   No   Date of injury_____

Automobile accident?   Yes   No   Date of injury_____

Other injury?   Yes   No   Date of injury_____

Insurance (Primary)   Company Name: _____

Street _____ City _____ State _____ Zip_____

Subscriber's Name _____

Relationship to Subscriber: _____

Policy #_____ Group #_____

Insurance (Secondary)   Company Name: _____

Street _____ City _____ State _____ Zip_____

Subscriber's Name _____

Relationship to Subscriber: _____

Policy #_____ Group #_____

Assignment of Benefits:

I directly assign all medical/surgical benefits, including major medical benefits and Medicare, to South Padre Medical Center. I understand that this
authorization for assignment remains in effect until I revoke it in writing. A photocopy of this assignment will be considered as valid as this original assignment.
I further understand that I am responsible for my indebtedness no matter what charges the insurance pays for.

Insured or Guardian's Signature _____ Date _____

SUPPLIES

South Padre Medical Center

Gerald Bond, MD
Ray Adams, MD
Joyce Harkness, MD
Anthony Clark, MD

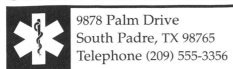

9878 Palm Drive
South Padre, TX 98765
Telephone (209) 555-3356

PATIENT INFORMATION

Please Print

Today's Date _____

Last Name _____ First Name _____ Initial _____

Date of Birth _____ Age _____ Sex _____ SS# _____-_____-_____

Home Address   Street _____ City _____

        State _____ Zip_____ Home Phone (_____)_____

Occupation _____ Employer _____

Employer Address   Street _____ City_____

        State _____ Zip _____ Work Phone (_____)_____

Are you currently a student?   Yes   No   Name of School _____

Spouse's Name _____ Marital Status   M   S   D   W   SEP

Spouse's SS# _____-_____-_____ Spouse's Employer _____

In case of emergency, notify _____ Relationship_____

        Home Phone (____) _____ Work Phone (____) _____

If you are a minor: Parent's _____SS# _____-_____-_____

        Street _____ City _____ State _____ Zip_____

        Home Phone (____) _____ Work Phone (____) _____

Reason for Visit _____

        Work related injury?   Yes   No   Date of injury_____

        Automobile accident?   Yes   No   Date of injury_____

        Other injury?   Yes   No   Date of injury_____

Insurance (Primary)   Company Name: _____

        Street _____ City _____ State _____ Zip_____

        Subscriber's Name _____

        Relationship to Subscriber: _____

        Policy #_____ Group #_____

Insurance (Secondary)   Company Name: _____

        Street _____ City _____ State _____ Zip_____

        Subscriber's Name _____

        Relationship to Subscriber: _____

        Policy #_____ Group #_____

Assignment of Benefits:

I directly assign all medical/surgical benefits, including major medical benefits and Medicare, to South Padre Medical Center. I understand that this authorization for assignment remains in effect until I revoke it in writing. A photocopy of this assignment will be considered as valid as this original assignment. I further understand that I am responsible for my indebtedness no matter what charges the insurance pays for.

Insured or Guardian's Signature _____ Date _____

SUPPLIES

HEALTH INSURANCE CLAIM FORM

APPROVED BY NATIONAL UNIFORM CLAIM COMMITTEE 08/05

☐☐ PICA   PICA ☐☐

| 1. MEDICARE ☐ (Medicare #) | MEDICAID ☐ (Medicaid #) | TRICARE CHAMPUS ☐ (Sponsor's SSN) | CHAMPVA ☐ (Member ID#) | GROUP HEALTH PLAN ☐ (SSN or ID) | FECA BLK LUNG ☐ (SSN) | OTHER ☐ (ID) | 1a. INSURED'S I.D. NUMBER   (For Program in Item 1) |

2. PATIENT'S NAME (Last Name, First Name, Middle Initial)

3. PATIENT'S BIRTH DATE MM DD YY — SEX M ☐ F ☐

4. INSURED'S NAME (Last Name, First Name, Middle Initial)

5. PATIENT'S ADDRESS (No., Street)

6. PATIENT RELATIONSHIP TO INSURED — Self ☐ Spouse ☐ Child ☐ Other ☐

7. INSURED'S ADDRESS (No., Street)

CITY | STATE

8. PATIENT STATUS — Single ☐ Married ☐ Other ☐ — Employed ☐ Full-Time Student ☐ Part-Time Student ☐

CITY | STATE

ZIP CODE | TELEPHONE (Include Area Code) ( )

ZIP CODE | TELEPHONE (Include Area Code) ( )

9. OTHER INSURED'S NAME (Last Name, First Name, Middle Initial)

10. IS PATIENT'S CONDITION RELATED TO:

11. INSURED'S POLICY GROUP OR FECA NUMBER

a. OTHER INSURED'S POLICY OR GROUP NUMBER

a. EMPLOYMENT? (Current or Previous) YES ☐ NO ☐

a. INSURED'S DATE OF BIRTH MM DD YY — SEX M ☐ F ☐

b. OTHER INSURED'S DATE OF BIRTH MM DD YY — SEX M ☐ F ☐

b. AUTO ACCIDENT? YES ☐ NO ☐ — PLACE (State)

b. EMPLOYER'S NAME OR SCHOOL NAME

c. EMPLOYER'S NAME OR SCHOOL NAME

c. OTHER ACCIDENT? YES ☐ NO ☐

c. INSURANCE PLAN NAME OR PROGRAM NAME

d. INSURANCE PLAN NAME OR PROGRAM NAME

10d. RESERVED FOR LOCAL USE

d. IS THERE ANOTHER HEALTH BENEFIT PLAN? YES ☐ NO ☐ — **If yes**, return to and complete item 9 a-d.

READ BACK OF FORM BEFORE COMPLETING & SIGNING THIS FORM.
12. PATIENT'S OR AUTHORIZED PERSON'S SIGNATURE I authorize the release of any medical or other information necessary to process this claim. I also request payment of government benefits either to myself or to the party who accepts assignment below.

SIGNED _____ DATE _____

13. INSURED'S OR AUTHORIZED PERSON'S SIGNATURE I authorize payment of medical benefits to the undersigned physician or supplier for services described below.

SIGNED _____

14. DATE OF CURRENT: MM DD YY — ◄ ILLNESS (First symptom) OR INJURY (Accident) OR PREGNANCY(LMP)

15. IF PATIENT HAS HAD SAME OR SIMILAR ILLNESS. GIVE FIRST DATE MM DD YY

16. DATES PATIENT UNABLE TO WORK IN CURRENT OCCUPATION MM DD YY FROM — TO MM DD YY

17. NAME OF REFERRING PROVIDER OR OTHER SOURCE | 17a. | 17b. NPI

18. HOSPITALIZATION DATES RELATED TO CURRENT SERVICES MM DD YY FROM — TO MM DD YY

19. RESERVED FOR LOCAL USE

20. OUTSIDE LAB? YES ☐ NO ☐ — $ CHARGES

21. DIAGNOSIS OR NATURE OF ILLNESS OR INJURY (Relate Items 1, 2, 3 or 4 to Item 24E by Line)

1. |___.___| 3. |___.___|

2. |___.___| 4. |___.___|

22. MEDICAID RESUBMISSION CODE — ORIGINAL REF. NO.

23. PRIOR AUTHORIZATION NUMBER

24. A. DATE(S) OF SERVICE						B. PLACE OF SERVICE	C. EMG	D. PROCEDURES, SERVICES, OR SUPPLIES (Explain Unusual Circumstances)		E. DIAGNOSIS POINTER	F. $ CHARGES	G. DAYS OR UNITS	H. EPSDT Family Plan	I. ID. QUAL.	J. RENDERING PROVIDER ID. #
From MM	DD	YY	To MM	DD	YY			CPT/HCPCS	MODIFIER						
1														NPI	
2														NPI	
3														NPI	
4														NPI	
5														NPI	
6														NPI	

25. FEDERAL TAX I.D. NUMBER — SSN ☐ EIN ☐

26. PATIENT'S ACCOUNT NO.

27. ACCEPT ASSIGNMENT? (For govt. claims, see back) YES ☐ NO ☐

28. TOTAL CHARGE $

29. AMOUNT PAID $

30. BALANCE DUE $

31. SIGNATURE OF PHYSICIAN OR SUPPLIER INCLUDING DEGREES OR CREDENTIALS (I certify that the statements on the reverse apply to this bill and are made a part thereof.)

SIGNED _____ DATE _____

32. SERVICE FACILITY LOCATION INFORMATION

a. | b.

33. BILLING PROVIDER INFO & PH # ( )

a. | b.

NUCC Instruction Manual available at: www.nucc.org

OMB APPROVAL PENDING

CARRIER

PATIENT AND INSURED INFORMATION

PHYSICIAN OR SUPPLIER INFORMATION

SUPPLIES

HEALTH INSURANCE CLAIM FORM

APPROVED BY NATIONAL UNIFORM CLAIM COMMITTEE 08/05

CARRIER

| | PICA | | | | | | | PICA | |

1. MEDICARE ☐ (Medicare #) MEDICAID ☐ (Medicaid #) TRICARE CHAMPUS ☐ (Sponsor's SSN) CHAMPVA ☐ (Member ID#) GROUP HEALTH PLAN ☐ (SSN or ID) FECA BLK LUNG ☐ (SSN) OTHER ☐ (ID)

1a. INSURED'S I.D. NUMBER (For Program in Item 1)

2. PATIENT'S NAME (Last Name, First Name, Middle Initial)

3. PATIENT'S BIRTH DATE MM DD YY SEX M ☐ F ☐

4. INSURED'S NAME (Last Name, First Name, Middle Initial)

5. PATIENT'S ADDRESS (No., Street)

6. PATIENT RELATIONSHIP TO INSURED Self ☐ Spouse ☐ Child ☐ Other ☐

7. INSURED'S ADDRESS (No., Street)

CITY   STATE

8. PATIENT STATUS Single ☐ Married ☐ Other ☐

CITY   STATE

ZIP CODE   TELEPHONE (Include Area Code) ( )

Employed ☐ Full-Time Student ☐ Part-Time Student ☐

ZIP CODE   TELEPHONE (Include Area Code) ( )

9. OTHER INSURED'S NAME (Last Name, First Name, Middle Initial)

10. IS PATIENT'S CONDITION RELATED TO:

11. INSURED'S POLICY GROUP OR FECA NUMBER

a. OTHER INSURED'S POLICY OR GROUP NUMBER

a. EMPLOYMENT? (Current or Previous) YES ☐ NO ☐

a. INSURED'S DATE OF BIRTH MM DD YY SEX M ☐ F ☐

b. OTHER INSURED'S DATE OF BIRTH MM DD YY SEX M ☐ F ☐

b. AUTO ACCIDENT? YES ☐ NO ☐ PLACE (State)

b. EMPLOYER'S NAME OR SCHOOL NAME

c. EMPLOYER'S NAME OR SCHOOL NAME

c. OTHER ACCIDENT? YES ☐ NO ☐

c. INSURANCE PLAN NAME OR PROGRAM NAME

d. INSURANCE PLAN NAME OR PROGRAM NAME

10d. RESERVED FOR LOCAL USE

d. IS THERE ANOTHER HEALTH BENEFIT PLAN? YES ☐ NO ☐ **If yes**, return to and complete item 9 a-d.

READ BACK OF FORM BEFORE COMPLETING & SIGNING THIS FORM.

12. PATIENT'S OR AUTHORIZED PERSON'S SIGNATURE I authorize the release of any medical or other information necessary to process this claim. I also request payment of government benefits either to myself or to the party who accepts assignment below.

SIGNED _____   DATE _____

13. INSURED'S OR AUTHORIZED PERSON'S SIGNATURE I authorize payment of medical benefits to the undersigned physician or supplier for services described below.

SIGNED _____

PATIENT AND INSURED INFORMATION

14. DATE OF CURRENT: MM DD YY ILLNESS (First symptom) OR INJURY (Accident) OR PREGNANCY(LMP)

15. IF PATIENT HAS HAD SAME OR SIMILAR ILLNESS. GIVE FIRST DATE MM DD YY

16. DATES PATIENT UNABLE TO WORK IN CURRENT OCCUPATION FROM MM DD YY TO MM DD YY

17. NAME OF REFERRING PROVIDER OR OTHER SOURCE

17a.
17b. NPI

18. HOSPITALIZATION DATES RELATED TO CURRENT SERVICES FROM MM DD YY TO MM DD YY

19. RESERVED FOR LOCAL USE

20. OUTSIDE LAB? YES ☐ NO ☐ $ CHARGES

21. DIAGNOSIS OR NATURE OF ILLNESS OR INJURY (Relate Items 1, 2, 3 or 4 to Item 24E by Line)

1. |___.___| 3. |___.___|
2. |___.___| 4. |___.___|

22. MEDICAID RESUBMISSION CODE   ORIGINAL REF. NO.

23. PRIOR AUTHORIZATION NUMBER

24. A. DATE(S) OF SERVICE From MM DD YY To MM DD YY	B. PLACE OF SERVICE	C. EMG	D. PROCEDURES, SERVICES, OR SUPPLIES (Explain Unusual Circumstances) CPT/HCPCS MODIFIER	E. DIAGNOSIS POINTER	F. $ CHARGES	G. DAYS OR UNITS	H. EPSDT Family Plan	I. ID. QUAL.	J. RENDERING PROVIDER ID. #
1									NPI
2									NPI
3									NPI
4									NPI
5									NPI
6									NPI

25. FEDERAL TAX I.D. NUMBER SSN ☐ EIN ☐

26. PATIENT'S ACCOUNT NO.

27. ACCEPT ASSIGNMENT? (For govt. claims, see back) YES ☐ NO ☐

28. TOTAL CHARGE $

29. AMOUNT PAID $

30. BALANCE DUE $

31. SIGNATURE OF PHYSICIAN OR SUPPLIER INCLUDING DEGREES OR CREDENTIALS (I certify that the statements on the reverse apply to this bill and are made a part thereof.)

SIGNED _____   DATE _____

32. SERVICE FACILITY LOCATION INFORMATION

a.   b.

33. BILLING PROVIDER INFO & PH # ( )

a.   b.

PHYSICIAN OR SUPPLIER INFORMATION

SUPPLIES

NUCC Instruction Manual available at: www.nucc.org

OMB APPROVAL PENDING

HEALTH INSURANCE CLAIM FORM

APPROVED BY NATIONAL UNIFORM CLAIM COMMITTEE 08/05

☐☐ PICA

PICA ☐☐

| 1. MEDICARE ☐ (Medicare #) | MEDICAID ☐ (Medicaid #) | TRICARE CHAMPUS ☐ (Sponsor's SSN) | CHAMPVA ☐ (Member ID#) | GROUP HEALTH PLAN ☐ (SSN or ID) | FECA BLK LUNG ☐ (SSN) | OTHER ☐ (ID) | 1a. INSURED'S I.D. NUMBER (For Program in Item 1) |

2. PATIENT'S NAME (Last Name, First Name, Middle Initial)

3. PATIENT'S BIRTH DATE MM DD YY   SEX M ☐ F ☐

4. INSURED'S NAME (Last Name, First Name, Middle Initial)

5. PATIENT'S ADDRESS (No., Street)

6. PATIENT RELATIONSHIP TO INSURED
Self ☐ Spouse ☐ Child ☐ Other ☐

7. INSURED'S ADDRESS (No., Street)

CITY   STATE

8. PATIENT STATUS
Single ☐ Married ☐ Other ☐
Employed ☐ Full-Time Student ☐ Part-Time Student ☐

CITY   STATE

ZIP CODE   TELEPHONE (Include Area Code) (   )

ZIP CODE   TELEPHONE (Include Area Code) (   )

9. OTHER INSURED'S NAME (Last Name, First Name, Middle Initial)

10. IS PATIENT'S CONDITION RELATED TO:

11. INSURED'S POLICY GROUP OR FECA NUMBER

a. OTHER INSURED'S POLICY OR GROUP NUMBER

a. EMPLOYMENT? (Current or Previous)
☐ YES ☐ NO

a. INSURED'S DATE OF BIRTH MM DD YY   SEX M ☐ F ☐

b. OTHER INSURED'S DATE OF BIRTH MM DD YY   SEX M ☐ F ☐

b. AUTO ACCIDENT?   PLACE (State)
☐ YES ☐ NO

b. EMPLOYER'S NAME OR SCHOOL NAME

c. EMPLOYER'S NAME OR SCHOOL NAME

c. OTHER ACCIDENT?
☐ YES ☐ NO

c. INSURANCE PLAN NAME OR PROGRAM NAME

d. INSURANCE PLAN NAME OR PROGRAM NAME

10d. RESERVED FOR LOCAL USE

d. IS THERE ANOTHER HEALTH BENEFIT PLAN?
☐ YES ☐ NO **If yes**, return to and complete item 9 a-d.

READ BACK OF FORM BEFORE COMPLETING & SIGNING THIS FORM.
12. PATIENT'S OR AUTHORIZED PERSON'S SIGNATURE I authorize the release of any medical or other information necessary to process this claim. I also request payment of government benefits either to myself or to the party who accepts assignment below.

SIGNED _____ DATE _____

13. INSURED'S OR AUTHORIZED PERSON'S SIGNATURE I authorize payment of medical benefits to the undersigned physician or supplier for services described below.

SIGNED _____

14. DATE OF CURRENT: MM DD YY ◄ ILLNESS (First symptom) OR INJURY (Accident) OR PREGNANCY(LMP)

15. IF PATIENT HAS HAD SAME OR SIMILAR ILLNESS. GIVE FIRST DATE MM DD YY

16. DATES PATIENT UNABLE TO WORK IN CURRENT OCCUPATION
FROM MM DD YY TO MM DD YY

17. NAME OF REFERRING PROVIDER OR OTHER SOURCE

17a.
17b. NPI

18. HOSPITALIZATION DATES RELATED TO CURRENT SERVICES
FROM MM DD YY TO MM DD YY

19. RESERVED FOR LOCAL USE

20. OUTSIDE LAB? ☐ YES ☐ NO $ CHARGES

21. DIAGNOSIS OR NATURE OF ILLNESS OR INJURY (Relate Items 1, 2, 3 or 4 to Item 24E by Line)

1. |___.___| 3. |___.___|

2. |___.___| 4. |___.___|

22. MEDICAID RESUBMISSION CODE   ORIGINAL REF. NO.

23. PRIOR AUTHORIZATION NUMBER

24. A. DATE(S) OF SERVICE						B. PLACE OF SERVICE	C. EMG	D. PROCEDURES, SERVICES, OR SUPPLIES (Explain Unusual Circumstances)		E. DIAGNOSIS POINTER	F. $ CHARGES	G. DAYS OR UNITS	H. EPSDT Family Plan	I. ID. QUAL.	J. RENDERING PROVIDER ID. #
From MM	DD	YY	To MM	DD	YY			CPT/HCPCS	MODIFIER						
1														NPI	
2														NPI	
3														NPI	
4														NPI	
5														NPI	
6														NPI	

25. FEDERAL TAX I.D. NUMBER   SSN ☐ EIN ☐

26. PATIENT'S ACCOUNT NO.

27. ACCEPT ASSIGNMENT? (For govt. claims, see back) ☐ YES ☐ NO

28. TOTAL CHARGE $

29. AMOUNT PAID $

30. BALANCE DUE $

31. SIGNATURE OF PHYSICIAN OR SUPPLIER INCLUDING DEGREES OR CREDENTIALS (I certify that the statements on the reverse apply to this bill and are made a part thereof.)

SIGNED _____ DATE _____

32. SERVICE FACILITY LOCATION INFORMATION

a.   b.

33. BILLING PROVIDER INFO & PH # (   )

a.   b.

NUCC Instruction Manual available at: www.nucc.org

OMB APPROVAL PENDING

SUPPLIES

CARRIER ↑

PATIENT AND INSURED INFORMATION

PHYSICIAN OR SUPPLIER INFORMATION

HEALTH INSURANCE CLAIM FORM

APPROVED BY NATIONAL UNIFORM CLAIM COMMITTEE 08/05

| | PICA | | | | | | | | | | PICA | | |

1. MEDICARE	MEDICAID	TRICARE CHAMPUS	CHAMPVA	GROUP HEALTH PLAN	FECA BLK LUNG	OTHER	1a. INSURED'S I.D. NUMBER	(For Program in Item 1)
(Medicare #)	(Medicaid #)	(Sponsor's SSN)	(Member ID#)	(SSN or ID)	(SSN)	(ID)		

2. PATIENT'S NAME (Last Name, First Name, Middle Initial)	3. PATIENT'S BIRTH DATE MM DD YY SEX M F	4. INSURED'S NAME (Last Name, First Name, Middle Initial)

5. PATIENT'S ADDRESS (No., Street)	6. PATIENT RELATIONSHIP TO INSURED Self Spouse Child Other	7. INSURED'S ADDRESS (No., Street)

CITY	STATE	8. PATIENT STATUS Single Married Other	CITY	STATE

ZIP CODE	TELEPHONE (Include Area Code) ( )	Employed Full-Time Student Part-Time Student	ZIP CODE	TELEPHONE (Include Area Code) ( )

9. OTHER INSURED'S NAME (Last Name, First Name, Middle Initial)	10. IS PATIENT'S CONDITION RELATED TO:	11. INSURED'S POLICY GROUP OR FECA NUMBER

a. OTHER INSURED'S POLICY OR GROUP NUMBER	a. EMPLOYMENT? (Current or Previous) YES NO	a. INSURED'S DATE OF BIRTH MM DD YY SEX M F

b. OTHER INSURED'S DATE OF BIRTH MM DD YY SEX M F	b. AUTO ACCIDENT? PLACE (State) YES NO	b. EMPLOYER'S NAME OR SCHOOL NAME

c. EMPLOYER'S NAME OR SCHOOL NAME	c. OTHER ACCIDENT? YES NO	c. INSURANCE PLAN NAME OR PROGRAM NAME

d. INSURANCE PLAN NAME OR PROGRAM NAME	10d. RESERVED FOR LOCAL USE	d. IS THERE ANOTHER HEALTH BENEFIT PLAN? YES NO If yes, return to and complete item 9 a-d.

READ BACK OF FORM BEFORE COMPLETING & SIGNING THIS FORM.

12. PATIENT'S OR AUTHORIZED PERSON'S SIGNATURE I authorize the release of any medical or other information necessary to process this claim. I also request payment of government benefits either to myself or to the party who accepts assignment below.

SIGNED _____ DATE _____

13. INSURED'S OR AUTHORIZED PERSON'S SIGNATURE I authorize payment of medical benefits to the undersigned physician or supplier for services described below.

SIGNED _____

14. DATE OF CURRENT: MM DD YY ◄ ILLNESS (First symptom) OR INJURY (Accident) OR PREGNANCY(LMP)	15. IF PATIENT HAS HAD SAME OR SIMILAR ILLNESS. GIVE FIRST DATE MM DD YY	16. DATES PATIENT UNABLE TO WORK IN CURRENT OCCUPATION MM DD YY MM DD YY FROM TO

| 17. NAME OF REFERRING PROVIDER OR OTHER SOURCE | 17a. | 18. HOSPITALIZATION DATES RELATED TO CURRENT SERVICES MM DD YY MM DD YY |
| | 17b. NPI | FROM TO |

19. RESERVED FOR LOCAL USE	20. OUTSIDE LAB? YES NO $ CHARGES

21. DIAGNOSIS OR NATURE OF ILLNESS OR INJURY (Relate Items 1, 2, 3 or 4 to Item 24E by Line)

1. |___.___ 3. |___.___

2. |___.___ 4. |___.___

22. MEDICAID RESUBMISSION CODE ORIGINAL REF. NO.
23. PRIOR AUTHORIZATION NUMBER

24. A. DATE(S) OF SERVICE From MM DD YY To MM DD YY	B. PLACE OF SERVICE	C. EMG	D. PROCEDURES, SERVICES, OR SUPPLIES (Explain Unusual Circumstances) CPT/HCPCS MODIFIER	E. DIAGNOSIS POINTER	F. $ CHARGES	G. DAYS OR UNITS	H. EPSDT Family Plan	I. ID. QUAL.	J. RENDERING PROVIDER ID. #
1									NPI
2									NPI
3									NPI
4									NPI
5									NPI
6									NPI

25. FEDERAL TAX I.D. NUMBER SSN EIN	26. PATIENT'S ACCOUNT NO.	27. ACCEPT ASSIGNMENT? (For govt. claims, see back) YES NO	28. TOTAL CHARGE $	29. AMOUNT PAID $	30. BALANCE DUE $

31. SIGNATURE OF PHYSICIAN OR SUPPLIER INCLUDING DEGREES OR CREDENTIALS (I certify that the statements on the reverse apply to this bill and are made a part thereof.) SIGNED _____ DATE _____	32. SERVICE FACILITY LOCATION INFORMATION a. b.	33. BILLING PROVIDER INFO & PH # ( ) a. b.

NUCC Instruction Manual available at: www.nucc.org

OMB APPROVAL PENDING

SUPPLIES

CARRIER →

| | PICA | | | | | | | | PICA | |

1. MEDICARE ☐ (Medicare #) MEDICAID ☐ (Medicaid #) TRICARE CHAMPUS ☐ (Sponsor's SSN) CHAMPVA ☐ (Member ID#) GROUP HEALTH PLAN ☐ (SSN or ID) FECA BLK LUNG ☐ (SSN) OTHER ☐ (ID)

1a. INSURED'S I.D. NUMBER (For Program in Item 1)

2. PATIENT'S NAME (Last Name, First Name, Middle Initial)

3. PATIENT'S BIRTH DATE MM ☐ DD ☐ YY **SEX** M ☐ F ☐

4. INSURED'S NAME (Last Name, First Name, Middle Initial)

5. PATIENT'S ADDRESS (No., Street)

6. PATIENT RELATIONSHIP TO INSURED Self ☐ Spouse ☐ Child ☐ Other ☐

7. INSURED'S ADDRESS (No., Street)

CITY   STATE

8. PATIENT STATUS Single ☐ Married ☐ Other ☐   Employed ☐ Full-Time Student ☐ Part-Time Student ☐

CITY   STATE

ZIP CODE   TELEPHONE (Include Area Code) ( )

ZIP CODE   TELEPHONE (Include Area Code) ( )

9. OTHER INSURED'S NAME (Last Name, First Name, Middle Initial)

10. IS PATIENT'S CONDITION RELATED TO:

11. INSURED'S POLICY GROUP OR FECA NUMBER

a. OTHER INSURED'S POLICY OR GROUP NUMBER

a. EMPLOYMENT? (Current or Previous) YES ☐ NO ☐

a. INSURED'S DATE OF BIRTH MM ☐ DD ☐ YY **SEX** M ☐ F ☐

b. OTHER INSURED'S DATE OF BIRTH MM ☐ DD ☐ YY **SEX** M ☐ F ☐

b. AUTO ACCIDENT? YES ☐ NO ☐ **PLACE (State)** ☐

b. EMPLOYER'S NAME OR SCHOOL NAME

c. EMPLOYER'S NAME OR SCHOOL NAME

c. OTHER ACCIDENT? YES ☐ NO ☐

c. INSURANCE PLAN NAME OR PROGRAM NAME

d. INSURANCE PLAN NAME OR PROGRAM NAME

10d. RESERVED FOR LOCAL USE

d. IS THERE ANOTHER HEALTH BENEFIT PLAN? YES ☐ NO ☐ **If yes,** return to and complete item 9 a-d.

READ BACK OF FORM BEFORE COMPLETING & SIGNING THIS FORM.
12. PATIENT'S OR AUTHORIZED PERSON'S SIGNATURE I authorize the release of any medical or other information necessary to process this claim. I also request payment of government benefits either to myself or to the party who accepts assignment below.

SIGNED _____ DATE _____

13. INSURED'S OR AUTHORIZED PERSON'S SIGNATURE I authorize payment of medical benefits to the undersigned physician or supplier for services described below.

SIGNED _____

PATIENT AND INSURED INFORMATION →

14. DATE OF CURRENT: MM ☐ DD ☐ YY ◄ ILLNESS (First symptom) OR INJURY (Accident) OR PREGNANCY(LMP)

15. IF PATIENT HAS HAD SAME OR SIMILAR ILLNESS. GIVE FIRST DATE MM ☐ DD ☐ YY

16. DATES PATIENT UNABLE TO WORK IN CURRENT OCCUPATION FROM MM ☐ DD ☐ YY TO MM ☐ DD ☐ YY

17. NAME OF REFERRING PROVIDER OR OTHER SOURCE

17a.
17b. NPI

18. HOSPITALIZATION DATES RELATED TO CURRENT SERVICES FROM MM ☐ DD ☐ YY TO MM ☐ DD ☐ YY

19. RESERVED FOR LOCAL USE

20. OUTSIDE LAB? YES ☐ NO ☐ $ CHARGES

21. DIAGNOSIS OR NATURE OF ILLNESS OR INJURY (Relate Items 1, 2, 3 or 4 to Item 24E by Line)

1. ⌐___.___   3. ⌐___.___
2. ⌐___.___   4. ⌐___.___

22. MEDICAID RESUBMISSION CODE   ORIGINAL REF. NO.

23. PRIOR AUTHORIZATION NUMBER

24. A. DATE(S) OF SERVICE						B. PLACE OF SERVICE	C. EMG	D. PROCEDURES, SERVICES, OR SUPPLIES (Explain Unusual Circumstances)		E. DIAGNOSIS POINTER	F. $ CHARGES	G. DAYS OR UNITS	H. EPSDT Family Plan	I. ID. QUAL.	J. RENDERING PROVIDER ID. #
From MM	DD	YY	To MM	DD	YY			CPT/HCPCS	MODIFIER						
1														NPI	
2														NPI	
3														NPI	
4														NPI	
5														NPI	
6														NPI	

25. FEDERAL TAX I.D. NUMBER SSN ☐ EIN ☐

26. PATIENT'S ACCOUNT NO.

27. ACCEPT ASSIGNMENT? (For govt. claims, see back) YES ☐ NO ☐

28. TOTAL CHARGE $

29. AMOUNT PAID $

30. BALANCE DUE $

31. SIGNATURE OF PHYSICIAN OR SUPPLIER INCLUDING DEGREES OR CREDENTIALS (I certify that the statements on the reverse apply to this bill and are made a part thereof.)

SIGNED _____ DATE _____

32. SERVICE FACILITY LOCATION INFORMATION

a.   b.

33. BILLING PROVIDER INFO & PH # ( )

a.   b.

PHYSICIAN OR SUPPLIER INFORMATION →

SUPPLIES

NUCC Instruction Manual available at: www.nucc.org   OMB APPROVAL PENDING

1500

HEALTH INSURANCE CLAIM FORM

APPROVED BY NATIONAL UNIFORM CLAIM COMMITTEE 08/05

☐☐ PICA

PICA ☐☐

1. ☐ MEDICARE (Medicare #) ☐ MEDICAID (Medicaid #) ☐ TRICARE CHAMPUS (Sponsor's SSN) ☐ CHAMPVA (Member ID#) ☐ GROUP HEALTH PLAN (SSN or ID) ☐ FECA BLK LUNG (SSN) ☐ OTHER (ID)

1a. INSURED'S I.D. NUMBER (For Program in Item 1)

2. PATIENT'S NAME (Last Name, First Name, Middle Initial)

3. PATIENT'S BIRTH DATE MM | DD | YY   SEX M ☐ F ☐

4. INSURED'S NAME (Last Name, First Name, Middle Initial)

5. PATIENT'S ADDRESS (No., Street)

6. PATIENT RELATIONSHIP TO INSURED
Self ☐ Spouse ☐ Child ☐ Other ☐

7. INSURED'S ADDRESS (No., Street)

CITY   STATE

8. PATIENT STATUS
Single ☐ Married ☐ Other ☐
Employed ☐ Full-Time Student ☐ Part-Time Student ☐

CITY   STATE

ZIP CODE   TELEPHONE (Include Area Code) (   )

ZIP CODE   TELEPHONE (Include Area Code) (   )

9. OTHER INSURED'S NAME (Last Name, First Name, Middle Initial)

10. IS PATIENT'S CONDITION RELATED TO:

11. INSURED'S POLICY GROUP OR FECA NUMBER

a. OTHER INSURED'S POLICY OR GROUP NUMBER

a. EMPLOYMENT? (Current or Previous) ☐ YES ☐ NO

a. INSURED'S DATE OF BIRTH MM | DD | YY   SEX M ☐ F ☐

b. OTHER INSURED'S DATE OF BIRTH MM | DD | YY   SEX M ☐ F ☐

b. AUTO ACCIDENT? ☐ YES ☐ NO   PLACE (State) [   ]

b. EMPLOYER'S NAME OR SCHOOL NAME

c. EMPLOYER'S NAME OR SCHOOL NAME

c. OTHER ACCIDENT? ☐ YES ☐ NO

c. INSURANCE PLAN NAME OR PROGRAM NAME

d. INSURANCE PLAN NAME OR PROGRAM NAME

10d. RESERVED FOR LOCAL USE

d. IS THERE ANOTHER HEALTH BENEFIT PLAN?
☐ YES ☐ NO   If yes, return to and complete item 9 a-d.

READ BACK OF FORM BEFORE COMPLETING & SIGNING THIS FORM.
12. PATIENT'S OR AUTHORIZED PERSON'S SIGNATURE I authorize the release of any medical or other information necessary to process this claim. I also request payment of government benefits either to myself or to the party who accepts assignment below.

SIGNED _____ DATE _____

13. INSURED'S OR AUTHORIZED PERSON'S SIGNATURE I authorize payment of medical benefits to the undersigned physician or supplier for services described below.

SIGNED _____

14. DATE OF CURRENT: MM | DD | YY ◄ ILLNESS (First symptom) OR INJURY (Accident) OR PREGNANCY(LMP)

15. IF PATIENT HAS HAD SAME OR SIMILAR ILLNESS. GIVE FIRST DATE MM | DD | YY

16. DATES PATIENT UNABLE TO WORK IN CURRENT OCCUPATION
FROM MM | DD | YY TO MM | DD | YY

17. NAME OF REFERRING PROVIDER OR OTHER SOURCE

17a.
17b. NPI

18. HOSPITALIZATION DATES RELATED TO CURRENT SERVICES
FROM MM | DD | YY TO MM | DD | YY

19. RESERVED FOR LOCAL USE

20. OUTSIDE LAB? ☐ YES ☐ NO $ CHARGES

21. DIAGNOSIS OR NATURE OF ILLNESS OR INJURY (Relate Items 1, 2, 3 or 4 to Item 24E by Line)
1. |___. ___|
2. |___. ___|
3. |___. ___|
4. |___. ___|

22. MEDICAID RESUBMISSION CODE   ORIGINAL REF. NO.

23. PRIOR AUTHORIZATION NUMBER

24. A. DATE(S) OF SERVICE From MM DD YY	To MM DD YY	B. PLACE OF SERVICE	C. EMG	D. PROCEDURES, SERVICES, OR SUPPLIES (Explain Unusual Circumstances) CPT/HCPCS	MODIFIER	E. DIAGNOSIS POINTER	F. $ CHARGES	G. DAYS OR UNITS	H. EPSDT Family Plan	I. ID. QUAL.	J. RENDERING PROVIDER ID. #
1										NPI	
2										NPI	
3										NPI	
4										NPI	
5										NPI	
6										NPI	

25. FEDERAL TAX I.D. NUMBER ☐ SSN ☐ EIN

26. PATIENT'S ACCOUNT NO.

27. ACCEPT ASSIGNMENT? (For govt. claims, see back) ☐ YES ☐ NO

28. TOTAL CHARGE $

29. AMOUNT PAID $

30. BALANCE DUE $

31. SIGNATURE OF PHYSICIAN OR SUPPLIER INCLUDING DEGREES OR CREDENTIALS (I certify that the statements on the reverse apply to this bill and are made a part thereof.)

SIGNED _____ DATE _____

32. SERVICE FACILITY LOCATION INFORMATION
a.   b.

33. BILLING PROVIDER INFO & PH # (   )
a.   b.

NUCC Instruction Manual available at: www.nucc.org

OMB APPROVAL PENDING

TASK 7.1   481

South Padre Medical Center

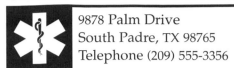

9878 Palm Drive
South Padre, TX 98765
Telephone (209) 555-3356

PATIENT INFORMATION

Please Print

Today's Date _____

Last Name _____ First Name _____ Initial _____

Date of Birth _____ Age _____ Sex _____ SS# _____-_____-_____

Home Address   Street _____ City _____

                    State _____ Zip_____ Home Phone (_____)_____

Occupation _____ Employer _____

Employer Address   Street _____ City_____

                    State _____ Zip _____ Work Phone (_____)_____

Are you currently a student?   Yes   No   Name of School _____

Spouse's Name _____ Marital Status   M   S   D   W   SEP

Spouse's SS# _____-_____-_____ Spouse's Employer _____

In case of emergency, notify _____ Relationship_____

                    Home Phone (____) _____ Work Phone (____) _____

If you are a minor: Parent's _____SS# _____-_____-_____

                    Street _____ City _____ State _____ Zip_____

                    Home Phone (____) _____ Work Phone (____) _____

Reason for Visit _____

                    Work related injury?   Yes   No   Date of injury_____

                    Automobile accident?   Yes   No   Date of injury_____

                    Other injury?   Yes   No   Date of injury_____

Insurance (Primary)   Company Name: _____

                    Street _____ City _____ State _____ Zip_____

                    Subscriber's Name _____

                    Relationship to Subscriber: _____

                    Policy #_____ Group #_____

Insurance (Secondary)   Company Name: _____

                    Street _____ City _____ State _____ Zip_____

                    Subscriber's Name _____

                    Relationship to Subscriber: _____

                    Policy #_____ Group #_____

Assignment of Benefits:

I directly assign all medical/surgical benefits, including major medical benefits and Medicare, to South Padre Medical Center. I understand that this authorization for assignment remains in effect until I revoke it in writing. A photocopy of this assignment will be considered as valid as this original assignment. I further understand that I am responsible for my indebtedness no matter what charges the insurance pays for.

Insured or Guardian's Signature _____ Date _____

SUPPLIES

South Padre Medical Center

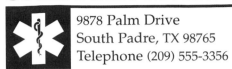

Gerald Bond, MD
Ray Adams, MD
Joyce Harkness, MD
Anthony Clark, MD

9878 Palm Drive
South Padre, TX 98765
Telephone (209) 555-3356

PATIENT INFORMATION

Please Print

Today's Date _____

Last Name _____ First Name _____ Initial _____

Date of Birth _____ Age _____ Sex _____ SS# _____-_____-_____

Home Address   Street _____ City _____

State _____ Zip_____ Home Phone (_____)_____

Occupation _____ Employer _____

Employer Address   Street _____ City_____

State _____ Zip _____ Work Phone (_____)_____

Are you currently a student?   Yes   No   Name of School _____

Spouse's Name _____ Marital Status   M   S   D   W   SEP

Spouse's SS# _____-_____-_____ Spouse's Employer _____

In case of emergency, notify _____ Relationship_____

Home Phone (____) _____ Work Phone (____) _____

If you are a minor: Parent's _____SS# _____-_____-_____

Street _____ City _____ State _____ Zip_____

Home Phone (____) _____ Work Phone (____) _____

Reason for Visit _____

Work related injury?	Yes	No	Date of injury	_____
Automobile accident?	Yes	No	Date of injury	_____
Other injury?	Yes	No	Date of injury	_____

Insurance (Primary)   Company Name: _____

Street _____ City _____ State _____ Zip_____

Subscriber's Name _____

Relationship to Subscriber: _____

Policy #_____ Group #_____

Insurance (Secondary)   Company Name: _____

Street _____ City _____ State _____ Zip_____

Subscriber's Name _____

Relationship to Subscriber: _____

Policy #_____ Group #_____

Assignment of Benefits:

I directly assign all medical/surgical benefits, including major medical benefits and Medicare, to South Padre Medical Center. I understand that this authorization for assignment remains in effect until I revoke it in writing. A photocopy of this assignment will be considered as valid as this original assignment. I further understand that I am responsible for my indebtedness no matter what charges the insurance pays for.

Insured or Guardian's Signature _____ Date _____

TASK **7.2**   485

SUPPLIES

South Padre Medical Center

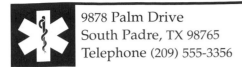

Gerald Bond, MD
Ray Adams, MD
Joyce Harkness, MD
Anthony Clark, MD

9878 Palm Drive
South Padre, TX 98765
Telephone (209) 555-3356

PATIENT INFORMATION
Please Print

Today's Date _____

Last Name _____ First Name _____ Initial _____

Date of Birth _____ Age _____ Sex _____ SS# _____-_____-_____

Home Address   Street _____ City _____

State _____ Zip _____ Home Phone (_____)_____

Occupation _____ Employer _____

Employer Address   Street _____ City_____

State _____ Zip _____ Work Phone (_____)_____

Are you currently a student?   Yes   No   Name of School _____

Spouse's Name _____ Marital Status   M   S   D   W   SEP

Spouse's SS# _____-_____-_____ Spouse's Employer _____

In case of emergency, notify _____ Relationship_____

Home Phone (_____) _____ Work Phone (_____) _____

If you are a minor: Parent's _____SS# _____-_____-_____

Street _____ City _____ State _____ Zip_____

Home Phone (_____) _____ Work Phone (_____) _____

Reason for Visit _____

Work related injury?	Yes	No	Date of injury	_____
Automobile accident?	Yes	No	Date of injury	_____
Other injury?	Yes	No	Date of injury	_____

Insurance (Primary)   Company Name: _____

Street _____ City _____ State _____ Zip_____

Subscriber's Name _____

Relationship to Subscriber: _____

Policy #_____ Group #_____

Insurance (Secondary) Company Name: _____

Street _____ City _____ State _____ Zip_____

Subscriber's Name _____

Relationship to Subscriber: _____

Policy #_____ Group #_____

Assignment of Benefits:

I directly assign all medical/surgical benefits, including major medical benefits and Medicare, to South Padre Medical Center. I understand that this authorization for assignment remains in effect until I revoke it in writing. A photocopy of this assignment will be considered as valid as this original assignment. I further understand that I am responsible for my indebtedness no matter what charges the insurance pays for.

Insured or Guardian's Signature _____ Date _____

SUPPLIES

South Padre Medical Center

Patient's Name _____ Age _____ Sex _____ Marital Status S M W D

Address _____ Insurance _____

Telephone _____ Referred _____

Date	Subsequent Findings

SUPPLIES

South Padre Medical Center

Patient's Name _____ Age _____ Sex _____ Marital Status S M W D

Address _____ Insurance _____

Telephone _____ Referred _____

Date	Subsequent Findings

SUPPLIES

South Padre Medical Center

Patient's Name _____ Age _____ Sex _____ Marital Status S M W D

Address _____ Insurance _____

Telephone _____ Referred _____

Date	Subsequent Findings

SUPPLIES

<u>New York City Cardiac Conference</u>

Dr. Harkness will leave Friday, April 18
Her flight is at 5:30am
Needs to be at the airport at 4:45 am
Her flight # is 19
Non-stop flight from South Padre to New York City
Arrive in New York City at 9:00am
Check-in New York City Hotel
Conference starts at 10:00am in the Green Room
Finishes at approx. 7:30pm
Leave New York City Saturday morning
Flight is at 7:30am, Flight #229
Non-stop flight from New York City to South Padre
Be at airport at 6:45am
Arrive at South Padre Airport at 12:00pm

****Reminder to Dr. Harkness to bring portfolio for conference and to pick up airline ticket at the check-in desk when she arrives at the airport.

SUPPLIES

REQUEST FOR PREAUTHORIZATION FOR SURGERY

Surgeon: Gerald Bond, MD
(circle one)   Ray Adams, MD
               Joyce Harkness, MD
               Anthony Clark, MD

PATIENT NAME: _____   FACILITY: _____

DATE OF BIRTH: _____   ADMIT DATE: _____

ACCOUNT #: _____   SURGERY DATE: _____

INSURANCE: _____   POLICY#: _____

PROCEDURE: _____

DIAGNOSIS: _____

AUTHORIZATION: _____

COMPLETED BY: _____

DATE COMPLETED: _____

SUPPLIES

REQUEST FOR PREAUTHORIZATION FOR SURGERY

Surgeon: Gerald Bond, MD
(circle one)   Ray Adams, MD
              Joyce Harkness, MD
              Anthony Clark, MD

PATIENT NAME: _____   FACILITY: _____

DATE OF BIRTH: _____   ADMIT DATE: _____

ACCOUNT #: _____   SURGERY DATE: _____

INSURANCE: _____   POLICY#: _____

PROCEDURE: _____

DIAGNOSIS: _____

AUTHORIZATION: _____

COMPLETED BY: _____

DATE COMPLETED: _____

SUPPLIES

REQUEST FOR PREAUTHORIZATION FOR SURGERY

Surgeon: Gerald Bond, MD
(circle one) Ray Adams, MD
Joyce Harkness, MD
Anthony Clark, MD

PATIENT NAME: _____   FACILITY: _____

DATE OF BIRTH: _____   ADMIT DATE: _____

ACCOUNT #: _____   SURGERY DATE: _____

INSURANCE: _____   POLICY#: _____

PROCEDURE: _____

DIAGNOSIS: _____

AUTHORIZATION: _____

COMPLETED BY: _____

DATE COMPLETED: _____

SUPPLIES

REQUEST FOR PREAUTHORIZATION FOR SURGERY

Surgeon: Gerald Bond, MD
(circle one)   Ray Adams, MD
               Joyce Harkness, MD
               Anthony Clark, MD

PATIENT NAME: _____   FACILITY: _____

DATE OF BIRTII: _____   ADMIT DATE: _____

ACCOUNT #: _____   SURGERY DATE: _____

INSURANCE: _____   POLICY#: _____

PROCEDURE: _____

DIAGNOSIS: _____

AUTHORIZATION: _____

COMPLETED BY: _____

DATE COMPLETED: _____

SUPPLIES

REQUEST FOR PREAUTHORIZATION FOR SURGERY

Surgeon: Gerald Bond, MD
(circle one)   Ray Adams, MD
                Joyce Harkness, MD
                Anthony Clark, MD

PATIENT NAME: _____   FACILITY: _____

DATE OF BIRTH: _____   ADMIT DATE: _____

ACCOUNT #: _____   SURGERY DATE: _____

INSURANCE: _____   POLICY#: _____

PROCEDURE: _____

DIAGNOSIS: _____

AUTHORIZATION: _____

COMPLETED BY: _____

DATE COMPLETED: _____

SUPPLIES

REQUEST FOR PREAUTHORIZATION FOR SURGERY

Surgeon: Gerald Bond, MD
(circle one) Ray Adams, MD
               Joyce Harkness, MD
               Anthony Clark, MD

PATIENT NAME: _____   FACILITY: _____

DATE OF BIRTH: _____   ADMIT DATE: _____

ACCOUNT #: _____   SURGERY DATE: _____

INSURANCE: _____   POLICY#: _____

PROCEDURE: _____

DIAGNOSIS: _____

AUTHORIZATION: _____

COMPLETED BY: _____

DATE COMPLETED: _____

SUPPLIES

South Padre Medical Center

SURGICAL REQUEST AND INFORMATION

This portion is to be completed by requesting surgeon.

Surgeon: ☒ Gerald Bond, MD
         ❑ Ray Adams, MD
         ❑ Joyce Harkness, MD
         ❑ Anthony Clark, MD

Schedule: ❑ URGENT   ☒ IMMEDIATE   ❑ PATIENT CONVENIENCE

Date Requested: ___04-16-08___   Time Requested: ___8:10 AM___

Patient Name: ___KLINT, SAM J.___   ACCOUNT #: ___00000-0012___

Procedure: ___BIOPSY OF KIDNEY___

Procedure Code(s): ___50200___

Diagnosis(es): ___RENAL FAILURE___

Diagnosis(es) Code(s): ___586___

Estimated Surgery Time: ___1 HOUR   OUTPATIENT___

Surgical Assistant Requested: ___—___

Additional Information: ___—___

This portion is to be completed by scheduling personnel.

Surgery Date: _____   Time: _____
            Day   Date

Authorization Obtained: ❑ YES   ❑ NO   ❑ REQUESTED

If authorization has been requested and response is pending, list date and contact information from the initial request.

Requested From: _____   Date: _____
            (Carrier and person)

Telephone: _____   Ext: _____

Completed By: _____

Date Completed: _____

SUPPLIES

South Padre Medical Center

SURGICAL REQUEST AND INFORMATION

This portion is to be completed by requesting surgeon.

Surgeon: ☒ Gerald Bond, MD
❏ Ray Adams, MD
❏ Joyce Harkness, MD
❏ Anthony Clark, MD

Schedule: ❏ URGENT ☒ IMMEDIATE ❏ PATIENT CONVENIENCE

Date Requested: ___04-16-08___ Time Requested: ___8:45 AM___

Patient Name: ___HARKLAND, EMMY L.___ ACCOUNT #: 00000-0110

Procedure: ___BREAST BIOPSY___

Procedure Code(s): ___19101___

Diagnosis(es): ___BREAST MASS___

Diagnosis(es) Code(s): ___239.3___

Estimated Surgery Time: ___1 HOUR___ ___OUTPATIENT___

Surgical Assistant Requested: _____

Additional Information: _____

This portion is to be completed by scheduling personnel.

Surgery Date: _____ Time: _____
         Day   Date

Authorization Obtained: ❏ YES ❏ NO ❏ REQUESTED

If authorization has been requested and response is pending, list date and contact information from the initial request.

Requested From: _____ Date: _____
         (Carrier and person)

Telephone: _____ Ext: _____

Completed By: _____

Date Completed: _____

SUPPLIES

South Padre Medical Center

SURGICAL REQUEST AND INFORMATION

This portion is to be completed by requesting surgeon.

Surgeon:
☒ Gerald Bond, MD
❏ Ray Adams, MD
❏ Joyce Harkness, MD
❏ Anthony Clark, MD

Schedule: ❏ URGENT ☒ IMMEDIATE ❏ PATIENT CONVENIENCE

Date Requested: _04-16-08_   Time Requested: _9:05 AM_

Patient Name: _BATES, MICHELLE L._   ACCOUNT #: _00000-0069_

Procedure: _NEEDLE BIOPSY RT BREAST_

Procedure Code(s): _19102_

Diagnosis(es): _BREAST NEOPLASM_

Diagnosis(es) Code(s): _239.3_

Estimated Surgery Time: _1 HOUR   OUTPATIENT_

Surgical Assistant Requested: _——_

Additional Information: _——_

This portion is to be completed by scheduling personnel.

Surgery Date: _____   Time: _____
         Day   Date

Authorization Obtained: ❏ YES   ❏ NO   ❏ REQUESTED

If authorization has been requested and response is pending, list date and contact information from the initial request.

Requested From: _____   Date: _____
        (Carrier and person)

Telephone: _____   Ext: _____

Completed By: _____

Date Completed: _____

SUPPLIES

South Padre Medical Center

SURGICAL REQUEST AND INFORMATION

This portion is to be completed by requesting surgeon.

Surgeon:
- ❏ Gerald Bond, MD
- ❏ Ray Adams, MD
- ❏ Joyce Harkness, MD
- ☒ Anthony Clark, MD

Schedule: ❏ URGENT   ☒ IMMEDIATE   ❏ PATIENT CONVENIENCE

Date Requested: ___04-16-08___   Time Requested: ___10:28 am___

Patient Name: ___Adams, Tony W.___   account #: 00000-0223

Procedure: ___Biopsy of Lymph Node, Excisional___

Procedure Code(s): ___38510___

Diagnosis(es): ___Lymphadenopathy___

Diagnosis(es) Code(s): ___785.6___

Estimated Surgery Time: ___1 hour   Inpatient___

Surgical Assistant Requested: ___Tony Andrews___

Additional Information: ___—___

This portion is to be completed by scheduling personnel.

Surgery Date: _____   Time: _____
        Day   Date

Authorization Obtained: ❏ YES   ❏ NO   ❏ REQUESTED

If authorization has been requested and response is pending, list date and contact information from the initial request.

Requested From: _____   Date: _____
         (Carrier and person)

Telephone: _____   Ext: _____

Completed By: _____

Date Completed: _____

SUPPLIES

South Padre Medical Center

SURGICAL REQUEST AND INFORMATION

This portion is to be completed by requesting surgeon.

Surgeon:
- ❏ Gerald Bond, MD
- ❏ Ray Adams, MD
- ☒ Joyce Harkness, MD
- ❏ Anthony Clark, MD

Schedule: ❏ URGENT   ☒ IMMEDIATE   ❏ PATIENT CONVENIENCE

Date Requested: _____04-16-08_____   Time Requested: _____10:40 am_____

Patient Name: _____Anderson, Charlie M._____   account #: 00000-0009 _____

Procedure: _____Echocardiogram_____

Procedure Code(s): _____93318_____

Diagnosis(es): _____Atrial Fibrillation_____

Diagnosis(es) Code(s): _____427.31_____

Estimated Surgery Time: _____45 minutes_____   outpatient _____

Surgical Assistant Requested: _____—_____

Additional Information: _____—_____

This portion is to be completed by scheduling personnel.

Surgery Date: _____   Time: _____
          Day   Date

Authorization Obtained: ❏ YES   ❏ NO   ❏ REQUESTED

If authorization has been requested and response is pending, list date and contact information from the initial request.

Requested From: _____   Date: _____
          (Carrier and person)

Telephone: _____   Ext: _____

Completed By: _____

Date Completed: _____

SUPPLIES

South Padre Medical Center

SURGICAL REQUEST AND INFORMATION

This portion is to be completed by requesting surgeon.

Surgeon:
- ❏ Gerald Bond, MD
- ❏ Ray Adams, MD
- ❏ Joyce Harkness, MD
- ☒ Anthony Clark, MD

Schedule: ❏ URGENT ☒ IMMEDIATE ❏ PATIENT CONVENIENCE

Date Requested: ___04/16/08___   Time Requested: ___10:45 am___

Patient Name: ___Wood, Tina J.___   account #: 00000-2123

Procedure: ___Cervical Diskectomy (2 disc, anterior)___

Procedure Code(s): ___63075, 63076___

Diagnosis(es): ___Herniated disc   C5-7___

Diagnosis(es) Code(s): ___722.0___

Estimated Surgery Time: ___1.5 hours   Inpatient___

Surgical Assistant Requested: ___Peggy Johnson___

Additional Information: _____

This portion is to be completed by scheduling personnel.

Surgery Date: _____   Time: _____
            Day   Date

Authorization Obtained: ❏ YES ❏ NO ❏ REQUESTED

If authorization has been requested and response is pending, list date and contact information from the initial request.

Requested From: _____   Date: _____
              (Carrier and person)

Telephone: _____   Ext: _____

Completed By: _____

Date Completed: _____

SUPPLIES

South Padre Medical Center

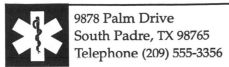

Gerald Bond, MD
Ray Adams, MD
Joyce Harkness, MD
Anthony Clark, MD

9878 Palm Drive
South Padre, TX 98765
Telephone (209) 555-3356

PATIENT INFORMATION
Please Print

Today's Date __04/16/08__

Last Name __Klint__   First Name __Sam__   Initial __J__

Date of Birth __02/11/46__   Age __62__   Sex __M__   SS# __504-11-4545__

Home Address   Street __5403 Fairview Dr.__   City __South Padre__

State __TX__   Zip __98765__   Home Phone (__209__) __555-0990__

Occupation __None – disabled__   Employer __N/A__

Employer Address   Street _____   City _____

State _____   Zip _____   Work Phone (_____)_____

Are you currently a student?   Yes   (No)   Name of School _____

Spouse's Name __Faye Klint__   Marital Status   (M)   S   D   W   SEP

Spouse's SS# ___-___-___   Spouse's Employer _____

In case of emergency, notify _____   Relationship _____

Home Phone (_____) _____   Work Phone (_____) _____

If you are a minor: Parent's Name _____   SS# ___-___-___

Street _____   City _____   State _____   Zip _____

Home Phone (_____) _____   Work Phone (_____) _____

Reason for Visit __Renal failure__

Work related injury?   Yes   (No)   Date of injury _____

Automobile accident?   Yes   (No)   Date of injury _____

Other injury?   Yes   (No)   Date of injury _____

Insurance (Primary)   Company Name: __BC/BS of Texas__

Street __1514 West Road__   City __Houston__   State __TX__   Zip __99881__

Subscriber's Name __Self__

Relationship to Subscriber: _____

Policy # __MKL2211__   Group # __A1280__

Insurance (Secondary)   Company Name: _____

Street _____   City _____   State _____   Zip _____

Subscriber's Name _____

Relationship to Subscriber: _____

Policy # _____   Group # _____

Assignment of Benefits:

I directly assign all medical/surgical benefits, including major medical benefits and Medicare, to South Padre Medical Center. I understand that this authorization for assignment remains in effect until I revoke it in writing. A photocopy of this assignment will be considered as valid as this original assignment. I further understand that I am responsible for my indebtedness no matter what charges the insurance pays for.

Insured or Guardian's Signature _____   Date _____

SUPPLIES

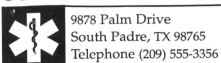

South Padre Medical Center

Gerald Bond, MD
Ray Adams, MD
Joyce Harkness, MD
Anthony Clark, MD

9878 Palm Drive
South Padre, TX 98765
Telephone (209) 555-3356

PATIENT INFORMATION
Please Print

Today's Date **04/16/08**

Last Name **Harkland**　　First Name **Emmy**　　Initial **L**

Date of Birth **04/06/42**　Age **66**　Sex **F**　SS# **009-99-0099**

Home Address　Street **1818 Oak Street**　City **South Padre**

　　State **TX**　Zip **98765**　Home Phone **(209) 555-5209**

Occupation **Retired**　　Employer **N/A**

Employer Address　Street _____　City _____

　　State _____　Zip _____　Work Phone (_____)_____

Are you currently a student?　Yes　(No)　Name of School _____

Spouse's Name _____　Marital Status　M　S　D　(W)　SEP

Spouse's SS# ___-___-____　Spouse's Employer _____

In case of emergency, notify _____　Relationship_____

　　Home Phone (____) _____　Work Phone (____) _____

If you are a minor:　Parent's Name_____　SS#___-___-____

　　Street _____　City _____　State _____　Zip_____

　　Home Phone (____) _____　Work Phone (____) _____

Reason for Visit **Lump in breast**

　　Work related injury?　Yes　(No)　Date of injury_____

　　Automobile accident?　Yes　(No)　Date of injury_____

　　Other injury?　Yes　(No)　Date of injury_____

Insurance (Primary)　Company Name: **Medicare**

　　Street **402 Main Street** City **South Padre** State **TX** Zip **98765**

　　Subscriber's Name _____

　　Relationship to Subscriber: **Emmy Harkland**

　　Policy # **009990099A**　Group #_____

Insurance (Secondary)　Company Name: _____

　　Street _____　City _____　State _____　Zip_____

　　Subscriber's Name _____

　　Relationship to Subscriber: _____

　　Policy #_____　Group #_____

Assignment of Benefits:

I directly assign all medical/surgical benefits, including major medical benefits and Medicare, to South Padre Medical Center. I understand that this authorization for assignment remains in effect until I revoke it in writing. A photocopy of this assignment will be considered as valid as this original assignment. I further understand that I am responsible for my indebtedness no matter what charges the insurance pays for.

Insured or Guardian's Signature _____　Date _____

SUPPLIES

South Padre Medical Center

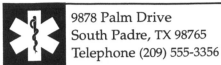

Gerald Bond, MD
Ray Adams, MD
Joyce Harkness, MD
Anthony Clark, MD

9878 Palm Drive
South Padre, TX 98765
Telephone (209) 555-3356

PATIENT INFORMATION
Please Print

Today's Date __04/16/08__

Last Name __Bates__ First Name __Michelle__ Initial __L__

Date of Birth __11/09/61__ Age __46__ Sex __F__ SS# __502-66-0066__

Home Address Street __2204 2nd Ave__ City __South Padre__

State __TX__ Zip __98765__ Home Phone __(209) 555-9737__

Occupation __Nurse__ Employer __South Padre Nursing Home__

Employer Address Street _____ City _____

State _____ Zip _____ Work Phone (_____)_____

Are you currently a student? Yes (No) Name of School _____

Spouse's Name __Dean__ Marital Status (M) S D W SEP

Spouse's SS# __180-52-9987__ Spouse's Employer __B & L Incorporated__

In case of emergency, notify __Dean__ Relationship __Spouse__

Home Phone (209) __555-9737__ Work Phone (209) __555-1827__

If you are a minor: Parent's Name _____ SS# ____-__-____

Street _____ City _____ State ____ Zip_____

Home Phone (____)_____ Work Phone (____)_____

Reason for Visit __Breast mass__

Work related injury? Yes (No) Date of injury_____

Automobile accident? Yes (No) Date of injury_____

Other injury? Yes (No) Date of injury_____

Insurance (Primary) Company Name: __South Padre Insurance__

Street __2702 Oak Line Dr.__ City __South Padre__ State __TX__ Zip __98765__

Subscriber's Name __Michelle Bates__

Relationship to Subscriber: __Self__

Policy # __KMK9236__ Group #_____

Insurance (Secondary) Company Name: _____

Street _____ City _____ State ____ Zip_____

Subscriber's Name _____

Relationship to Subscriber: _____

Policy #_____ Group #_____

Assignment of Benefits:

I directly assign all medical/surgical benefits, including major medical benefits and Medicare, to South Padre Medical Center. I understand that this authorization for assignment remains in effect until I revoke it in writing. A photocopy of this assignment will be considered as valid as this original assignment. I further understand that I am responsible for my indebtedness no matter what charges the insurance pays for.

Insured or Guardian's Signature _____ Date _____

SUPPLIES

TASK **8.2** 525

South Padre Medical Center

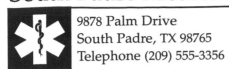

9878 Palm Drive
South Padre, TX 98765
Telephone (209) 555-3356

PATIENT INFORMATION

Please Print

Today's Date __04/16/08__

Last Name __Adams__ First Name __Tony__ Initial __W__

Date of Birth __05/22/48__ Age __59__ Sex __M__ SS# __509-81-8382__

Home Address Street __1616 Todd Ave__ City __South Padre__

State __TX__ Zip __98765__ Home Phone (__209__) __555-1114__

Occupation __Lawyer__ Employer __Adams Law Firm__

Employer Address Street _____ City _____

State _____ Zip _____ Work Phone (____)_____

Are you currently a student? Yes (No) Name of School _____

Spouse's Name _____ Marital Status M S (D) W SEP

Spouse's SS# ___-___-___ Spouse's Employer _____

In case of emergency, notify _____ Relationship _____

Home Phone (____)_____ Work Phone (____)_____

If you are a minor: Parent's Name _____ SS#___-___-___

Street _____ City _____ State ____ Zip____

Home Phone (____)_____ Work Phone (____)_____

Reason for Visit __Excision Lymph Node/Neck__

Work related injury? Yes (No) Date of injury_____

Automobile accident? Yes (No) Date of injury_____

Other injury? Yes (No) Date of injury_____

Insurance (Primary) Company Name: __Texas Health__

Street __1256 56th Ave S.__ City __Houston__ State __TX__ Zip __99881__

Subscriber's Name _____

Relationship to Subscriber: __Self__

Policy # __XCV4568__ Group #_____

Insurance (Secondary) Company Name: _____

Street _____ City _____ State ____ Zip____

Subscriber's Name _____

Relationship to Subscriber: _____

Policy #_____ Group #_____

Assignment of Benefits:

I directly assign all medical/surgical benefits, including major medical benefits and Medicare, to South Padre Medical Center. I understand that this authorization for assignment remains in effect until I revoke it in writing. A photocopy of this assignment will be considered as valid as this original assignment. I further understand that I am responsible for my indebtedness no matter what charges the insurance pays for.

Insured or Guardian's Signature _____ Date _____

SUPPLIES

South Padre Medical Center

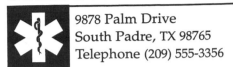

9878 Palm Drive
South Padre, TX 98765
Telephone (209) 555-3356

PATIENT INFORMATION
Please Print

Today's Date __04/16/08__

Last Name __Anderson__   First Name __Charlie__   Initial __M__

Date of Birth __04/23/31__   Age __76__   Sex __M__   SS# __011__-__22__-__3210__

Home Address   Street __919 36th Ave South__ City __South Padre__

State __TX__   Zip __98765__ Home Phone (__209__) __555-8838__

Occupation __Retired__   Employer __N/A__

Employer Address   Street _____ City _____

State _____ Zip _____ Work Phone (_____)_____

Are you currently a student?   Yes   (No)   Name of School _____

Spouse's Name _____   Marital Status   M   S   D   (W)   SEP

Spouse's SS# ____-____-____ Spouse's Employer _____

In case of emergency, notify _____ Relationship _____

Home Phone (____) _____ Work Phone (____) _____

If you are a minor: Parent's Name _____ SS# ____-____-____

Street _____ City _____ State _____ Zip_____

Home Phone (____) _____ Work Phone (____) _____

Reason for Visit __Echocardiogram__

Work related injury?   Yes   (No)   Date of injury_____

Automobile accident?   Yes   (No)   Date of injury_____

Other injury?   Yes   (No)   Date of injury_____

Insurance (Primary)   Company Name: __Medicare__

Street __402 Main Street__ City __South Padre__ State __TX__ Zip __98765__

Subscriber's Name _____

Relationship to Subscriber: __self__

Policy # __011223210A__   Group #_____

Insurance (Secondary)   Company Name: _____

Street _____ City _____ State _____ Zip_____

Subscriber's Name _____

Relationship to Subscriber: _____

Policy #_____   Group #_____

Assignment of Benefits:

I directly assign all medical/surgical benefits, including major medical benefits and Medicare, to South Padre Medical Center. I understand that this authorization for assignment remains in effect until I revoke it in writing. A photocopy of this assignment will be considered as valid as this original assignment. I further understand that I am responsible for my indebtedness no matter what charges the insurance pays for.

Insured or Guardian's Signature _____ Date _____

SUPPLIES

South Padre Medical Center

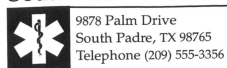

Gerald Bond, MD
Ray Adams, MD
Joyce Harkness, MD
Anthony Clark, MD

9878 Palm Drive
South Padre, TX 98765
Telephone (209) 555-3356

PATIENT INFORMATION
Please Print

Today's Date __04|16|08__

Last Name __Wood__ First Name __Tina__ Initial __J__

Date of Birth __12|25|77__ Age __30__ Sex __F__ SS# __207-48-1842__

Home Address Street __222 Cherry Elm Rd apt. 15__ City __South Padre__

State __TX__ Zip __98765__ Home Phone __(209) 555-6169__

Occupation __Machine operator__ Employer __South Padre Potato Plant__

Employer Address Street _____ City _____

State _____ Zip _____ Work Phone __(209) 555-5805__

Are you currently a student? Yes (No) Name of School _____

Spouse's Name _____ Marital Status M (S) D W SEP

Spouse's SS# ___-___-___ Spouse's Employer _____

In case of emergency, notify _____ Relationship _____

Home Phone (___) _____ Work Phone (___) _____

If you are a minor: Parent's Name _____ SS# ___-___-___

Street _____ City _____ State _____ Zip_____

Home Phone (___) _____ Work Phone (___) _____

Reason for Visit __Cervical Diskectomy__

Work related injury? (Yes) No Date of injury __11/16/07__

Automobile accident? Yes (No) Date of injury _____

Other injury? Yes (No) Date of injury _____

Insurance (Primary) Company Name: __Workers Compensation__

Street __10 State Highway__ City __Houston__ State __TX__ Zip __99881__

Subscriber's Name _____

Relationship to Subscriber: _____

Policy # __MKI4231__ Group # _____

Insurance (Secondary) Company Name: __BC/BS of Texas__

Street _____ City _____ State _____ Zip_____

Subscriber's Name _____

Relationship to Subscriber: __Self__

Policy # __PXM4031__ Group # _____

Assignment of Benefits:

I directly assign all medical/surgical benefits, including major medical benefits and Medicare, to South Padre Medical Center. I understand that this authorization for assignment remains in effect until I revoke it in writing. A photocopy of this assignment will be considered as valid as this original assignment. I further understand that I am responsible for my indebtedness no matter what charges the insurance pays for.

Insured or Guardian's Signature _____ Date _____

SUPPLIES

South Padre Medical Center
Reception Inventory List

INVENTORY NUMBER	PRODUCT NAME	DESCRIPTION	DATE PURCHASED	ROOM	APRIL 17, 2008
RE1601	Normon	Reception Chair	01/15/XX	Reception	
RE1602	Normon	Reception Chair	01/15/XX	Reception	
RE1603	Normon	Reception Chair	01/15/XX	Reception	
RE1604	Normon	Reception Chair	01/15/XX	Reception	
RE1605	Normon	Reception Chair	01/15/XX	Reception	
RE1606	Normon	Reception Chair	01/15/XX	Reception	
RE1607	Normon	Reception Chair	01/15/XX	Reception	
RE1608	Normon	Reception Chair	01/15/XX	Reception	
RE1609	Normon	Reception Chair	01/15/XX	Reception	
RE1610	Normon	Reception Chair	01/15/XX	Reception	
RE1611	Normon	Reception Chair	01/15/XX	Reception	
RE1612	Normon	Reception Chair	01/15/XX	Reception	
RE6401	ThrillFlat	Table, round	08/03/XX	Reception	
RE6402	ThrillFlat	Table, round	08/03/XX	Reception	
RE6984	Swift	Stand, brochure	12/07/XX	Reception	
RE9021	Gabrial	Chair, child	03/06/XX	Reception	
RE9203	Swift	Picture, abstract	04/05/XX	Reception	
RE9204	Gabrial	Table, child	11/11/XX	Reception	
RE6111	Swift	Picture, abstract	01/04/XX	Reception	
RE6985	Normon	Rack, Magazine	01/15/XX	Reception	

SUPPLIES

South Padre Medical Center

Patient's Name _____ Age _____ Sex _____ Marital Status   S   M   W   D

Address _____ Insurance _____

Telephone _____ Referred _____

Date	Subsequent Findings

SUPPLIES

South Padre Medical Center

Patient's Name _____ Age _____ Sex _____ Marital Status S M W D

Address _____ Insurance _____

Telephone _____ Referred _____

Date	Subsequent Findings

SUPPLIES

South Padre Medical Center

Patient's Name _____ Age _____ Sex _____ Marital Status S M W D

Address _____ Insurance _____

Telephone _____ Referred _____

Date	Subsequent Findings

SUPPLIES

South Padre Medical Center

Patient's Name _____ Age _____ Sex _____ Marital Status S M W D

Address _____ Insurance _____

Telephone _____ Referred _____

Date	Subsequent Findings

SUPPLIES

South Padre Medical Center

Patient's Name _____ Age _____ Sex _____ Marital Status S M W D

Address _____ Insurance _____

Telephone _____ Referred _____

Date	Subsequent Findings

SUPPLIES

South Padre Medical Center

Patient's Name _____ Age _____ Sex _____ Marital Status   S   M   W   D

Address _____ Insurance _____

Telephone _____ Referred _____

Date	Subsequent Findings

SUPPLIES

PRIORITY ☐

Telephone Record

Patient _____ Age _____

Caller _____

Telephone _____

Referred to _____

Chart # _____

Chart Attached ☐ YES ☐ NO

Date __ / __ / __ Time _____ Rec'd By _____

Message _____
_____
_____

Temp	Allergies

Response _____
_____

PHY/RN Initials	Date __ / __ / __	Time	Handled By

PRIORITY ☐

Telephone Record

Patient _____ Age _____

Caller _____

Telephone _____

Referred to _____

Chart # _____

Chart Attached ☐ YES ☐ NO

Date __ / __ / __ Time _____ Rec'd By _____

Message _____
_____
_____

Temp	Allergies

Response _____
_____

PHY/RN Initials	Date __ / __ / __	Time	Handled By

PRIORITY ☐

Telephone Record

Patient _____ Age _____

Caller _____

Telephone _____

Referred to _____

Chart # _____

Chart Attached ☐ YES ☐ NO

Date __ / __ / __ Time _____ Rec'd By _____

Message _____
_____
_____

Temp	Allergies

Response _____
_____

PHY/RN Initials	Date __ / __ / __	Time	Handled By

PRIORITY ☐

Telephone Record

Patient _____ Age _____

Caller _____

Telephone _____

Referred to _____

Chart # _____

Chart Attached ☐ YES ☐ NO

Date __ / __ / __ Time _____ Rec'd By _____

Message _____
_____
_____

Temp	Allergies

Response _____
_____

PHY/RN Initials	Date __ / __ / __	Time	Handled By

SUPPLIES

PRIORITY ☐

Telephone Record

Patient _____ Age _____

Caller _____

Telephone _____

Referred to _____

Chart # _____

Chart Attached ☐ YES ☐ NO

Date ___/___/___ Time _____ Rec'd By _____

Message
_____
_____

| Temp | Allergies |

Response
_____

| PHY/RN Initials | Date ___/___/___ | Time | Handled By |

SUPPLIES

TASK **10.1**   549

SOUTH PADRE HOSPITAL

980 Lagona Drive • South Padre, TX 98765 • Telephone (209) 555-4289

OPERATIVE REPORT

SUPPLIES

SOUTH
PADRE
HOSPITAL

980 Lagona Drive • South Padre, TX 98765 • Telephone (209) 555-4289

OPERATIVE REPORT

SUPPLIES

SOUTH PADRE HOSPITAL

980 Lagona Drive • South Padre, TX 98765 • Telephone (209) 555-4289

OPERATIVE REPORT

SUPPLIES

SOUTH PADRE HOSPITAL

980 Lagona Drive • South Padre, TX 98765 • Telephone (209) 555-4289

OPERATIVE REPORT

SUPPLIES

SOUTH PADRE HOSPITAL

980 Lagona Drive • South Padre, TX 98765 • Telephone (209) 555-4289

OPERATIVE REPORT

SUPPLIES

SOUTH
PADRE
HOSPITAL

980 Lagona Drive • South Padre, TX 98765 • Telephone (209) 555-4289

CARDIOLOGY REPORT

SUPPLIES

SOUTH PADRE HOSPITAL

980 Lagona Drive • South Padre, TX 98765 • Telephone (209) 555-4289

RADIOLOGY REPORT

SUPPLIES